Caiques

Their Care, Breeding and Some Natural History

John C. McMichael, Ph.D.,
Fellow of the American Academy of Microbiology

Avian Publications
6380 Monroe St. NE
Minneapolis, MN 55432

Bruce Burchett Publisher
www.avianpublications.com
bruce@avianpublications.com
Phone & FAX 763-571-8902

ISBN 0-910335-74-5

Printed in USA

Table of Contents

Pionites melanocephalus melanocephalus

George Edwards published this lithograph of a caique he found on the docks of London. This may be the first illustration of a caique ever published. In his 1751 book entitled **A Natural History of Uncommon Birds** (118) he called it the "White-Breasted Parrot." (Courtesy of the Division of Rare and Manuscript Collections, Cornell University Library.)

Preface

I began to write about caiques shortly after I began to breed caiques back in 1986. There were only a few people breeding them then and there was little information on their care and husbandry. This book evolved from my first attempts to provide a care manual to the buyers of my chicks. Over the years, I wrote many versions. Along the way, I found myself digging further and further in the caique literature. I may not have found every article published on caiques, but I have made a good attempt. With each new tidbit of information, however, the manuscript progressed from a simple care manual into one covering just about everything known about caiques. I could not have written it without what I learned from other caique owners and breeders. I also had the assistance of many librarians, veterinarians, field scientists, and lab scientists. I was a regular visitor to the Carnegie Museum Library and the Cornell University Libraries. I thank all of those individuals for their efforts in developing this manuscript.

I hope this book provides the reader with a good understanding of caiques. I have divided it into three parts. The first part provides information on caring for pet caiques. The second part provides information about breeding caiques. The third and last part delves into some esoteric and scientific topics related to caiques. There you will find the technical descriptions of the species and subspecies, a discussion of taxonomy, speculation on how they evolved into two species and five subspecies, a discussion of caique ecology, a consideration of their conservation in the wild, and a look into caique color variants. There are also a number of appendices, mostly lists too long to include in the text. Finally, an extensive bibliography recognizes the contribution of the many people whose pioneering observations and ideas form much of the basis of this book.

Preface

I began to write about caiques shortly after I began to breed caiques back in 1986. There were only a few people breeding them then and there was little information on their care and husbandry. This book evolved from my first attempts to provide a care manual to the buyers of my chicks. Over the years, I wrote many versions. Along the way, I found myself digging further and further in the caique literature. I may not have found every article published on caiques, but I have made a good attempt. With each new tidbit of information, however, the manuscript progressed from a simple care manual into one covering just about everything known about caiques. I could not have written it without what I learned from other caique owners and breeders. I also had the assistance of many librarians, veterinarians, field scientists, and lab scientists. I was a regular visitor to the Carnegie Museum Library and the Cornell University Libraries. I thank all of those individuals for their efforts in developing this manuscript.

I hope this book provides the reader with a good understanding of caiques. I have divided it into three parts. The first part provides information on caring for pet caiques. The second part provides information about breeding caiques. The third and last part delves into some esoteric and scientific topics related to caiques. There you will find the technical descriptions of the species and subspecies, a discussion of taxonomy, speculation on how they evolved into two species and five subspecies, a discussion of caique ecology, a consideration of their conservation in the wild, and a look into caique color variants. There are also a number of appendices, mostly lists too long to include in the text. Finally, an extensive bibliography recognizes the contribution of the many people whose pioneering observations and ideas form much of the basis of this book.

Introduction

I have kept many parrot species, and in my biased opinion, the parrots of the *Pionites* genus we call caiques are the best of all. They are intelligent, curious, stubborn, affectionate, fearless and devoted. Some people call them the "clowns" of the parrot world because of their amusing antics. Rosemary Low (233), who wrote the most definitive book available on parrot aviculture states, "No other parrot has a personality quite the same." For her, only the lories and fig parrots come close to comparing with a caique's disposition. Alfred Wallace (450), co-discoverer of evolution noted "...the Mariána[1] was a lively little creature, inquisitive as a monkey, and playful as a kitten. It was never quiet, running over the whole canoe, climbing into very crack and cranny, diving into all the baskets, pans, and pots it could discover, and tasting everything they contained." In 1915, Charles Dawson (102) a missionary in British Guiana made a similar allusion to them being like monkeys and kittens. He noted their penchant for play stating: "The children and he would run races or play hide and seek; and when it was his turn to hide and they couldn't find him, he would come slyly out of his hiding place and nip the bare foot of the nearest child." I have never known my caiques to play hide and seek, but anyone that has owned a young caique knows its penchant for play.

The willingness of caiques to play and socialize with people probably is due to their preference to socialize in small groups of ten or more birds in the wild. However, you may not find a caique the best parrot if you absolutely have to have a bird that talks in a language you understand. Most learn a few words and some become very proficient, but most do not. They all seem to learn to whistle even though they cannot carry a tune very well. Their sounds are more like what Astley (14) wrote about his brown-necked parrot (*Poicephalus robustus*)—they make "canoodling" sounds. If you keep a caique as single pet, it is more likely to learn to talk when you keep them in groups. This is probably because a single caique receives more of your attention. When they do talk, their voices are usually low and you need to listen carefully to decipher what they are saying. They can use words in context. They will greet you with "Hello" and ask "What 'cha doing?" Still, do not expect the talents of an African grey. Caiques are more renowned for their personality than their speech.

Before going further, if you own or are considering the purchase of a caique, you should learn the proper pronunciation of caique. If you look up the word 'caique' in most dictionaries, you will find it means a small sailing boat that plies the Bosporus. This is clearly not a bird, but you pronounce it the same. The accepted American pronunciation is a variation of "kigh-eek" or "kah-eek." You will hear many other pronunciations ranging from cake to kike—ignore them. Caique appears to be a corruption of Caïca, an early genus name probably derived from one of the Caribe languages spoken in northern South America. Aviculturalists have applied this name to them from at least the late nineteenth century and Hopkinson (190) formalized it as the English name[2] in 1914.

Until the 1990's, most of the caiques sold in the United States were imported wild-caught birds. Bronson (50), writing in 1950, noted the local people commonly kept them as pets within their native range, but in the United States, you could only find them in zoological gardens. With few exceptions, imported wild-caught caiques did not make good pets. You could not handle these wild-caught caiques without suffering a bloody bite. This seems to have been the experience of many early writers prior to the wide availability of hand-fed chicks. For example, in 1969 Cyril Rogers (355) stated that they were "more suitable as aviary birds than as cage pets." Even earlier, Karl Russ (362) noted that a pair of caiques would savagely attack one's hand if he foolishly put it inside their cage, yet he did note their playfulness. This has changed. Now that we know more about their husbandry, a hand-reared caique is one of the more desirable pet birds and caiques now populate the memoirs of famous people such as the pianist Peter Duchin (114).

While there has been a surge in popularity of caiques as pets in North America and Europe

---

[1] Mariána or marianha is a common name for the caique in Brazil. It translates as "little Mary" in English.

[2] Despite its long use by aviculturalists, most scientific writers do not accept caique as the English name. In their papers, they usually refer to them as either the "white-bellied parrot" or "black-headed parrot."

(50, 78, 373), they were always popular with the inhabitants of South America (115, 185, 204). Stolzmann (422) noted in the late nineteenth century they were very desirable in Peru where they were the most commonly kept parrot. While surveying the Amazon River for the United States Navy, Herndon (178) came across a fully tonsured Franciscan friar in his robes "generally bearing upon his shoulder a beautiful and saucy bird of the parrot kind, called a chiriclis[3]" upon his visit to the town of Sarayacu[4] in Peru. Herndon was so enchanted; the friar gave it to him. He wrote, "It was beautiful, gentle, and affectionate, and so gallant that I called it my Mohawk chief."

When W.L. Sclater (379) visited British Guiana, he noted, "The Caica is remarkable for its excessive friendliness and sociability. I brought a specimen of it home with me, which is certainly the tamest bird I have ever come across." On the Mulford Amazon Expedition of 1921-1922, the local owners were very reluctant to part with their pet yellow-thighed caiques, but a member of the expedition, Bill Mann, "found a woman who owned four as pets. She was willing to trade the birds for money to buy a new dress, but her husband forbid it. One day, she sent word that she could trade the birds while her husband was out. The husband arrived just as Mann was leaving with the birds and a 'shrill-pitched argument' broke out between husband and wife[5]" (115).

Other long-term visitors to Amazonia have kept caiques as pets. For example, the botanical artist Margaret Mee kept a pet black-headed caique she named Curica (259). It is our good fortune that we have discovered their pet qualities too, and this has led to an increase in the number of people breeding them.

Despite their greater availability, hand-reared caiques and the larger parrots remain expensive. Before 1980, the main reason was that they did not breed well in captivity. Charles Darwin (96), writing in 1868, noted that parrots in general almost never bred in captivity, and later aviculturalists such as Furner (137) despaired of ever getting his birds to breed. However, partly motivated by the parrot fever scare of 1929 and

1930[6], Gilbert Lee persevered and in 1932 was the first to successfully breed and rear caiques (219, 322).

Even after that breakthrough, breeding proved a challenge and it was not until the 1970's that pioneers such as Dr. George Smith and Tom Ireland learned how to breed caiques dependably. They faced a number of challenges. The most daunting was that caiques are monomorphic and there was no reliable way for determining their sex in order to set up opposite sex pairs. The advent of surgical sexing solved that problem. Even with that breakthrough, most of the imported pairs would not breed more than once a year. Fortunately, over the past twenty years, we have learned more about their husbandry and the early efforts of the pioneer breeders have produced a pool of domestically bred stock less shy about breeding in captivity. Now, instead of producing a single clutch, it is common to hear of pairs producing three or more clutches a year.

Yet, caiques remain expensive. This is because rearing a pet quality bird is a labor-intensive and time-consuming process. Not many people are willing to invest the amount of time needed to produce a pet-quality bird without some sort of financial reward. So while the price of a caique may drop, do not look for them to become as cheap as budgerigars or cockatiels.

---

[3] Chiriclis or chiricles is the local Spanish word for the caique in Ecuador and Peru. It is probably derived form chilicres, the Quichua word for the caique.
[4] Sarayacu is located on the Ucayali River within the range of the pallid subspecies.
[5] They presented these birds to the National Zoo when the expedition returned to the United States (New York Times, July 16, 1922).

[6] You can find a series of inflammatory reports on the occurrence of parrot fever in the United States in the New York Times from this period.

2

Part I. Care of Pet Caiques

Bird owner life style adjustments

Is a pet parrot right for you?

Before considering a pet of any kind, you should ask some basic questions of yourself. Do you have any health problem that would preclude you having that pet? Can you commit to caring for an animal that is completely dependent on you? How tolerant are you and your neighbors of the noises that pets make?

Your health or the health of other persons in your household should be a major consideration. If you tend to have allergies, you may develop them toward your parrot (323, 424). Fortunately, bird allergies rarely lead to hypersensitivity pneumonitis (301), but some people have had to give up their beloved pets because of this. If you notice you are developing an allergic reaction when around your bird, it is very important to see your physician before it becomes too severe. While a caique may be a better choice than a cockatoo, which produces a powder-like dander, their dust can still elicit a strong allergic reaction in a sensitive individual. Even if you do not have allergies, it is wise to invest in a good air cleaning devise to preclude these problems. (There is a section devoted to this and other human health concerns beginning on page 34.)

There is another set of people who should not keep pet birds—people with tuberculosis. There is a recent report of an African Grey parrot that contracted the disease from its owner (369). The danger is that the infected bird might be able to transmit it back to other people and this presents a public health issue.

Parrots, like mammalian pets, need care every day. If you like to take frequent or extended vacations, or must travel on business that requires you leaving them for long periods without care, it is probably not a good idea to own a parrot. Parrots are creatures of routine; they like to know what to expect every day. Neglecting them, especially a single pet bird, often leads to serious psychological disorders for the bird. They tolerate short separations of a week or two as long as the separations are not too frequent and the birds continue to receive good care, but pet parrots do not like you to lock them away in a cage and forget them. They are highly social and need companionship just like people.

If you or the people who live with or near you have a low noise tolerance, think carefully before purchasing any parrot. This may be a particular problem for people suffering from chronic or recurrent headaches such as migraines. In general, the larger the parrot, the louder its noise; while caiques are not exceptionally noisy, they still need to vocalize, particularly during their morning and evening call times. This is less of a problem for people who live in single-family homes, but can be a particular problem for apartment dwellers and others who must deal with close neighbors.

One last consideration that may preclude parrot ownership concerns whether you are in the commercial poultry business. It is not a good idea to keep pet birds on a poultry farm. The chance of transmission of diseases from one species to the other is probably too high for you to consider any bird as a pet. If you elect to have a pet bird, be sure you keep it well away from your poultry flock and institute strict sanitary procedures to prevent the intertransmission of diseases between the species.

Getting started

If this is your first parrot, you need to arm yourself with at least two things: the proper equipment and the proper knowledge. The most important items you will need are a cage, a play stand, and a training stick. (There is a section devoted to cage selection beginning on page 5.) A play stand is important for the management of your bird. The better stands provide food cups and a climbing area. Caiques quickly learn that they are supposed to stay on or near their play stand, although once they develop confidence they will break this rule. A stand from which the bird cannot climb to the floor is the best for keeping your bird confined to its perch.

Another important tool is a training stick. A hard wood ladder is an excellent substitute for the straight training stick and has the advantage that you can use it to pick your bird up off the floor without having to stoop as you would with a straight stick. All bird trainers recommend that you stick train your bird. The main reason for stick training is to manage your bird should it become temperamental, refuses get on your hand, or tries to bite you.

Once you have the cage and other equipment, you need knowledge about the bird's husbandry in order to keep it the sweet thing you want it to be. To get you started, here are some basic rules:

* Feed your bird properly. (There is a large section devoted to feeding caiques beginning on page 9 as well as lists of foods and their preparation in appendices A and B).

* Handle your bird everyday. You need to do this to maintain the bond; if neglected too long your bird may no longer want your attention.

* Develop a regular schedule. Let your bird know when it can expect to eat and be out of its cage. The schedule need not be rigid, but it should be consistent. Most caiques greatly appreciate being out of their cage.

* Talk to your bird. Start using its name immediately. Your bird will learn its name and respond to it.

* Always use the up or similar command when picking up your bird. Using this command should become second nature. It is also a good idea to teach it the down command for when you want it to get off your hand or stick.

* Never pick up the bird just because it is screaming. Wait until it is quiet, and then pick it up. Picking up the bird to get it to stop vocalizing is sending a message to the bird on how to manipulate you.

* Be firm, but show respect. For example, do not allow your bird to ignore your up command. Be persistent until it steps onto your finger or a stick. Do not allow it to learn that it can avoid important commands.

* Never hit your bird. It is better to show your displeasure by banishing it to some place it dislikes such as a timeout box. A timeout box can be an actual box or a cage isolated so the bird cannot have interaction with you or other birds. (Never put it back in its cage. Putting it back in its cage will either cause it to hate its cage, or stimulate it to do the same action to get back to its cage.)

* Play with your bird, especially young birds. This is how they learn to socialize with you and learn each other's limits, such as not to nip too hard and not to perch on top of your head.

* Parrot-proof your home. For more on this, see the next section.

* Make a recording of the voice of your caique and hope you never need to use it. The reason for this is to help lure it back to you should it escape. Bird watchers often use the recorded sounds of wild caiques to entice them close enough to observe. You can buy recordings of wild caiques from places such as the Cornell Ornithology Lab (460).

* Do not expect your caique to be perfect. There are no perfect people, and there are no perfect pets.

These rules provide a start for mutual understanding. A well-adjusted bird knows what to expect. You have to provide not just a home and food, but companionship. A pet bird that bonds with you will want to spend all its waking hours near you, as it would with its mate in the wild. It should learn, however, that it must be in its cage for much of the day in order to conform to human social norms. We have to do the best we can to meet their demands, and this requires discipline on the part of both the bird and its human being.

Detail of caique from a black and white print in *The Parrot Book* by Allen Silver, ca. 1933 (390). Caiques are a forest species, so it is curious that the artist embellished it with grass.

Parrot-proofing your home

After you buy any parrot, you must parrot-proof your home. This is like human baby proofing, except for birds. Please take this very seriously; your bird's life may be at stake. The most important things that you must do are:

1. Remove all items made of lead. Lead is extremely toxic for both people and birds. Parrots like to chew on this soft metal. Some parrots seem to like the "sweet" flavor of old lead-based paint. Pay particular attention to removing the lead weights from your curtains and drapes. These often

become one of your bird's favorite play areas. Other things made of lead are fishing weights, leaded windows, the capsule-foil on wine bottles, glazes on antique and imported pottery, bell clappers, and old window putty (77). Even brass keys contain a small amount of lead.

2. Eliminate or limit your use of polytetrafluoroethylene (PTFE) coated cooking utensils, especially the drip pans under your range burners. Vendors sell PTFE under a number of brand names including Teflon®, Hostaflon, and CuFlon. Manufacturers also use PTFE in a wide range of other products such as clothing irons, space heaters and even heat lamps. When a PTFE product overheats, it emits a gas that is extremely poisonous for birds. Only a few minutes of exposure to this gas will kill most birds. This is one reason you should not keep your bird caged in the kitchen.

3. Stop smoking. Birds are generally more sensitive to air pollutants than people are. This was why miners took canaries with them into the mine. Pulmonary disease (92) and recurrent respiratory infection (391) in birds are associated with secondary smoke[7]. Not only is the smoke dangerous, but parrots pick up the nicotine and tars off one's fingers on their feet. This can be so noxious that the bird may chew on its feet and mutilate itself. In this vein, if you do smoke, do not allow your bird access to ashtrays and cigarette butts.

4. If you must keep your birds in a small kitchen, do not fry with oil without proper ventilation. There is a report that olive oil is particularly toxic when used for frying. This was the sad experience of a parrot owner when he decided to fry food in his small, poorly ventilated travel trailer (297).

5. Remove toxic plants to another room or altogether. Not all plants are poisonous, so you must be selective in what plants they can reach and chew. Fortunately, most toxins are dose dependent, so if your bird consumes only a small amount there is usually little to worry about. Still, if your bird happens to chew on a plant and you are uncertain if it is harmful, you should first call the local poison control center listed in the front of your phone directory. They will tell you if it is poisonous for people; if it is, it is probably poisonous for birds too. For more information related to toxicity of a plant for animals, phone the National Animal Poison Control Center Hotline at (800) 548-2423 or (900) 680-0000. This Hotline charges a flat rate when you use the first number and a per minute rate if you use the second number. There is a short list of common toxic plants in Appendix D. It is not comprehensive, but includes some of the common toxic plants.

6. Make a habit of putting the toilet seat down. This is not an edict from Miss Manners, but sound advice to prevent the accidental drowning of your bird.

7. You need additional parrot-proofing if you leave your bird's wings unclipped. You need to be careful about using ceiling fans. Remove large mirrors. Use a sheer or other curtain on your windows. While birds do not usually injure themselves seriously when they fly into mirrors and windows, it is very traumatic when they do. While discussing windows, be sure they have screens or keep them closed. One of the most common reasons for the loss of pet birds is escape.

The cage

Cage selection

No commercial cage meets all the needs of a caique. When you look for a cage, try to find a one with greater horizontal than vertical space. Cages made for cockatiels, although of lighter construction than parrot cages are acceptable. Caiques do not have beaks large enough to bend the bars or break the welds of these cages and they cost less.

While the roomier the cage the better, pet caiques do not require a spacious cage if you allow them out every day. Pet caiques usually prefer climbing to flying, so you do not have to supply them with a large flight cage. Because they prefer to climb, the clear acrylic or Plexiglas cages that offer no grip for a bird's feet are poor choices.

If you build your own cage, make it from high quality galvanized wire such as 2" x 1/2" or 2" x 1" or similar mesh. Do not use small-meshed hardware cloth (191, 334); the galvanizing on hardware cloth seems to release zinc more readily as "white rust" than the better quality larger meshed wire. Zinc is toxic for your bird. You need to wash any cage constructed with galvanized wire with a dilute acid, such as vinegar, before placing a bird in it.

---

[7] Surprisingly, the data supporting second-hand smoke as dangerous to people has not held up too well. (Hyping Health Risks, G.C. Kabat, Columbia Univ. Press, 2008)

Most pet caiques prefer sleeping in a cavity. For this reason, I suggest attaching a roost box. The only reason not to provide a roost box is to prevent a pair from breeding. A roost box is the same as a nest box; the difference is that the bird uses it for sleeping instead of hatching eggs. Of course, your caique may lay eggs in the box, too. If you cannot do this, buy one of the cloth tents for your parrot to sleep in.

Even in the wild, caiques roost in cavities (459). Early explorers of Amazonia also noted that the pet caiques they encountered preferred to sleep in cavities. This is something they never mention for other parrots. Stolzmann, during his trip to Peru (422), noted that a pet caique he encountered liked to sleep under a box or pot and would chortle with delight when placed there. Wallace (450) noted that one tribe of Indians on the upper Rio Negro had a great affinity for pet birds and they "had nine pretty little black-headed parrots, which every night would go of their own accord into a basket prepared for them to sleep in."

Some recent cage and box designs make it easy to attach a roost box. Unfortunately, most commercial cages do not. You can easily install one, though. When you buy your cage, also buy a large budgie or cockatiel nest box. If you buy a budgie box, enlarge the entrance hole enough for your caique to enter.

If your cage does not provide an opening for the attachment of the box, you may have to cut two or three bars. The number depends on the spacing of the bars and the width of the entry hole to the roost box. It is best to install the box on the outside of the cage with large flat washers and fender bolts. Some boxes have pre-drilled holes, but you may have to drill two holes in the box through which to put the bolts. When possible, position the bolts just above a horizontal bar so that the box will not creep down the cage. It is also a good idea to place the nut on the exterior of the box so you can tell if your bird has loosened it.

You may place wood shavings or other bedding in the box, but birds do not always accept them. Only use shavings made from untreated wood, not wood intended for outdoor construction. Treated wood contains either chromated copper arsenate (CCA) or ammoniacal copper arsenate (ACA) as a preservative. Cedar chips are not recommended either; they contain plicatic acid that can irritate the respiratory system. Pet shops stock wood shavings intended for nest boxes.

If your bird has recently weaned, it may not realize that it is not supposed to defecate in its roost box. If this is the case, line the bottom of the box with paper towels and change them every morning. Once the chick has stopped defecating in its box, you can switch to wood chips. Giving your bird a roost box relieves you of the need to cover the cage at night.

Postcard of a painting by Catherine Klein (b. 1861). She attended the Berlin Art School in what was then Berlin, Prussia. Her specialty was pictures of flowers done in gauche. They often used decals of this painting to decorate lamps and shades in the early twentieth century. (Card in possession of the author.)

You may also wish to consider splatter shields. Unlike most other parrot species that eat their food and just drop it when they are done, caiques have a habit of flicking their food about. There are several ways to respond to this. One way is to buy a rectangular cage with the short glass or plastic seed guard inserts at the bottom. Then, replace the inserts with a sheet of the clear rigid polyacrylic plastic so that it covers the entire side of the cage. You can buy these clear plastic sheets and the tool for cutting them at most home centers.

Cut the sheet so it slips into the slot originally intended for the shorter seed guard. Secure the top of the sheet to the cage with a heavy spring clip available from an office supply store.

This shield will keep your bird from decorating everything near its cage. Splatter shields work well on the backs of most of caique cages, and you can install them on the sides as well. You should leave them off the front in order to allow easy entry and air circulation. Now, rather than cleaning the entire area around the bird, you can just remove the plastic sheet and wash off the debris in either your bathtub or with a hose outside. These shields will save you time and money by keeping the area around the outside of the cage free of the gooey fruits that dry to a hard crust on your floor and furnishings.

Most new cages include perches, but you will probably have to replace a perch sometime. Perch chewing is not usually the problem for pet caique owners as it is for breeder birds, but some birds chew more than others do. The standard perches sold in pet stores are fine, but most aviculturists do not recommend using just dowel rod perches because the diameter of the perch selected may not be the most comfortable for your bird. To save money, you can buy perches at a home center or simply cut one off a convenient tree.

When you buy a perch, be sure to buy one made of hard wood—the harder the better. If you buy a soft pine one, you may be back buying another perch in less than a week. One way caiques entertain themselves is chewing their perches and the softer the wood the more inviting it is to chew. This is not unique to caiques, and many bird shops sell manzanita branch perches. Manzanita is exceptionally hard, but even these may be chewed and need replacement.

A home center is a good place to buy both dowels and regular hard wood lumber for perches. As previously noted for wood chips, avoid treated lumber. When you buy dowels, select a diameter of ½ to ¾ inch. The dowel rods sold by home centers are of hard wood so they should last some time. However, short lengths of rectangular 1" x 2" and 2" x 2" hardwood lumber will serve as well. Both oak and fir are suitable for caiques.

If you do not want to buy perches at all, you may use branches cut from a tree. For this, select branches of appropriate diameter from trees that are safe for your bird to chew. (A short but incomplete list of acceptable and unacceptable trees for perches is included in Appendix D.) After cutting the branches to length, sterilize or disinfect them. If the branch is short enough, you can sterilize it by baking it in an oven for 20 minutes at 225°F. If it is too long to fit your oven, soak it in a dilute solution of chlorine bleach or Nolvasan, and then rinse it well before installation.

Finally, do not mount all the perches horizontally. Mount one or two at a steep vertical angle. Caiques are good climbers and climbing up and down the steep perches provides them entertainment. Some bird owners also install the cement-like perches meant to help keep the bird's nails trim. This seems to work for some birds, but not all.

You will also need some toys for the cage. Caiques love toys, particularly ones that make a noise. So add a toy with a bell or one that squeaks or rattles. You should add at least one toy made of soft wood to provide something for the bird to chew. They also like colored toys, especially red ones. Pet stores sell toys made especially for birds, but you can buy toys meant for human infants that are just as nice and usually less expensive. Because of liability concerns, those meant for infants may be safer than those made specifically for birds.

Sometimes you do not have to spend any extra money at all. Caiques like the colored caps off plastic bottles, plastic flatware, or other non-brittle plastic items. A crumpled up newspaper can provide a caique with hours of entertainment. The only problem with toys is that you can fill the cage so full of them there is no room left for the bird.

Cage Placement.

Carefully consider where to place the cage in your home. Pet caiques enjoy being where the action is, so place the cage near where you spend much of your time. I do not recommend keeping the cage in the TV room if you spend your late evening hours there. Caiques, like most birds, like to get their sleep. You should allow them between 12 and 13 hours of daylight. They are usually in their boxes before eight PM. Sometimes excessive noise keeps them awake, and a tired bird can be cranky. (Often you can tell when your caique is sleepy by when it grinds its beak.)

Caiques enjoy looking out a window and they will spend hours watching all the outdoor activity. As long as it is not too cool, place the cage near a window so they may have this pleasure. Avoid placing the cage in the kitchen. Most of us no longer need worry about fumes from a poorly adjusted coal stove (97), but the fumes from Teflon pans (135) and self-cleaning ovens (417) can kill birds in a matter of seconds. If you elect not to put the plastic spatter shields on as mentioned earlier, place the cage in a room with a floor and walls you can easily clean.

One thing you must understand is that manufacturers design cages for the convenience of people, not birds. This means there are all sorts of openings in the cage for feed cups and other accessories, and your bird can escape through any one of them should the cage topple. This also means that cages are not suited for long-term outdoor use. Not only can your bird escape easily, but a bird in a cage is also an easy target for predators, including our common domestic carnivores. You may believe your bird in a cage is safe from cats, dogs and other predators, but people often lose their birds this way.

Another concern about placing a caique outside in its cage is that in the wild, caiques fly through and just above rain forest canopy and like having nearby cover to duck into if they sense danger. If you take your caique outdoors into the open, it keeps a constant eye to the sky. If it sees a large bird fly over or even a low-flying plane, it will panic and fly away in an erratic manner. In the wild, hawks and harpy eagles usually soar well above the canopy and are major predators of parrots (47) Thus, caiques have good reason to be wary of the open sky. Further, snakes and rats are predators that can also easily access outdoor cages. So if you want to keep your birds outdoors, build them a sturdy vermin-proof aviary with some shelter from the open sky.

Lighting the cage

Caiques are diurnal creatures and appreciate sunlight; however, they must be able to seek refuge in shade. If they receive too much sun and heat, they will lift their wings, open their beak, and pant. They do this to increase their surface area in order to dissipate heat. If the bird overheats for an extended time, it can have a heat stroke and die. Overheating is not a typical problem for pet parrots kept in your home where they accept the same or higher light levels as people.

Even in southern areas of the United States, your pet caique may need additional light. However, it is more important to provide supplemental light in the north where they have to endure the short dim days of winter. Breeders in the United States and in Canada often provide extra light. The broad-spectrum fluorescent lamps that match as nearly as possible the spectrum of the sun are excellent. Suitable broad-spectrum lamps with a color rendering greater than 90 are available at most home supply stores.

You should be sure, however, that the fixture has an electronic ballast. These usually cost

more, but they do not flicker. (A quick test for flicker is to wag your finger rapidly under the lamp. If you see multiple images of your finger, you are seeing flicker.) Birds can detect light at a frequency of about 160 frames per second compared to the 50 to 60 frames per second of people (152). Thus, a bird will see things with a strobe effect if the fixture flickers and this may be harmful. You should place the lamp about a foot (about 30 cm) above the cage and arrange the cord so it is inaccessible to the bird.

Some lamp vendors tout the beneficial effects of ultraviolet light for parrots and sell lamps with greater UV output. Given what we know about the effects of UV light on people, we should be careful. Elderly macaws that lived their whole lives outdoors in sunny Florida at Parrot Jungle developed cataracts (81). This is also the case for people who live in sunny locales, and for people there is strong correlation between cataracts and long-term exposure to UV light.

Some parrot species, particularly those of African origin, may benefit from UV radiation. Stanford noted that UV radiation increased calcium ion levels in African grey parrots; however, this was not seen for a group of *Pionus* species (415) which are Neotropical. Assuming caiques, because they are also Neotropical, are more like the *Pionus* parrots than the African grey, there is no need for UV exposure. As long as you feed caiques a fortified seed or formulated diet, which includes vitamin D3, there is no need for UV light irradiation.

Cleaning the cage

Good hygiene is necessary for the health of your bird. Since our birds live with us in our homes, you cannot simply hose down their quarters. You are the judge of how often you need to clean your bird's cage. Some owners allow their pets out of the cage most of the day, so they do not need to clean the cage as often. Because breeder birds are usually confined to their cages, you need to clean their cages at least once a day. The total floor area of the cage is the major factor affecting how often you need to clean a cage. In general, the larger the area of the cage floor the less often you need to clean. Try not to be too compulsive about cleaning up after every defecation. Your biggest concern should be that the birds do not get feces on themselves.

A convenient way to manage cage cleaning is to layer newspapers, sheets of brown craft paper that comes on a roll, or other wide pieces of paper in four or five layers on the cage floor. Then you can simply roll up the top layer and pitch it out when it is fouled. This is what the Centers for Disease Control recommends (200), noting that the particulate type beddings are prone to produce dust that can spread disease. The corncob bedding is particularly unsatisfactory. When used during warm weather, molds can grow on it after it becomes damp from bird droppings or other debris. Some pet stores sell a clay-based material or ground walnut hulls. These come with a sifter you use to sift out the large aggregates that form when the material gets wet. There are reports that birds sometimes ingest the corncob and walnut shell. This can have disastrous consequences. If you must use one of these products, try the absorbable crown bedding paper pellets and be sure to use a floor grid to prevent the bird from reaching them. Paper pellets are less likely to result in an impaction when ingested. For me, newspapers and craft paper work well enough, and they are inexpensive.

Periodically, you have to scrub the cage. For this, you have two choices. You may buy either a good stiff brush or a power washer. A brush is the only hand tool that works well on cage bars decorated with dried fruit. I have tried steamers. They only work well on solid surfaces, not cage bars, and you end up using a brush anyway. I think there is potential for steamers, but only if you can afford one of the commercial ones that combine steam with a vacuum to suck off the debris after it is loosened.

A power washer is easy and quicker but unless you have a special indoor enclosure, you have to use it outside. When you use a power washer, pick a bright sunny day, and after being sure the birds are secure in a spare cage, take the dirty cage outside. Thoroughly clean it by directing the stream of pressurized water to all parts of the cage. Most power washers have an option for siphoning from a solution of dilute detergent and you may add a mild sanitizer such as Nolvasan if you wish.

I soak the perches and other small accessories in a sanitizer for at least 20 minutes, and then scrub down the cage itself. I then rinse the cage and accessories two or three times with water and allow them to dry in direct sunlight. If you do this when the sun is high in the sky, that is when your doctor tells you to stay out of the sun, the ultraviolet rays provide another way for sterilizing your cage. When sunning the cage, rotate it to expose all sides to the direct rays for a short while.

If you use a brush, you may use sanitizers that are more powerful. There is a list of these in Appendix E. When you use them, however, you need to take extra precautions for you and your bird's protection. You need proper ventilation, hand protection, and you should never use them in a power washer.

Chlorine bleach is one of the most effective of the more powerful sanitizers. It is also the cheapest. It is good to use on solid surfaces and for soaking small parts. There is a caution; chlorine bleach corrodes metal if you expose it too long. It is best if you only use it for plastic and ceramic items. Fortunately, there are other good sanitizers for metals.

You can clean most metal cages with Lysol. Lysol is more germicidal than most of the other sanitizers, but you should never use it on plastic parts. You cannot rinse phenol away from the plastic, and the strong smell of phenol will persist in the plastic for months. Except possibly for Nolvasan, most sanitizers irritate your skin, so always wear rubber gloves when sanitizing the cage.

Finally, it is a good idea to rotate the use of sanitizers. This helps prevent microbes, especially molds, from becoming established. If you use the same sanitizer repeatedly, the mold may develop resistance and come back again. So, if you used chlorine beach the last time you sanitized, use something like Nolvasan the next time.

Nourishment

Feeding

The feeding of parrots is a controversial topic and there are many viewpoints, some rational and some not. The debate, however, seems to be resolving in favor of formulated diets, better known as pellets, over strict seed diets. Nonetheless, all parrots have a beak well adapted for hulling seed and the ancestor of today's parrots was very likely a seedeater (188). Complicating the debate is that different parrot species have evolved different dietary needs. For example, budgerigars and cockatiels can completely sustain themselves on a seed-based diet, lories and lorikeets need nectar and pollen, hyacinthine macaws can survive on only palm nuts, while the Pesquet's parrot is almost exclusively frugivorous (327). Further complicating this is that bacteria in the crop may facilitate the digestion of some foods (295). No one has made a systematic study of the caique's diet in the wild, but we know that caiques eat seed in the wild from a report on their stomach contents. I have also compiled a list of other things they eat in the wild, and it is clear that caiques eat a large variety of plant and animal-origin foods (see Appendix C).

Caiques, like most parrots of the neotropics, are foragers. They move about the rainforest from one tree to the next eating the fruit from one, the seed of another, or the blossoms of yet another depending on the season. While it is impossible for us to emulate foraging in the wild, you can simulate it on a small scale by doing such things as placing different foods in different bowls in the cage, providing different kinds of foods outside the cage, and varying fresh foods according to the season. To provide caiques a challenge, give them an occasional almond in the shell so they have to chew in order to get to the nut.

Caiques appreciate variety. In the wild, they must change food sources whenever the fruiting season of one tree species ends, and they must move to another. This may be the reason they seem to become bored with even some of their favorite foods, such as corn-on-the-cob that they eat with relish at the beginning of the season. A changing diet may even be important for a caique's mental health.

Formulated diets (Pellets). Most modern aviculturalists recommend that a commercial formulated diet in the form of pellets, form the nutritional basis of the caique's diet. Unlike seed diets, the fat content of pellets is nearly always less than 15 percent, and those intended for obese birds can contain as little as three percent (457). In addition, manufacturers often make pellets using an extrusion cooking method that reduces the mycotoxin level (69). Nearly every brand of formulated diet will provide adequate nutrition for non-breeding caiques, but caiques definitely prefer some brands to others. They usually pick around in their pellet bowl and prefer colored pellets to the non-colored ones. Most prefer to eat the red, orange and purple pellets first. This is consistent with most caiques' preference for red fruits (62). Yet, each caique seems to have an individual preference. One will pick out all the yellow and green pellets and leave the red and purple ones behind, while another has the opposite preference. Fortunately, there is no difference in the nutritional value from color to color.

Another consideration when selecting a pellet diet is that caiques prefer sweet tasting foods. If you have trouble choosing which to feed to a caique, taste the pellets yourself and pick the sweetest. The best thing about feeding a pellet diet is that you need not worry whether your bird is getting proper nutrition. The companies that manufacture these diets have set themselves the goal of formulating their diets to supply complete nutrition.

Still, there are a number of caveats associated with feeding pellets. The most important is that you should never supply additional vitamins or minerals if you feed pellets because they are already present in the pellet. A second is that different parrot species have different nutritional requirements (327) and except for formulations specific for the African grey and Eclectus parrots, companies formulate their pellets for the generic parrot, not for the caique. A third problem with pellets is that they usually do not stimulate the same interest that other foods do. For this last reason, some pellet manufacturers recommend that you provide your bird with fresh fruits, vegetables, and seeds as a treat (249). What you should aim for is a diet of about half pellets in order for your birds to have an adequate intake of all nutrients (179).

Another problem with pellets is that some formulations contain compounds intended to stabilize some of the ingredients. Among these is ethoxyquin. Manufacturers add this to prevent fats from becoming rancid and to provide longer shelf life. There is no evidence that these additions are deleterious, but there have been no long-term studies to confirm this. Because of uncertainty about these additives, the Federal Drug Administration (FDA) notes that you should not feed the same product on a long-term basis to dogs and cats. It also recommends that pet owners rotate the source of pet foods among manufacturers (39). In view of the 2006-2007 contamination of pet foods with melamine that killed many cats and dogs and went undetected for so long, brand rotation should become the practice among pet bird owners as well.

It is best to accustom caiques to pellets at an early age. Older caiques raised on seeds often resist moving to pellets and it is a long-term process to convert them from a seed-based diet to a pellet diet. No one recommends abruptly ending the feeding of seed in order to force the bird to eat pellets. Parrots suffer too much from neophobia[8] (130, 263) for this to work.

There are a number of approaches for converting birds to pellets. Most manufacturers

---

[8] Neophobia is the fear of the new. This is very common among parrots, although caiques suffer less from this than other parrots. Among caiques, neophobia is most common toward new toys. Sometimes you need to habituate parrots to new items by placing them near their cage for a while before introducing them.

offer instructions on how to convert parrots to pellets. Pellets should be available at all times in a bowl located in the upper portion of the cage where the bird is more likely to encounter them and, if inclined, eat them. Caiques almost never binge on pellets. Therefore, as long as the pellets stay clean and dry, you may leave them in the cage several days and refresh them as needed. Still, you should replace them completely with fresh pellets at least once a week or if your bird fouls them with its feces or other food.

Seed. At one time, there were no formulated diets and every parrot owner had to rely on seed and fruit diets (443), and in World War I England, they did not even have fruit (51). In the early period of aviculture, parrots such as cockatiels, grass parakeets and cockatoos had the greatest longevity in captivity. These were primarily seedeaters (276). However, one cannot recommend an exclusive seed for the more omnivorous parrots such as caiques. These parrots departed from the predominately seed eating evolutionary track. Now, most aviculturalists feed their parrots a pellet diet. Still, anyone who has ever owned a parrot can attest to the fact that parrots greatly appreciate seeds and eat them in a ritualized fashion. They position the seed in their bill in just the right way to remove the hull, crush and then ingest the kernel. Also like other parrots, caiques prefer certain seeds to others. Curiously, unlike most other foods, caiques tend not to flick the empty seed hulls (394).

There are several commercial seed mixtures available. Those sold for parrots are usually fortified with vitamins and other nutrients. Despite the fortification, I recommend providing them in a rationed manner of a tablespoon or so a day. If you use a seed-only diet, proper nutrition is difficult to achieve. The commercial purveyors of seed diets prepare them under the assumption that parrots will eat all the seeds in the mix, hull and all. This never happens.

Further, some commercial seed diets exceed 32 percent in fat based on the contents of the hulled seeds (457). This is a particular problem with mixes containing nuts and sunflower seeds. Nearly all parrots will eat these before eating any of the other seeds. Because nuts and sunflower seeds contain a disproportionate amount of fat, parrots on this diet often become obese and develop excessive lipid levels in their blood. This can lead to a condition in which some of their feathers lack melanin giving them a pied appearance known as "localized melanic leucism" (57). If you insist on feeding a strict seed-based diet, purchase a safflower-based one and be sure it is fortified. You should also limit the amount of seed available to the bird as a way to encourage it to eat all the seeds in the mix. With seed diets, you need to be much more concerned about potential nutritional gaps than with the pellet diets. In addition to the seeds, you should provide plenty of fresh vegetables and fruits.

There are some other cautions when using a seed diet. Avoid seed mixes meant for wild birds. Wild birdseed mixes do not provide a balanced diet and a report on wild birdseed purchased in Texas found that 17 percent of them contained unacceptable levels of aflatoxin (177). Aflatoxin is a poison produced by a number of mold species that usually affects the liver. Further, some birdseed mixtures contain rapeseed (184). If you must feed one of these mixtures in an emergency, be sure it contains a rapeseed variety known as Canola™. (Canola is a registered trademark of the Canola Council of Canada.) Canola is a form of rapeseed low in the glucosinolates that are harmful to poultry. This is the same seed from which they make Canola oil.

Fresh fruits and vegetables. While the formulated or pellet diets provide a good nutritional base, you should provide an interesting selection of other foods for social enrichment, to fill nutritional gaps, and to simulate foraging. Fresh fruits and vegetables fulfill at least part of this need. While pellets are a concentrated source of nutrients, fruits and vegetables are largely comprised of water, and, unless eaten in large amounts, do not compromise the nutrition provided by the pellets (249). With few exceptions, you may provide caiques the same fruits and vegetables people eat. There are lists of some of the acceptable, less acceptable, and toxic foods in the tables of Appendix B. You will find that caiques usually prefer fruits to vegetables because they are sweeter, but every caique has its own preference quirks.

In the wild, caiques forage most frequently just after sunrise and just before dusk (181). For this reason, provide their fruits and vegetables in the morning and remove them in the late afternoon before they have a chance to spoil. If you provide fresh fruits and vegetables, they do not usually become moldy within that short interval even if you live in a warm area[9]. Prepare the fresh produce by chopping them into pieces that a caique can easily pick up with its foot. There are some notes in the next few pages and in Appendix A on how to

---

[9] The only time I ever had a problem with mold was during an anomalous period when it rained continuously for several weeks during a Florida summer.

prepare a few of the more common fruits and vegetables.

Balsa wood carving of a pallid black-headed caique (Pionites melanocephalus pallidus) purchased in Quito, Ecuador. (Carving in possession of the author.)

In some places in the world, parrot owners feed local fruits and berries not readily available in North American markets. These include the fruits of the Hawthorn (*Crataegus* sp.), European mountain ash (*Sorbus aucuparia*) and rose hips. Margaret Mee, who lived in Amazonia, fed her pet black-headed caique fresh "Solandra berries" (259). This is probably the fruit of the *Solandra gutatta*, which, except for its fruit, is very toxic. Some other fruits, such as the mountain ash fruit, require cooking before people eat them and, presumably, you need to do this for birds as well. Some people feed their parrots palm fruits such as that of the Queen Palm (*Arecasterum romanzoffianum*) (230). Hyacinth macaws eat the nuts of several species of palm, and palm cockatoos relish the fruit of the pandanus tree. I have had little experience feeding any of these foods to caiques, and I suggest you search out more information on them before you

feed them. Even in North America, one occasionally finds things such as radish pods, squash blossoms and oriental okra at farmers' markets that are not available in most supermarkets.

There is one caution related to feeding fresh produce. If you own a farm and grow your own fruits and vegetable, take care to keep them free of animal fecal material. *Salmonella* and *Escherichia coli* O147:H7 are a particular problem in this situation and can cause human infections. Birds are particularly susceptible to these bacteria. In this vein, you also need to consider the potential contamination of organically grown fruits and vegetables from some farms. Contamination of seed sprouts seems to be a particular problem and the Centers for Disease Control has reported several incidents of disease in people due to sprouts contaminated with bacteria[10].

Nectar. le Vaillant (217) reported in 1801 that wild caiques consumed so much nectar and sweet fruit that their white breasts became discolored. A more recent study has taken this further and reported that *P. l. leucogaster* is one of several parrots that serve as agents for pollinating *Platonia insignis*[11] (250). To induce them to provide this service, the flowers of this tree developed a cup-like shape with the pollen-bearing anthers clustered around the upper edge. Thus, when a bird puts its beak into the flower to take nectar, it picks up pollen on its head and carries it to the next flower. There are also reports of caiques eating the flowers of *Symphonia globulifera* (144) which belongs to the same Moronoboideae family of trees as *Platonia insignis*. Caiques also eat the flowers of the *Inga laterifolia* as well as those of some species of the *Norantea* and *Eschweilera* genera.

During my visit to the Tambopata Research Center, Dr. Brightsmith noted that he had observed caiques biting into the base of flowers, presumably the flower's nectary. Penard (309) and McLoughlin (257) made similar observations. McLoughlin noted that a flock of black-headed caiques that had foraged in a tree above him left behind red tubular blossoms scattered on the ground and only the base of the flower was missing. One feature of all the flowers that caiques have been reported to eat is that they are brightly colored pink, red or orange. This suggests that coloration of these flowers is a signal to the birds that nectar is available in them. We do not fully

---

[10] You can confirm this by going to the CDC website and typing in "sprouts" in the search window.

[11] *P. insignis* is a very tall tree called bacuri in Brazil. They make jams and jellies from the fruit that the local population relishes.

12

understand the implications in terms of total nutrition, but the many reports of nectar theft from the flowers of several species and the mutualistic[12] relationship with *P. insignis* is proof of nectar consumption by caiques in the wild.

Long before I became aware of the nectivorous ways of caiques, I was providing my birds with ginger ale or juice when out of their cages. After learning about their nectar consumption, I experimented with a number of nectar-like liquids. Based on the analysis of the sugar content of the *Symphonia globulifera* (144), I prepared a solution of five percent dextrose and five percent fructose. My caiques seemed to like this solution. I also experimented with a commercial formulated nectar mix meant for lories and lorikeets, as well as the complete liquid nutrition preparations meant for people, such as the Sustical and Ensure brands. My caiques seemed to like all of them.

You can provide a small cup of nectar in the morning and allow your bird to take its fill. You may serve any nectar-like liquid except diluted honey. While honey has the same sugar composition as nectar, the spores of the bacterium *Clostridium botulinum* sometimes contaminate it and pasteurization does not kill them. The Centers for Disease Control recommend against feeding honey to young children, and all birds except vultures are susceptible to botulism. This is the reason you should not put diluted honey into a hummingbird feeder.

The commercial lory mixes and the human nutritionals, such as Sustical or Ensure, may be used to supplement the requirements of birds that are not eating or do not eat a balanced diet—particularly those on a seed diet. The nectar I use most frequently is ginger ale or a clear juice such as cranberry juice. If you want to give your caiques something special, they like the açai juice made from a palm fruit caiques eat in the wild. This is available in some health food stores.

You should note, however, that not all aviculturalists believe giving nectar is good for caiques. While Them (432) added vitamins to the bird's sugar water, Ireland (195) believed nectar

caused caiques to be more aggressive. If you feed nectar, be sure to discard the leftover liquid at the end of the day and replace it fresh every morning.

British cigarette card. There were 25 cards of different parrots in this series C.W.S. stands for Co-operative Wholesale Society. The size of the original card is only 2 ¾ x 1 ½ inches. (Original in possession of author.)

Animal-origin foods. Some parrot owners avoid giving parrots animal-origin foods. However, most parrots are omnivorous and eat both plant and animal-origin foods. There are a number of reports of parrots eating small animals in the wild, including one of macaws catching fish (4). Insect larvae seem to be a favorite (246, 380, 386). Termites are another (257, 386), as are snails (386) and crawfish (348). Just like people, a varied diet is important for achieving a balanced diet. For example, people are unable to synthesize the amino acids known as essential amino acids. These include arginine, histidine, isoleucine, leucine, lysine, methionine, phenylalanine, threonine, tryptophan, and valine. Plants are a very poor source of some of these, but animal flesh is very good.

The amino acids essential for parrots are largely unknown (364), but Risdon (349) discovered that parrots seemed to rear healthier chicks when fed a variety of meats, and Stoodley (418) and Low (232) recommended providing them with fish or beef broth. I give my birds a small half-

---

[12] Mutualism is a relationship between two organisms that benefits them both. In this case, the tree rewards the caique with nectar in order to achieve cross-pollination. A curious fact about the Neotropical rainforest is that it has a low level of wind-borne pollen. The extreme diversity of tree species means that members of a species are usually spaced so far apart wind pollination is inefficient, so nearly all trees depend on animal vectors.

inch cube of cheese every day and some cooked meat at least once a week. If you want to give your bird a special treat, though, offer it a cooked chicken bone. A caique will shred it into splinters to reach the marrow. Fortunately, unlike dogs and cats, you do not need to be worried about a parrot having an obstruction from ingesting bones (4). Although they are not a favorite food, some parrots like cooked eggs, which have fewer problems associated with them than other animal-origin foods.

McLoughlin (257), after he learned that the conure *Aratinga pertinax* not only nested in termitaria but also ate the termites, offered termites to a hand-reared caique and it relished them. This bird also liked grasshoppers and small caterpillars. On occasion, I give my breeders a treat of a waxworm larva (*Galleria mellonella*) (206), especially when they are feeding young. Some bird owners provide crickets—live, frozen or freeze-dried. Parrots also greatly appreciate the small grubs of the flour moth (237). Thus, while a flour moth infestation may not be pleasant; your caique can make the most of your misfortune.

I have tried mealworms (*Tenibrio molitor*), but my caiques did not accept them as readily. Mealworms are considered a hard-bodied larva and Low (233) noted that most parrots prefer soft-bodied larvae. If you are adventuresome, you may rear larvae of the blowfly (family Calliphoridae) for your birds (120). There is one warning: You should be very careful about feeding your parrot insect larvae collected from the wild. There is a report of birds suffering from poisoning when they were fed inchworms collected off an azalea (474). You should also avoid feeding insects collected off shrubs and flowers contaminated with pesticides. If you wish to try live foods, crickets, waxworms and mealworms are usually available at pet stores specializing in reptiles.

Letting your bird have milk and dairy products is controversial. For some reason, many people believe birds are like people who suffer from lactose intolerance, but the evidence does not support this. Indeed, milk is a protein and calcium-rich staple offered by many aviculturalists. Bechstein (21) found milk very beneficial for birds in the early nineteenth century; Low (233) believed it was important to provide milk to birds when they are rearing their young; while Stoodley (418) advocated providing skim milk as a source of essential amino acids.

Some people believe the main problem with offering milk is that it contains lactose. Birds cannot digest lactose. Those who say you should not feed milk claim that other bacteria in the bird's gut can sometimes ferment it and this usually results in diarrhea. The diarrhea, if it occurs, is not a severe problem and avian nutritionist Tom Roudybush (359) did not see any problem with providing parrots with milk, especially low fat milk, as long as the bird's total diet contained less than ten percent lactose. One study indicates that lactose can comprise up to 20 percent of the diet without adversely affecting the growth of young chickens (130, 131), while another study indicated that feeding lactose to young chickens actually accelerated their growth (363). Some recent studies even suggest that lactose can serve as a prebiotic that can help fend off some bacterial infections in chickens (85, 86, 476). I agree with Roudybush that feeding milk in small amounts is not harmful, and my pets often share my breakfast of milk and cereal even though I do not offer it as a regular menu item.

If you remain concerned about lactose, you can still feed your bird cheese or yogurt. Bacteria or other microorganisms consume the lactose in these fermented products. These foods are excellent sources of the calcium and amino acids that parrots need, especially when they are breeding. The chief problem with these foods is that they usually contain high levels of saturated fats. I provide my caiques with a small half-inch cube or smaller of cheddar cheese daily. They tend to prefer yellow cheese to white cheese.

Cooked foods. You need to cook some foods before feeding them to your bird. For example, you should cook all meats and beans that you serve your caique for the same reasons we do this for people including to prevent disease, release nutrients, and destroy toxins. Some foods you need to cook to make them palatable. These include pasta; dried grains such as corn, rice and barley; and dried pulses such as peas (1, 30, 253). Lupins, soybeans, lima beans and all beans need to be cooked not just to make them palatable, but to destroy toxins (262, 284, 291).

There are a few commercial products intended for parrots that require cooking. These are usually mixes of a number of dried foods. A major advocate of providing cooked foods was the late John Stoodley (418). The way he recommended preparing the dry pulses was to soak them overnight in water, rinse them with fresh water, then bring them to a boil in fresh water. Once cool, he mixed them with wheat that he sprouted for two days. He recommended using a mixture of pulses—

14

everything from butter beans to split peas, occasionally replacing a portion of them with dried corn. The largest portion, that is about two fifths of the mixture, should be soybeans because they are protein rich.

Another food parrot lovers like to make for their pet birds is "birdie bread." There are a number of recipes for this bread. The easiest one is to prepare a commercial corn bread mix according to the package directions, but then add the whole egg including its crushed shell before baking. You can find additional recipes on the Internet and in bird magazines. I have found, however, that caiques do not eat enough of these to warrant making them on a regular basis.

Vitamins. You frequently see avian vitamins for sale in pet shops. Unless a veterinarian advises you to do this, you should only use these if you feed an unfortified seed and vegetable diet. Never provide additional vitamins if any portion of the bird's diet includes pellets or a fortified seed diet. All pellet diets contain vitamins and most seed mixes are vitamin fortified. Read the labels on the seed mix before you decide to add vitamins because too large a dose of certain vitamins, particularly the fat-soluble ones such as vitamin A and vitamin D can be dangerous. Further, most birds synthesize their own vitamin C (79, 209). We suspect caiques do, but we do not know for sure. If you feel compelled to provide vitamins, sprinkle them over the bird's favorite fruits taking care to follow the manufacturer's instructions. Never add vitamins to the bird's water because this encourages bacterial growth.

Mineral supplements. Almost all aviculturalists provide a mineral supplement. The argument for providing a mineral supplement for caiques is that they visit the clay-licks known as colpas in the wild (186). The real reason parrots visit colpas is unknown. One line of thought is that by consuming this clay, parrots are better able to deal with the natural toxins in the seeds and foods they eat in the wild (181). Another is that the clay simply provides needed minerals such as calcium (283). Still another is that the parrots are just seeking sodium chloride like mammals do (40, 387). Oddly, parrots in other parts of neotropics, such as in Costa Rico, do not need to visit colpas. Recently, Brightsmith (40) reported that parrots frequent the colpas more often during the breeding season just before they lay their eggs and just after their chicks hatch. This suggests they are seeking minerals in a behavior similar to captive female caiques when they breed. I have offered my caiques clay sterilized in an oven both as a dry dust bath and as a wet paste. My caiques completely ignored it regardless of the form. There may be several reasons they rejected it. One may be that it was not the proper type of clay. Parrots only eat from one layer in the clay bank in preference to others (143). The clay I saw the caiques "eating" at the copla at the Tambopata Research Center in Peru seemed to be a mineral crumble that broke apart as the bird held it in its claw while gnawing on it. Maybe some resourceful person will eventually discover the clay caiques prefer and market it.

Caiques rarely if ever chew on the gypsum-based mineral blocks sold in pet stores. Those I have attached to my birds' cages only seem to gather debris and get dirty. However, Loro Parque makes its own calcium supplement blocks and provides them to all its parrots (420). The blocks are prepared from a mixture of several calcium rich minerals including oyster shell, calcium carbonate, clay, limestone, cuttlebone and rock salt. They use the ground forms of these minerals with white cement as the binder. Sweeney noted that nearly all the parrots take to grinding their beak against these blocks and in the process obtain the small amount of calcium they need. I tried making my own mineral blocks based on the Loro Parque recipe, but my birds ignored them.

I do not offer grit. Parrots do not require grit because they do not grind their food in a gizzard, like poultry. If you watch carefully, you will note that parrots hull the seed first and then squeeze the pulp in their beak to extract the soft pulp and smaller particulate matter. They then drop the hull and coarser parts onto the cage floor, so they have little need for any grit. In the past, I offered oyster shell. Many parrot owners provide this, but my caiques completely ignored it.

The one mineral-like item they seem to like is cuttlebone. You may present it in several ways. You can secure it to the inside of the cage or, alternatively, buy the cuttlebone chunks and drop them into the roost box. Most of the time, the birds ignore the cuttlebone, but when the mood strikes, a caique will attack it and chew it into fine powder. If it is a female, this is often a sign that she is going to lay an egg soon. On the other hand, they may be just doing this for entertainment.

Tonic foods. People typically give their birds tonic foods to improve their health and vitality. Often these are the same ones touted for human use such as wheat grass, spirulina, and bee pollen. Early in the twentieth century, castor oil, epsom salts, onion, rock salt, and whiskey were the touted tonics for birds (283). These are hardly what we would consider good tonics today. Thus, the concept of what constitutes a tonic food changes with the era. Despite this, or perhaps because of the fad nature of tonics, a whole industry has sprung up to sell these products. Usually they disappear as their fad status fades.

Some proponents of tonic foods (421) recommend feeding parrots things like aloe, garlic, fresh ginger, and sea vegetables. There is no definitive evidence in people of the benefit of eating aloe (446) despite the many testimonials. If you feed it to your bird, be sure to feed *Aloe vera* since there are many species of aloe in cultivation and we do not know their toxicity. While garlic may be a good tonic for people, it can be harmful for birds. There is a report of a dusky-headed conure (*Aratinga weddellii*) dying from enforced feeding of garlic (449). To me, fresh ginger has a very pleasant odor, but my caiques ignored it. I do not put much stock in any of these tonics, but to give them a fair chance, I have tried feeding many of them with the exception of aloe, seaweed and pollen. My caiques did not much like any of the tonic foods I offered. They avoided the fruits sprinkled with wheat grass and spirulina and immediately dropped the ginger and garlic after they tried them. My birds seem quite healthy despite not eating them! There is little harm in giving a small quantity of these items to your birds, but do not expect them to be appreciated.

A few bird keepers recommend feeding small amounts of charcoal as a cleansing purgative (358), and sometimes charcoal is sold specifically for birds and parrots. Activated charcoal is used to treat cases of severe poisoning with known toxins of both people and animals, and for that purpose, they must administer a very large dose. However, I see little to recommend it for routine cleansing of the gut. Charcoal binds to many different molecules, so it not only sequesters toxins, but also vitamins and other beneficial molecules.

Dangerous foods. Dangerous foods fall into three main categories. The first are foods that are intrinsically dangerous because they are poisonous. The second are dangerous not because they are poisonous, but deleterious if consumed in excess. The third group is comprised of foods contaminated with toxin-producing fungi or other pathogenic organisms. There are other kinds of dangerous foods, such as allergens, but I do not consider them here.

As a rule, foods that are poisonous for people are probably poisonous to your birds.

However, some of the foods safe for people may be too toxic to give your bird. Similarly, parrots may be able to eat foods that are poisonous to people. The most common of the foods safe for people but not parrots are chocolate, members of the allium group of plants, certain cooking oils, and alcohol. There are studies showing that avocado is harmful to cockatiels (164, 385), but Smith noted that feral flocks of parrots in Florida partake of them on a regular basis (403).

There are anecdotal reports of chocolate toxicity. In one, a parrot ate some chocolate cake and immediately became very ill (471), and in another, an African grey ate a chocolate donut and died (82). Chocolate contains a compound called theobromine that is toxic for cats and dogs and it may be for birds, too (172). You must never feed chocolate.

Avoid feeding an excessive amount of the members of the allium family including onions, leeks and garlic. As noted previously, garlic fed in large amounts will kill your caique, and they tend to be toxic to other avian species, as well. Feeding too much onion or garlic can cause Heinz body hemolytic anemia. Also, read the labels on prepared foods to confirm they do not contain large amounts of onion and garlic if you feed them on a routine basis (466).

Although most of us are unlikely to use it in our cooking, dendé palm oil is important in some cuisines in Africa and South America. When fed to some species of birds in excess, it causes them to develop a pleasing yellow plumage; however, this plumage is the result of liver disease induced by the oil (386). Thus, I recommend against feeding caiques any oil, including the red palm oil sold as a dietary supplement. This may not apply to species such as the African grey and macaws. Indeed, oil rich palm fruits constitute the bulk of the diet of the hyacinth macaw in the wild.

Finally, alcohol can cause your bird not just to get drunk but can be deadly. You may think this is cute, but chronic use affects birds just as badly as it does people. A list of additional human foods, known or suspected to be outright poisonous for parrots, are included Appendix D.

Most of the foods that are dangerous when fed in excess are high in fat content. One of the most common diseases of the larger parrots is atherosclerosis (19). This is a frequent condition among parrots that eat too many sunflower seeds or nuts, although lack of exercise and other stimulation probably contribute (401). If you feed a diet too rich in fats, birds become obese and this can lead to a heart attack and death. Likewise, you should also not allow your bird too much salt. Giving your bird salt is as bad for them as for us. If your bird consumes large amounts of salt, it may develop kidney disease. Coffee may also fall into this category. It is thought that caffeine in high amounts can alter respiration, increased heart rates, dehydration and kidney damage in birds. However, other than a depression in fertility among chickens (296), there is little evidence to support its toxicity in birds.

It is not only important to provide nutritious food, but it must be free of bacteria and molds. For example, monkey biscuit dipped in water or juice is a favorite of caiques, but you need to be careful not to leave it in the cage very long because bacteria or molds will grow on it. You need to be especially aware of mold contamination. Molds produce mycotoxins that are dangerous for both birds and people. This is a particular problem for grains, peanuts, meats, cheese, certain fruits, and bread. This is one of the reasons to avoid providing seed meant for wild birds. Aflatoxin is a frequent contaminate of peanuts. This is a particularly potent mycotoxin produced by *Aspergillus flavus*. You should only feed the unsalted peanuts meant for human consumption since these are monitored for this toxin. Grapes are another food frequently contaminated with mycotoxin. At least two kinds of mold that grow on grapes produce the mycotoxin ochratoxin A. Be sure to avoid feeding grapes that are obviously moldy or have unusually fragile skins. You should not feed any food that has an off odor or is obviously moldy. It is not worth the risk. This is why it is important not to allow fruits and vegetables to remain overnight in the bird's cages. Some also think spoiled and rotten fruit causes diarrhea in parrots.

Entertainment foods. You should give some foods to your bird more for entertainment than nutrition. A freshly cut leafy limb or twig off a tree is one of these. Of course, be sure it is from one of the safe trees listed in Appendix D that has not been sprayed with an insecticide. It need not be a deciduous tree. One of the things that Loro Parque provides its parrots is a bough of a pine native to the Canary Islands. I have seen caiques pruning leaves and small twigs off large trees in the wild and captive caiques like to do the same. There are many other things of this nature.

If you are able to acquire carrots, beets, turnips and other such vegetables with their tops,

give the tops to the birds. If the spacing of the bars on the top of the cage is close enough, you can dangle the stems of Swiss chard, turnips, etc. over the wires of the cage near a perch. Caiques like to chew on both the core and leaves of cauliflower and broccoli. If you buy Brussels sprouts on the stock, mount the leftover stock as a perch. This stock is very tough, and it takes the bird a long time to chew through it. Give them the husks from your corn-on-the-cob and the skeleton of stems left after picking off a bunch of grapes. Little things like these provide them hours of entertainment and helps keep their beaks in trim.

Flowers are also among the foods you may provide for entertainment. In the wild, flowers may comprise a significant portion of a caique's diet. I have listed a few of these in the list of foods eaten by wild caiques (Appendix C). One reason for eating flowers is to secure nectar, as mentioned previously. However, caiques appreciate flowers that do not produce much nectar such as nasturtium flowers and squash blossoms. You may also provide some of the same flowers given to lories. Schroeder (372), a specialist on lories, has listed a number including citrus blossoms, the yellow florets of broccoli, pansies, violets, rosemary blossoms, budding sunflowers, young dandelion blooms, roses, and monarda blooms. He recommends against giving apple blossoms or tomato blooms. In general, any blossom safe for people to eat is probably safe for your bird. So, add a flower or two from your garden to liven up your bird's life.

Treats. Caiques are especially fond of certain foods. Among their most favored treats are sunflower seeds, nuts, dried banana slices, dried figs, and chicken bones. Nearly every caique likes these. Caiques, however, sometimes develop individual tastes. Several of mine have a great fondness for cheese and prefer it to other foods. Andy, one of my pets, has a great fondness for carrots in just about every way they are prepared, whether cooked or raw. In addition, there are numerous commercial parrot treats. Caiques like them, but with so many cheaper treats available, there is little reason to buy them.

Washing foods. There are a number of food-borne pathogens and you can greatly reduce exposure to them by simply washing the food. Among the human pathogens encountered on fresh produce are salmonella, *E. coli*, and hepatitis A. Obviously, you cannot wash things like pellets and seed, but you can wash fruits and vegetables. There are a number of products sold for this purpose; however, these are no more effective than using city tap water (New York Time, Dec. 17, 2003).

Here are some pointers on how to wash produce: First, never wash produce before storing. This spreads bacteria and accelerates spoilage. Buy leafy produce such as lettuce and cabbage with their outer leaves still attached. Contaminants mostly occur on the outer leaves and you can remove these prior to serving. Scrub firm produce such as apples, peppers, etc. under running water. Do the same for root vegetables using a vegetable brush. Rinse delicate produce such as berries in a colander with at least two changes of water, swirling during each wash. Finally, do not forget to wash produce with rinds such as melons and squash because you can contaminate their flesh when you cut into them. In other words, follow the same rules you would for people.

The serving bowl. You must clean the bowls used for the fruits and vegetables every day. The detachable stainless steel or plastic containers that attach to the inside of cage or sit on the cage floor are excellent for this because you can easily wash and disinfect them. You should put them through the dishwasher every few days. If you cannot do this, soak the bowls for a few minutes in ten percent sodium hypochlorite bleach, e.g. Clorox®, and rinse them well afterwards. Those used for dry foods do not need cleaning as often. Some stores, mostly farm animal feed stores, sell galvanized feeders that hook on the side of the cage. Avoid using these especially for water, acidic fruits and vegetables. The galvanized surface of these feeders contains zinc, which is toxic. You may use ceramic and pottery bowls, but avoid the ones made in foreign countries. These often leach lead. If you suspect lead is present in one of your feeding containers, test it with a lead test kit available at your local hardware store.

Feeding times. Captive parrots eat nearly any time in the day, but in the wild, they forage more frequently in the early morning and in the evening just before dusk (181). Offer your caique a treat the first thing in the morning. Pecans or walnuts are a special favorite, but you may offer nearly any of its favorite foods. Shortly afterwards, give your caique their fresh fruits and vegetables and permit them access to these foods most of the day, being sure to remove the leftovers in the evening. Allow your birds access to pellets at all times, but check the pellets at least once a day to see how much your birds have consumed or if your bird has fouled them. If fouling is a frequent occurrence, relocate the dish or the perch above it. You can provide a small amount of a safflower-based seed mix, but limit it to a tablespoon or less. The seed and treats are usually welcome anytime, but take care not to overindulge your bird. Treats are an important aid in socializing your bird and you should use them to create a special relationship.

To summarize, most bird nutritionists recommend that a formulated pellet diet form the basis of your caique's diet. Any of the commercial products will do, although caiques usually like the multicolored ones best. Provide seeds as a treat when your caiques are out of their cages. Do not use a sunflower-based seed mix, because they would eat the sunflower seeds to the exclusion of the other seeds in the mix. However, you can give your caique a few sunflower seeds or nuts as a treat. Caiques are also very fond of fruits, cooked meats, and, to a lesser extent, vegetables. Give your caiques a variety of fruits and vegetables, and a very small hunk of cheese or meat on a daily basis. It is best to let the season determine what fruits and vegetables to feed. In winter, give citrus and papaya; in the summer, fresh sweet corn and berries, etc. As an imitation of the nectar they would take in the wild, offer caiques juice, ginger ale, or other sugar sweetened caffeine-free beverage when out on their stand. You may also offer them occasional bits of human food straight from the table. A strict pellet diet is far too boring for a caique, and supplementing the diet with fruits, vegetables and other foods is an important source of environmental enrichment. In short, feed your bird the formulated diets to keep it in good health and the other foods to make its life more interesting.

Water

Water should be available to your bird at all times. Do not give your caique soft or distilled water; hard water is probably best since it contains calcium and other minerals your bird needs (404). You can supply the water in either a large open bowl or water bottle attached to the side of the cage. I prefer an open bowl on the bottom of the cage so that my birds can not only can get a drink, but also take a bath whenever they want. This method of watering, however, has its problems. The most common is the tendency of the bird to foul the water. Caiques have a tendency to dunk food in their water bowl. One of mine likes to dunk her nut treats between each bite. This results in a very dirty bowl. You need to change the water every day and more frequently if it is severely fouled. Once a week, you should sanitize the water bowls by running them through a dishwasher or rinsing with

18

ten percent chlorine bleach to remove the thin biofilm. If you use bleach, be sure to rinse the bowls well afterwards.

If your bird fouls its water bowl too often, you may need to switch to water bottles that mount outside the cage. Most bottles release water when the bird touches a ball valve at the tip of a tube. While this usually solves the bowl-fouling problem, it presents other problems. First, the bird may play with the bottle and release all the water at once, leaving itself without water. Another problem is that some caiques try to stuff food up the delivery tube when they try to emulate dunking their food in a bowl. This and incidental back flushing of material from the beak during normal drinking can introduce bacteria into the bottle. If you cannot change the water bottles on a daily basis, you should acidify the water with vinegar to a pH between 2.5 and 3. This is a common practice in large animal research colonies. Even with this precaution, you should inspect the water bottle every day and change it when fouled. You should wash and rinse the bottles with bleach once a week, just like the bowls.

Routine maintenance

Bathing

Most caiques love to bathe. In the wild, they are subject to frequent showers in the rainforest. They also leaf or sap bathe. For this, they rub the sides of their heads and bodies along leaves or a tree limb. If they have a fresh limb available, they will sometimes strip off the bark and bathe in the exuding sap. Indoors, they usually do not have fresh tree limbs available, but this does not discourage them. This may explain why some caiques have a shoe fetish. Many caiques like to get on your shoe and rub back and forth over it. In the wild, they probably do this with tree limbs.

When they use water for bathing, each individual caique has its own bathing technique. Some like to jump around in a bowl in the bottom of their cage. Others wait for you to turn on the faucet of your kitchen sink and then romp around under the water as it streams out. Others want you to mist them with a spray bottle. Others like you to lay a damp cloth on a counter or other flat surface so that they can rub themselves all over. Still others want to take a shower with you. Just be sure the water is not too hot and your caique can dry off quickly afterwards. If you keep your home cooler than 65°F during the winter, you ought to buy a heat lamp[13], preferably one of the red or ceramic types, to help your bird dry after its bath.

If you have a baby caique that has just weaned, it may be reluctant to bathe. This is normal and may last a year or more. You may have to be more aggressive about giving this baby a bath, especially when you begin to think you have a black-bellied caique.

Wing, beak, and nail trimming

Most pet caiques are poor fliers, but they can fly well enough to escape. Therefore, you should not take chances. If you ever plan to take your bird outdoors, you must clip your bird's wings. This is important in order to prevent it from accidentally injuring itself or escaping. Caiques become extremely agitated when they see large birds and planes flying overhead and will take flight without warning. You should trim the flight feathers on both wings of your birds so that if they fall or jump off their perch, they can control their fall. This, however, is not necessary to limit its flight. I have one bird on which I only trim one wing. This bird never flies if she can help it, and she positively detests the sight of the scissors. She only has to see them to become inflamed to the point that she will try to bite me, so I try to limit her trauma.

If you have never clipped a parrot's wings before, I recommend that you have it done by an avian veterinarian or other trained person the first few times. Watch, and have him explain what he is doing. Until you get the knack, it is easiest if two people do the clipping, one to hold the bird and one to clip the flight feathers. Some people can clip wings one handed, but this requires skill. Even for the mildest mannered bird, you will need a clean towel to wrap the bird to prevent it from nipping you. If you have more than one bird, be sure to use a fresh clean towel for each bird to prevent spread of disease.

The person holding the bird should drape the towel over the bird's back and then wrap it around the rest of the body. This is not always a tidy affair, and your bird will not like it. Then, gently place your thumb and forefinger in a circle around the bird's neck just below its head. If you are holding it correctly, the bird will not be able to reach you to give a nip and it usually relaxes a bit. You should occasionally hold the bird in this way

---

[13] One caveat is that you should avoid heat lamps with Teflon membranes.

sans the towel as part of play. If you do this often enough, the bird feels less threatened when you actually have to hold it for clipping or medical emergencies. Use the other hand to hold the bird's feet. The second person then pulls a wing out from the towel and clips the flight feathers.

There are two ways to clip the flight feathers. The most common but crude method is to clip off about two thirds of the flight feather's length all at once with a sharp pair of scissors. Take great care not to clip too close to the skin of the wing, and avoid clipping new feathers that have blood in them, i.e., "blood feathers." You may leave the two or three outermost flight feathers intact to give the bird a more esthetic appearance and a bit of control when it does try to fly.

A more professional way to clip a bird's wing is to clip each flight feather individually just behind where it is covered by the secondary covert feathers on the top surface of the wing. You do this with a pair of the notched scissors intended for clipping cat or dog nails. If you encounter a blood feather while clipping, leave it and next feather out intact. Leaving this feather will protect the blood feather while it grows. After you have finished clipping, give your bird a test flight by dropping it two or three feet over your bed or other soft landing spot. The bird should not be able to fly more than a yard or two from where you dropped it.

If you should happen to clip or break a blood feather and it bleeds profusely, use a pair of pliers and pull it out. This will take considerable force, but it is the best thing to do for the bird. Otherwise, it may bleed uncontrollably. To stop this bleeding, the best approach is to apply direct pressure until the blood stops. In the case of a feather follicle, you just squeeze it between your thumb and finger. If that fails, use a regular sewing needle and thread and suture the wound. A single suture should do. You can sterilize the needle with alcohol. Then, after about a week, snip off the suture. Do **not** apply styptic compound to the feather follicle or cuts in the skin. Styptic compounds can cause a cyst to form where the feather was pulled, resulting in a scar-like wound on the skin. Only use a styptic compound on the nails and beak.

If your caique is young and healthy, you will probably never have to trim its beak. Sometimes a bird, usually an older one, will need its beak trimmed if it wears asymmetrically. If it is malformed and there is an obvious need, you should take it to a veterinarian because this can be an indication of malnutrition or disease. Most caiques chew and climb so much the beak wears itself down. Sometimes if the beak is exceptionally long, the very tip of it will break off. This happened to me once when one of my breeders bit me. After he bit me, I was surprised to find a large piece of his maxilla in my wound. The bird's beak, however, looked better than before. Some parrot owners cope, that is blunt, the tip of the beak with a file as a way to stop the bird from being too nippy. I cannot recommend this. The tip of a parrot's beak has a large number of nerve endings in its tip and is very sensitive. When the tip of the beak is injured by coping or any other cause it may be so painful as to prevent the bird from eating.

Trimming nails is one task you should learn. Caiques tend to need this more often than other parrots. There are two reasons to clip your bird's nails. First, some birds seem to hone their nails so sharp that when they perch on your finger they dig uncomfortably into your flesh. The second reason is that some individual bird's nails grow so long they curl under and threaten to harm the fleshy part of its toes. This often happens if you are using the incorrect size perch for your bird, as discussed previously. You should make it a habit to check your bird's nails when you clip its wings.

There are several ways to trim your bird's nails. First, you may use the same kind of clippers used to clip dog and cat nails. This gives a blunt end to the nail which some find objectionable. The best tool for this is to use the short stubby scissors with the notch. If you use any of the clippers, however, you must always have on hand some kind of styptic compound. At some time in the nail clipping process, you are going to clip the nail too close to the toe and it will bleed. Apply one of the styptic powders available at your local pet shop to stop this bleeding. In an emergency, you can use a styptic pencil sold to stop bleeding from shaving nicks. **Never clip your bird's nails unless you have a styptic compound available**.

Once you have the clippers and styptic compound, have another person wrap and hold the bird in a towel just as for wing clipping. Then pull out the bird's claw and clip the nails. After you are finished clipping, watch the bird carefully to see if there is bleeding, and if there is, apply some of the styptic compound and lightly press directly on the end of the bleeding nail with your finger. Sometimes, especially if the bird is frightened, bleeding does not begin immediately. For this reason, you need to watch the bird for at least half an hour. The first few times will present a challenge because your bird will usually detest this operation.

20

With experience though, you will be able to gauge just where to clip without bringing blood.

An alternative way to trim your bird's nails is to use a wire cauterizer. The advantage of this method is that you cauterize the nail at the same time it is trimmed. The result is that there is never any bleeding. Some pet shops specializing in birds sell these cauterizers. They consist of a wire filament loop heated by the passage of an electric current. To trim the bird's nails, you place the nail taut against the wire loop, press the button to turn on the electricity, and draw the hot loop through the nail. The device I originally used, however, was of such poor quality I returned to the clippers. A good alternative may be to use one of the heated wire stripping devices that electricians use to remove insulation from wiring.

The professional way to trim nails is with a disposable coarse emery board, the same kind you use on your own nails. For this, you must have someone firmly hold the bird so that you can do the filing. When doing this, watch the board as you file. The filing can go quickly, and, if you see red on the board, stop. The red is blood. When done properly, this method of trimming gives the nail a more natural appearance, and allows the bird to grip perches better.

Keeping pairs as pets

One of the common questions from people who keep caiques as pets is whether they should get a "friend" for the pet they already own. The answer in a resounding yes, provided you do it right. I have two pairs that are pets and they are probably the best adjusted of all my birds. My pet pairs had the opportunity of choosing their own mates. Of course, they were not the ones I originally intended. In one case, a recently weaned hand-reared male, Andy, bonded almost immediately to a female, Ginger, that was about two years older. In the other case, Coco, one of my hand-reared females that had just weaned, bonded to Fred, a very stubborn male. My original plan was to set up Ginger with Fred because they were about the same age and likely to breed sooner. These four birds had other plans and they worked out just as well. The result is two pairs and four very nice pets.

In contrast, I have tried many times to interest my oldest female in a mate, beginning when she was nearly five years old. This did not meet with success. She now happily shares a cage with another female that all the males scorned. For this reason, I suggest that if you wish to set up a pair as pets, you should do it when the birds are young and flexible in their capacity to bond.

In my experience, pet caiques kept as pairs do not produce as many chicks as pairs set up for the sole purpose of breeding, and this has been the experience of others who keep pairs as pets. I believe there are two reasons for this. One is that the continual interaction with people keeps them interested in other things. I allow my pet pairs out of their cages and handle them every day. I only allow my breeder pairs out of their cages on rare occasions, even though some pairs are quite tame. Pet birds do appreciate having another bird to snuggle up to in a roost box, but you may have to remove the box to discourage breeding.

Caiques and other pets, including other birds

Caiques have individual responses to the presence of other birds. They usually ignore or try to attack smaller birds such as finches and smaller parrots. Herndon (178), who gathered a menagerie of animals on his trip down the Amazon River, noted that his "beautiful chiriclis" had no hesitation about taking food out of the beaks of larger parrots and macaws, but suspected that it bit off the bill of his small and "prettiest paroquet." However, in my experience, they usually give larger birds a wide berth, but it is hard to say just what a caique's response will be.

Young birds usually accept other birds more readily than older birds. Sometimes, single caiques develop a liking for a bird of another species, even a larger species such as a macaw. If they accept each other, your caique will spend hours sitting next to the other bird preening with only occasional spats. Before I obtained a mate for one of my female breeders, she developed a major attachment to a larger hawk-headed parrot. Alfred Wallace (450) had a similar experience with a black-headed caique and the mutual attraction it had with a hawk-headed parrot. The caique would trail after the hawk-head wherever he went, preening him whenever she got the chance. Rosemary Low (232) reported the attachment of caiques to a Quaker parakeet and to a lovebird. Other caiques, however, may detest, be indifferent to, or fear the other bird. It is difficult to predict what reaction your caique will have.

If you have mammalian pets, there are other problems. You should never keep a bird of any kind if you have a ferret. These animals are nocturnal, and will attack and kill even large Amazons while they sleep. If you have a cat or dog, you must monitor them when you allow them near your bird. Dogs, especially the small yippy ones, seem to frighten caiques more than cats. Cats, of course, should never be trusted near your bird and some breeders refuse to sell birds to people who have a cat. I have very little experience mixing these pets with birds, but you should be aware that if your dog or cat bites your bird it is imperative that you get the bird to a veterinarian immediately. Cat bites can be lethal for birds. It is not the bite itself, but a bacterium called *Pasteurella multocida*, a normal inhabitant of the cat's mouth, transmitted by the bite that is dangerous. This is not just a worry for your pet bird; it is one you should be concerned with yourself. Roughly 50 percent of all people bitten by a dog or cat develop an infection, most of which are due to this same organism (423). If this bacterium infects your bird, it can die within 24 to 48 hours. For this reason, you must always be present when these pets are together.

Caiques vary in their response to other small mammals, particularly rodents. Herndon's "chiriclis" (178) was so jealous of a "little Pinshi monkey" it would fly at it to drive it away. One of the black-headed caiques I raised spent much of its time in a screen-enclosed porch. Once, a chipmunk happened to find its way into the bird's cage. The caique immediately attacked, sending the chipmunk scurrying away after several bloody bites. However, when a squirrel happened to get into the cage, the caique hid in its roost box. Therefore, caiques may attack smaller rodents and leave the large ones alone.

Sex

Caiques are monomorphic, i.e., males and females are so similar in appearance you cannot tell which is which. Some naturalists suggest that monomophism is more frequent among monogamous bird species because they have less need to send signals to a potential mate every breeding season (411). Still, there may be some subtle phenotypic traits that allow distinguishing the sex of caiques. One is a report that yellow-thighed caiques have a sex-linked trait in which some males have a white toenail. Another is that the adult black-headed caique females tend to have a more white frosting in the yellow of their cheeks just below the eye (242). However, there is no completely reliable way for people to tell the sex of

a caique by sight, and one must resort to an alternate means of determining a bird's sex with certainty. There are a number of these—some highly reliable and others much less so. Appendix G lists a number of methods used to determine the sex of monomorphic birds as well as an estimate of their reliability for caiques.

Before about 1980, identifying the sex of a caique was a major challenge. The only reliable indication was when a bird laid an egg. This made setting up breeding pairs a matter of chance. Even the observation of copulation of one bird with another was not a sure sign because same sex birds often mount each other (195). Thus, the people who bred caiques had to resort to other poor indicators. Some thought they could see visual sexual differences in plumage (107), or tell a bird's sex by examining the closeness of a set of bones near the bird's vent by a method called pubic symphysis. The last method works well for some species, but not for caiques.

I even ran across a person who claimed that he could determine the sex by following the direction of motion of a steel sewing needle suspended by a thread over the bird's head. This person offered to demonstrate the method on Sammy, one of my pets whose sex I did not know at the time. He predicted that Sammy was a male—not much later Sammy laid an egg.

Some breeders claim they can distinguish sex by observing subtle visual and audio differences. Fran Gonzales (148) claimed that males have a more squared head shape, darker eye ring, and lower pitched voice than females. Except for head shape, I have not noted these among my caiques, and it requires some experience to perceive the head shape difference. Thankfully, however, we no longer need to depend on these methods.

There has been a succession of increasingly better approaches for determining a parrot's sex. An early one was hormone analysis (123). While it was non-invasive, only requiring a specimen of the bird's blood or feces, it proved unreliable and quickly lost favor. The first reliable method was a surgical method used by Arthur Risser at the San Diego Zoo called a laparotomy. This method required an incision into the bird's body cavity just large enough to inspect the sex organs (419). The development of laparoscopy, however, soon supplanted the need for this traumatic surgery and emerged as the preferred method for sex determination in the 1980's and early 1990's.

In the laparoscopy method, which like laparotomy is also referred to as the "surgical method," the veterinarian makes a tiny hole in the abdomen, inserts a laparoscope, and views the bird's sex organs. Because of the need to enter the body cavity, there is a small risk to your bird. This method works for most parrots, but some veterinarians think it is not always accurate, particularly if a caique is very young or out of season (326). When I was trying to secure male breeder birds, I purchased five birds in succession that veterinarians had previously surgically sexed as males. In every instance, my personal veterinarian found them to be females. Even my veterinarian indicated that one of my females was immature, but that bird laid her first egg three months later. Another bird, which the veterinarian indicated was a mature female, never laid an egg in the four years I owned her.

The late Dr. George Smith, a veterinarian whom I regarded as one of the world's leading authorities on caiques, also felt surgical sexing of caiques, particularly young birds, was unreliable. Still, this method was the most reliable at the time and many veterinarians still use it because it is the quickest method for determining a bird's sex and has the advantage of allowing the inspection of other internal organs.

Another method popular in the 1980's was karyotyping. It is also a good method, but few laboratories perform this assay anymore. The basis of this method is the difference in size of the chromosomes that determine the bird's sex. In birds, a set of chromosomes called the ZW pair determines sex. If a bird receives two Z chromosomes from each of its parents it is male, but if it receives a Z and a W, it is female. The W chromosome is smaller than the Z chromosome and one can see this size difference with a microscope when the cell is dividing. (You should note this is opposite from the XY chromosome inheritance pattern of mammals in which the smaller X chromosome is associated with being male.)

A major disadvantage of the karyotyping method is that it requires living blood cells. The blood is usually obtained by pulling several blood feathers. The test also requires a technician skilled in preparing the blood cells. This involves treating the cells with a mitogen to induce cellular division and observing them during the division process with a microscope. Thus, the accuracy of this method depended on the person doing the assay, and it fared poorly in a head-to-head comparison with surgical sexing (326). All these early clinical methods, except for the laparoscopic method, have nearly disappeared because a new, highly reliable, relatively non-invasive method has been developed—DNA sexing.

Actually, there are multiple DNA sexing methods. All are reliable. Halverson (161) gave one of the earliest descriptions of a DNA based assay—the restriction fragment length polymorphism (RLFP) method. In this method, enzymes called restriction enzymes cleave the DNA at specific sites defined by a nucleotide sequence. Halverson discovered a single DNA probe capable of annealing to the DNA of both the Z and W chromosomes; however, the lengths of the fragments resulting from the enzymatic digestion are different. Thus, when the digested DNA fragments are resolved according to size by agarose gel electrophoresis, one could determine the sex of the bird. If the probe anneals to only one size fragment, the bird is a male, since males have two Z chromosomes. If it anneals to two fragments of different sizes, the bird is a female—one of the fragments is from the Z chromosome and the second fragment of different size from the W chromosome.

There are alternative methods that detect other genes only found in the DNA of the female-determining W chromosome. Whatever the method, you only need a small drop of blood containing cells for the extraction of DNA. You can collect the blood by clipping a nail or pulling a feather. This has a big advantage over the karyotyping method since it does not require live blood cells. Avian veterinarians and some pet shops offer this service, and you can arrange for testing yourself at a number of laboratories with sites on the Internet. A disadvantage of this method of sexing is that it requires up to two weeks before you know the result.

Behavior is another way of telling sex. At one time, Dr. Smith (395) thought you could tell a male from a female by whether it makes a "piping with wing-lifting" movement when stimulated by the presence of another pair of caiques, but he later changed his mind. Nonetheless, I believe one still can use behavior to distinguish sex, although not reliably. When a flock sets up a pecking order, the top or alpha bird is usually a male. Further, males tend to be more open and aggressive, while females generally sit tight or flee. This difference would explain the success of Bernard Roer's rule for sexing monomorphic birds (171). One of his rules of parrot aviculture was that "the first bird you catch is the male, the second one you catch is the female." If you have a true pair, another way to tell is to bring another bird near them while in their cage; the male will usually place himself between the stranger and his mate.

Black-headed caiques (P. m. melanocephalus) of different ages. Recently weaned chick (left) and a mature male (right). The chick has a flesh colored beak; the mature bird a black beak. The chick's eye is dark; the mature bird has developed an orange-red iris. The chick usually has yellow to orange feathers scattered in its breast; the mature bird has a white breast. Chicks are also usually a bit smaller than mature birds. (Photo by author)

Some aviculturists believe that Neotropical parrots, including caiques, produce more male progeny than female progeny. It is possible for birds to control the sex of their progeny but this is more frequent among non-parrot species (278, 384). Smith (395) claimed this was the case for caiques, noting that his pairs produced twice as many males as females. Smith also suggested that female caiques tend to hatch last and from slightly smaller eggs and have greater difficulty surviving (396). I cannot say this has been my experience, and this is not seen for other Neotropical parrots (58, 75, 410). However, in an analysis of presumably randomly provided samples, a laboratory that does commercial DNA sexing of parrots (426) found they had sexed 247 male but only 201 female black-headed caiques and this difference was statistically significant. The result for the white-bellied caiques was less definitive, because of a smaller sample size. Of these, 20 were female and 26 were male, while the trend was the same, the result was not significant. If this result holds up, it suggests that a ratio of four females hatch for every five males. These data, however, are very soft and need further verification.

As far as selecting one sex as a pet over the other, it is a matter of what kind of traits you want in your bird. Males may have a greater propensity to talk, but females will talk. A more important consideration, I believe, is the bird's behavior. Generally, males are more fearless than females. They will jump off their perch and track you down when you leave the room for too long, while females are more likely to stay put. Males like to explore their surroundings more than females. Males also tend to be more destructive and are more likely to chew on your furnishings than females; however, females go into high gear chewing just before they go to nest. Males tend to remain chummier when they get older; older females, while they still like you to hold them, usually demand less attention. Of course, these comments are general and individual birds may not fit these behavioral profiles.

Lastly, while still on the topic of sexuality, I want to discuss departures from normal heterosexual bird relationships. Some parrots will rub their posteriors over your hand while making distinctly different sound. They are masturbating. This reality of life will not go away despite the forced firing of the former Surgeon General Dr. Jocylyn Elders when she recommended masturbation in the early Clinton administration. Bestiality is perhaps a better term, since they usually want to masturbate with their favorite person. Both sexes indulge in this. Females tend to do it only when they are in season, and they sometimes lay an infertile egg. Males will do it almost anytime. Not all birds engage in this behavior, but if they do, it does not mean they are maladjusted.

Parrots also have homosexual relationships. Early aviculturalists were keenly aware of this when they noticed that some same sex pairs of caiques were very content (195). There is even a report of a free-flying male scarlet macaw that developed a strong sexual attraction to a male blue and gold macaw, even in the presence of suitable mates of the same species (9). Sexuality is pervasive, even for birds. They are just following their natural instincts. Many dog owners are used to this behavior in their pets. Fortunately, birds usually only get it on with persons they know, and not with complete strangers, as do dogs.

Life cycle—maturation

As your caique matures

As a caique matures, it will change in both physical appearance and behavior. This will help you know if you are purchasing a young bird or an adult. Baby caiques are nearly adult in size when they wean; they will only gain a bit more weight. Changes, however, occur in other traits, which are a bit different among the subspecies.

Adult black-headed caiques have snowy white breasts. Babies usually, but not always, have yellow flecked, sometimes even golden breasts, until after the first molt or two. The beak is horn-colored in very young birds, but as it grows, it becomes black. The featherless periopthalmic area around the eye is often flesh-colored in young birds, but not always. It usually becomes black with age, but in some instances stays whitish. The eye of an adult has an orange-red iris, while the eyes of young birds have a brown iris and appear to be nearly black. The dark baby eyes will slowly change in the first year. Less noticeable will be the decrease in number of green-tinged feathers on the head and a slight broadening of the tail. The immature pallid form is reported to often have a few green feathers on their thighs that later molt to the lemon color that distinguishes them from the nominate black-headed form (432). Dr. Smith (399) reported that older black-headed caiques sometimes develop a few orange feathers in their crown.

Like the black-headed caique, young yellow-thighed caiques have dark eyes that undergo a change to a rust brown color. Their breasts are also flecked with yellow and become snowy white as they age. Some yellow-thighed chicks have green frosting on their legs that disappears in adulthood. Their feet usually darken but do not become as black as those of the black-headed caique, and occasionally their feet remain flesh-colored. Unlike the black-headed, their beaks do not grow in black. The most noticeable change is that young birds nearly always have dark feathers on their crowns. It often requires several molts before their heads are completely orange-apricot in color. This may occur in as few as six months or as long as four years (328).

Because I have never owned, let alone bred the green-thighed, I cannot provide a firsthand account of the changes for these during maturation. A breeder has informed me, however, that their maturation process is similar to that of the yellow-thighed except the chicks usually have more black on their heads. Further, they usually retain their black head feathers longer than the yellow-thighed, losing them just before the birds reach sexual maturity. Another difference from the yellow-thighed is that their feet remain flesh-colored instead of darkening.

Aging also leads to behavioral changes. Nearly anyone can handle a hand-reared chick, even strangers. This is when they are sweet and gentle towards everyone. At this age, they want the attention of people so much they will actually jump right onto anyone's finger. At about a year or more of age, however, your bird will go through what in human terms we would call the terrible twos. At that time, it may become nippy. Usually it nips you just enough to hurt, but not enough to break the skin. Bear with your bird, let it know your disapproval, but do not use physical punishment. As is the case for the terrible twos in people, this period will pass, although it may require a couple of years. Once your bird gets through this period, it will bond even more strongly to you.

Your bird may begin to have temper tantrums as it ages. Julian Huxley has written that people and animals are analogous to ships commanded by several captains (227). On the human vessel, all the captains remain on the bridge and give orders simultaneously. However, on the bird vessel the captains reach a gentleman's agreement whereby all the others leave the bridge whenever a stimulus causes one captain to take complete command. The temper tantrums of caiques are like this, i.e. they seem to have an on-off switch.

You can usually tell when your bird's temper is up by looking at its eye. Caiques and other South American parrots have two irises in their eye—one for controlling light exposure and another to express emotion. When they pin or flare their eyes, they are usually angry and lose control of rational behavior. This is called this pinning because the pupil of the eye becomes very small. In caiques, an increase in redness of the eye accompanies pinning, which is why this also called flaring. When you see this, it is a sign you need to be very careful. For some reason, the bird is no longer rational. The solution is to let it calm down on its own. If this is not possible, and the bird is in harm's way, use a thick towel, stick or bird ladder to pick up your bird and immediately place it on its perch or back in its cage. You will quickly learn the stimuli that usually set off this reaction.

Caiques are not domesticated in the sense that chickens and turkeys are. Their tameness is due to a process called imprinting, in which the chick upon opening its eyes, sees a human being instead of its parent, offering it food (227). That person becomes its ersatz mother. As with most concepts, imprinting is more complicated than this. In the first few years that I bred caiques, I learned that if I handled chicks left with the parents on a near daily basis, they became tame. This led to my co-parenting approach to rearing chicks. This means that the chicks imprint not just on their parents, but its siblings and even people during this early developmental period. There is also an element of learned behavior since you can tame many species of wild-caught parrots. Even so, pet caiques are only a few generations removed from the wild, and instinctive reactions often surface. For example, certain stimuli cause them to flee while others provoke attack. On occasion, you will have trouble discerning just what stimulates these reactions. Your tame bird is really a wild bird at heart, no matter what its age.

We know little about the geriatrics of parrots. One of the things we do know is that atherosclerosis may be one of the most common diseases of older parrots. There are no reports of this for caiques, but it is very frequent among Amazons, African greys, and macaws (19). In people, the risk factors for this condition include smoking, obesity and inactivity. There is also an indication that diet is an important risk factor among parrots, but no one has provided definitive proof (20). The data suggest that we need to keep our parrot friends trim and well exercised.

How long do caiques live?

Your bird will probably not die from old age. Birds generally live longer than mammals of comparable body size and data suggest that the larger the genome size the longer the life span of the bird (270). This may be the reason so many pet birds die after an unfortunate accident, are lost when they escape, or die of an infectious disease rather than from aging. If you avoid accidents and your bird remains healthy, you can expect it to be with you a long time.

In 1911, before aviculturists knew much about parrot nutrition or much else about parrot culture, the caiques in the London zoo lived an average of four years (267). The oldest caique, however, was twenty years old when it died. Brown (54) reported that a green-thighed and a yellow thighed acquired at unknown ages, only survived five and ten years respectively in the Philadelphia Zoo. By 1946, the average age at death was up to six years. However, Lady Poltimore (317) owned a pair reported to be 34 years old in 1958. Ralph Lima (222) reported in 1996 that several of his breeders were over 20 years old and George Smith reported in 1990 that several of his were more than 30 years old. Yet, a group of yellow-thighed caiques imported in 1980 to the United States lived to be only about 20 years of age (338). Brouwer (53), in a review of parrot longevity, reported that a female black-headed caique had lived to 22 years and a female white-bellied had lived to 26 years. A caique that died at age 45 in the London Zoo holds the present official record (8); however, there are unsubstantiated reports of birds in some zoos that are over 50 years old and still breeding.

Aviculture continues to improve, and it is likely your bird will be with you for a good portion of your life. The average age at which a well-cared for bird dies is still unknown, but the 45-year mark may be longer than you should expect.

Behavior

Personality

We tend to apply human personality traits to animals, and this may or may not be appropriate. It is becoming clear, however, that animals, like people, express a wide range of individual personalities. Scientists have not always recognized this, but now, animal personality studies are attracting considerable attention (101, 150). As of yet, scientists do not have a standard nomenclature for personality traits.

Most people who write about caique personality use a broad brush when they try to characterize the general personality of the species. Thus, they characterize caiques as charming (195, 233, 454), fearless (148, 233, 454, 470), mischievous (102, 233, 454), extroverted (399), brash (399), swaggering (399), bullying (399), intelligent (195), curious (148, 454, 470), uninhibited (148), stubborn (244) and playful (102, 186, 244, 454, 470). I have used some of these adjectives in the introduction. No author describes them as timid or fearful, but under certain situations, such as the presence of a much larger bird, they clearly are. While these traits provide a general idea of the personality of most caiques, one cannot state that every caique has all of these traits. Every caique has its own personality!

One personality trait among caiques that varies from bird to bird is neophobia. I mentioned this briefly in the food section. Neophobia means fear of the new, and is quite common among parrots (130, 263). In the case of caiques, this can take the form of fear of a new toy, food, person, etc. My personal experience suggests that each caique has a different degree of neophobia. Upon placing a new toy in a cage, one caique may immediately be attracted to it and begin playing with it, while another is fearful of the toy and distances itself from the perceived danger.

There probably is a spectrum in the personalities of caiques for each of the traits listed above. Most of us do not interact with a large number of caiques, so we fail to develop a full appreciation of the range of their individual personalities.

Fixed Action Patterns

A fixed action pattern is one in which a stimulus sets off a preprogrammed often innate reaction in an animal. The first to bring these patterns to our attention was the Nobel prize winning ethologist Konrad Lorenz (226). He referred to the stimulus as a "releaser" because it unleashes a specific reaction trajectory. For the most part these seem to reflect normal reactions, but some may seem peculiar to us. There are many examples of this pattern and I can only give a few examples here.

- The bathing of one caique is usually a stimulus for all the other caiques in one's flock to bathe.

- The need to defecate usually causes a caique, especially one that is breeding, to fly to the perch furthest from the nest box before it defecates.

- The alarm call by any bird, not just a caique, will send a flock into a frantic escape flight in all directions.

- Parent caiques respond to a chick begging by regurgitating food for them.

- Stolzmann (320) reported that caiques whistle when a storm is approaching.

Ethologists look at fixed action patterns as units of behavior, and the assemblage of these units is an ethogram (227) and a species' behavior is made of a complete set of these units. While they may not be obvious at first, you will quickly learn more about the fixed action patterns of your bird. You will also notice other fixed action patterns in the rest of this discussion of behavior. You see them in everything from teaching your bird to talk to toilet training to biting. Much of what constitutes bird training is the modification of the pre-existing fixed action patterns of your bird.

Bird talk

Most caiques lack a strong ability to talk. Instead, they are valued more for their ingratiating behavior. They do learn a few words, but their vocabulary is unlikely to be as large as that of an African grey or Amazon. They can learn to whistle and once they learn, it may be hard to keep them quiet. I have never made any serious attempt to teach any of my birds to talk because this is a difficult task when one has more than one caique. They prefer to talk caique with their fellow birds rather than take on the challenge of learning a human language. Recently, Beckers et al (22) demonstrated that Quaker parrots are able to use their tongues to control the formation of sounds produced in their sryinx in a way similar to how people use their tongues to control sounds produced in the larnyx. Indeed, people and parrots are the only species capable of this. This may also explain why caiques do not talk as well as other parrots; they may not be able to control their tongues well enough to enunciate our human words clearly.

Parrots, including caiques, learn to talk due to a phenomenon called call convergence (180). In the wild, when a male parrot meets a female parrot it likes and would like to mate with, it changes its call to imitate that of the female (at least in the case of budgies). Young male birds are more adept at this, but even female and older birds can do it. Thus, learning to talk is probably part of the bird's courtship behavior.

If you want to increase the chances of getting your bird to talk, here are some suggestions. First, the best talkers are usually young males. Second, it is best to keep the bird away from other birds so that it will focus its attention on you. You must interact with the bird frequently using the same words repeatedly and associating the words with some activity. For example, every time you visit the bird's cage say something like "What 'cha doin'." This is a phrase that caiques seem to find easy to learn. If your bird beaks or pumps on your finger, it is a good sign. That behavior means your bird is trying to bond with you and is more likely to try to imitate you. However, do not get your hopes up too much; caiques almost never learn to pronounce words as clearly as some other parrots. Typically, when they talk, they speak in a softer voice; you will probably have to accommodate yourself to their version of talking. If you decide to teach your bird, I wish you good luck.

Toilet training

Caiques are among the larger parrots that you can toilet train. Dr. Smith (397) noted that caiques have two habits that can aid you in training your caique. First, if your caique is a healthy adult, it will never defecate in its roost box; this means it has a great deal of control over its bowels. Second, just before a caique defecates it squats and waggles its tail. You can use these characteristics to toilet train your bird.

There are several steps to toilet training. First, decide on a stimulus to use to encourage the bird to eliminate, for example, a newspaper or receptacle such as a trash bin. Then, the first thing in the morning after you remove the bird from its cage and any other time you remove it from the cage provide the paper or chosen receptacle for the bird to defecate onto. Accompany this with a word or other signal such as "Potty." It is very important to say the word so the bird will be able to associate it with the need to defecate. Later, when you notice the bird wanting to defecate, say the word and offer the same receptacle. Immediately after the bird is finished reward it with a caress or treat. If all goes well, your bird should soon learn to do its toilet on command.

If you have not clipped your bird's wings, it is possible to train it to fly to its toilet when it needs to defecate. The owner only has to choose where the toilet is to be located. There is a report of a couple who allowed their parrot the liberty of their home and taught their bird to use the toilet in the bathroom (475). To do this they installed a perch well above the toilet where the bird would fly when the urge struck. There were only two problems; it would not flush, and it would not await its turn when the toilet was already occupied. Allowing a bird to fly free in your home is not usually recommended, but this may compensate in a small way for having your furniture and plaster chewed.

Hopping or dancing

One behavior that caiques exhibit that other parrots do not is a hopping or dancing action. This dancing takes the form of repetitive hopping in which bird jumps so that both feet leave the ground. Jean Stolzmann (422) reported this from his travels in Peru. He noted: "The inhabitants teach them to dance. In the evening they place them on a table lit by a candle, and sing or whistle and clap their hands, the parrots hop to this noise. For such a dancing parrot one pays between 40 to 50 FR." My caiques, particularly the male caiques, like to hop. I have not tried to train any of my birds to hop on command, but this may be possible. Often you can induce and prolong the hopping if you clap your hands in the cadence of the bird's hopping.

Biting

Parrots bite! Indeed, a caique's bite can be a painful, bloody affair. The bites are not as life threatening as those of dogs, which between 1979 and 1994 resulted in more than 279 deaths, mostly children (7). Still, there is no way of avoiding the fact that one day, what you thought was the sweetest bird in the world will bite you or someone else. This is one of its ways of communicating. You will have to learn just what stimuli sets off your bird.

A hand-reared pet caique under two years of age almost never bites with vicious intent. If it bites, it is almost certainly out of fear. Even a non-humanized parent-reared baby seldom bites. Young birds usually only bite as part of their play; this is their way of testing your tolerance level. Their playful bites are more pinches than bites, a part of their exploration of life.

When an adult bites with intent, it is very different. It will take a lot of understanding on your part to bear with your bird then. However, with patience, both you and your pet will come to understand how to deal with the biting. Oddly, some, but not all, pet caiques are remorseful after biting you, so there is a need to re-establish communication after both of you have calmed down. You need to show your bird that you still love it. That is the hard part!

There seems to be four biting patterns. The first two are unrelated to the sex of the bird. The third is most common in males. The fourth occurs only in females. The first of the biting patterns has to do with objects and is unrelated to sex. Each of my birds seems to have certain physical objects they loath and to avoid a bite, you must not hold or be near the offending item. This response fits the fixed action pattern in which a stimulus sets off an innate response (226). It is understandable that caiques may dislike scissors if you clip their wings with them, and all my pet birds know exactly in which kitchen drawer I keep the scissors. They not only hate the scissors, they hate the drawer. Therefore, I must always be careful to place my birds on a perch far away from that drawer before I open it.

They also equate other tools that operate in the same manner as being scissors. Therefore, I can never hold a bird when I use tools such as pliers, hedge clippers, or tongs. What is odd; however, are some of the other objects they sometimes learn to loathe. One of my males hates brooms. When I take out the broom and begin sweeping, he hops off his perch and attacks it. One of my females hates mixing bowls and tries to get into the cabinet to attack them. Another female hates the sound and sight of me pulling sticky-tape off a spool. I have a male caique that hates my hands but is very amenable to nuzzling with me if I keep my hands hidden. I suspect this is because I do all of his nail and wing trimming. It is wise not to get between your caique and the object it despises. If you do, you are likely to get a nasty bite even though it is not directed at you *per se*.

The second non-sex related biting pattern is the "how could you abandon me?" bite. I have one female that tries to bite me every time I return from a long business trip. A friend of mine has a male that is prone to the same response. Both of these birds are loners. Loners do not socialize with the other birds as much, so when you, their idol and normally faithful "mate," abandons them, they respond by biting you when you get back. I am now very aware of this biting pattern and take great care to avoid picking this caique up immediately after I return. I know when I can safely handle her because she no longer pins her eyes when I approach. This does not seem to be a problem for pet caiques kept in pairs.

Normally, females are gentler than males but they are less predictable. A nearly sure indication that a female is upset and about to bite is when her eyes flare. When a male flares his eyes he is excited, but it is not a reliable signal that he will bite. The unpredictable female biting pattern seems to be related to season, a sort of caique version of PMS. The female does not start this behavior until she reaches sexual maturity at two or three years of age. I have three pet females, and I am always startled the first time they bite. Typically, there is an increased frequency of biting by my female pets shortly after one of my breeder pairs goes to nest.

However, the out-of-nowhere bite can happen at other times during the year, as well. For instance, your favorite bird, that is sweet and has always desired your company, ferociously bites its favorite person. The female's tendency to bite usually lasts about a week. During this time, it is important to watch the bird's eye for flaring. Use a stick or ladder to move it from place to place. Keep it off your shoulder. Some birds will try to attack your face. One of the oddities of this pattern of biting is that the bird directs it toward her favorite person. Another person in the household, normally not the bird's favorite, will still be able to handle it without a hint of threat.

Usually this kind of biting is worst the first few seasons. As the bird ages, it usually learns to control this response and the bites become firm nips. However, even in older caiques the hormones can rage, so give them their space during this time. They are usually as shocked by their behavior as you, especially the older birds that seem to understand that something is happening beyond their control. Therefore, it is important for you to have patience and resist hitting the bird in retaliation.

Males, and occasionally females, have a biting pattern directed against other animate beings, usually another bird or human being. The bird decides that certain people and other birds are either friends or enemies. I had one pet male, Pony Boy, that allowed me to roughhouse with him and toss him about while he chuckled with glee. However, if my partner even went near him, the bird lunged and tried to bite. This behavior began the first day I got the bird, so I know my partner had done nothing to provoke this antipathy. One of my other males, Fred, detests me and two of my pet females, but completely tolerates my partner, another female and a younger male. I should add that Pony Boy and Fred also hate each other. While I can handle Fred, if I allow either of the two females near him, and I happen to be in between them, he bites me.

Some females also dislike certain people and not others. Sammy, my dominant female, seems to detest strange women with a certain voice quality. Yet, I have never known her to attack a man. In a variation of this pattern, the bird bites its favorite human being as a way of keeping him or her from straying too close to other birds or people. One of my males has this tendency. Therefore, you must always take care when you have your bird out around other birds and human strangers.

Biting is one of the downsides of caique ownership. It is something that will inevitably happen. Except for the sudden surprise female PMS biting, you will come to understand what stimuli elicit it. You will learn to keep the scissors and other stimuli out of sight. You will also learn the reason all bird trainers recommend training your bird to get on a stick or bird ladder. When your caique is in a biting mood, the only safe way to handle it is to coax it onto a stick or pick it up with a heavy leather glove or very heavy towel. The stick is preferred, and you should only use a glove or towel in extreme circumstances. Agaain, never hit the bird! You must realize that it is acting out of instinct.

You can apply negative reinforcement by putting it somewhere it does not want to be. For example, if the bird really wants to be out, put it in its cage for an hour or so. Sometimes, however, the cage is exactly where the bird wants to go. The idea is not to reward a caique for undesirable behavior. Therefore, if you notice that it is too eager to go back in its cage, put it in a safe place it does not like, for example, a timeout box or a darkened room for a short while. Do not leave it alone too long— just long enough for the bird to get the idea that it will be denied your presence if it persists in biting. Of course, if it is trying to bite a guest in your home, put it in its cage. In this case, it is better to protect your guest than train your bird.

Feather plucking and barbering

By far the most insidious behavioral problem of parrots is self-mutilation. The mildest form is the barbering of its feathers. In barbering, the bird compulsively chews the vane of its feathers but does not pluck it out. The next level of self-mutilation is feather plucking. In this case, the bird pulls its feathers out, leaving bare skin. While a little barbering may seem a minor problem, plucking and in rare instances, actual skin mutilation are causes for concern. Fortunately, this is not as frequent among caiques as for some other parrot species.

Sometimes, there is an underlying physical cause for plucking. Giardia, an endoparasite that colonizes the bird's gut, is the most frequently encountered. Giardia colonization seems to irritate the feather follicle in some way. Oddly, ectoparasites that colonize the skin it self seldom lead to plucking by larger parrots, although it can for lovebirds (18). Infections due to bacteria, fungi and viruses may also cause a bird to pluck. These may be the cause of the skin inflammation seen for some parrots (140), but there is little proof of this. However, in some viral infections, particularly parrot beak and feather disease (PBVD) and polyoma viral disease (PVD), the loss of feathers is due to disease progression and not plucking. There have also been attempts to link plucking to an allergenic reaction. A study of allergies in parrots that were plucking, noted that 93 percent (14/15) of birds developed a skin wheal to an allergen when challenged intradermally (239). In contrast, only two percent (1/41) of normal birds developed a wheal. Of the allergens tested, corn (maize) and sunflower were the most allergenic. Others dispute this connection, but if you were feeding corn or sunflower, there would be little harm in eliminating them from the bird's diet.

There may also be underlying metabolic causes such as hormonal imbalances, but there is little to support this. On the other hand, two of my female caiques that died, plucked their breasts the last few years of their life. When the veterinarian necropsied the birds, he diagnosed them as having long-term liver disease. I cannot say definitively that was the reason they plucked, but it is suspicious. Finally, nutrition, and possibly poisoning, may be a cause. Some early reports suggest you can treat these parrots with dietary supplements such as vitamins and minerals (18), but this is unproven.

Unfortunately, the main cause appears to be "psychogenic feather picking" and this is frustrating to treat. In African grey parrots, this appears to be due to stress and correlates with higher levels of corticosterone in their feces (294). Usually, some trigger initiates plucking by caiques. Among breeder caiques, one trigger appears to be a frustration related to a failure to rear chicks. I had one case of a hen that started plucking herself after her mate killed her chick, and another plucked her breast after she laid a clutch of sterile eggs.

Pet birds sometimes start plucking if you neglect them too long. When you become a parrot's mate, there is a built in biological reaction by the bird to believe that you should be there at all times. There are many tales of people leaving on vacation and returning to a plucked parrot. I once relocated a female pet caique to my bird room, thinking she would enjoy the visual interaction with the rest of my birds. She tolerated it for nearly six months before she began to pluck. It took me another three months to realize that what she wanted was to return to her original location where she could interact with me as frequently as possible.

A group at the University of California at Davis studying psychogenic feather picking by parrots, specifically orange-winged Amazons (*Amazona amazonica*), is starting to shed new light on parrot emotions and what leads to plucking (138, 139, 260, 261). Among their findings is that the condition is more prevalent among females than males, which is consistent with my observations for caiques. They also noticed a relationship between cage location and plucking. Their data suggest that birds located closest to the entry door of their aviary are more prone to plucking. They attribute this to the stress of people startling the birds when entering the aviary. I do not quite agree with this, since the cages of the birds that tended not to pluck were also adjacent to a wall. In my experience, caique-breeding pairs kept in cages adjacent to a wall are calmer than those in cages in the center of a room. Thus, another explanation is that being near a wall gives the pair a sense of added security since they realize nothing can attack them from that direction.

The research group's most important observation, I believe, is that plucking tends to run in family groups. This suggests heritability, but the data does not rule out early rearing experience. If it is heritable, it means that breeders can select against this trait. The researchers point out that selective breeding of chickens succeeded in eliminating chickens that pluck other chickens in just a few generations. If it is heritable, I suspect it will take much longer to eliminate plucking among parrots than it did for chickens. Most parrots do not begin to pluck until they are several years old, often as late as 10 or 15 years of age. By that time, a pair will have produced many clutches. Nonetheless, if plucking is heritable, breeders should select only well feathered birds for breeding as a start to eliminating this trait.

Currently, the best approach to plucking is to try to prevent it, and the best way to do this is to shield your bird from stress as much as possible. First, place your bird's cage in a place that gives it a sense of security. Until we know more, I suggest placing the cage against a wall at a distance from any entry doors. The other thing we can do is provide enrichment. Caiques are very inquisitive and you can do this by providing them with a periodic change in toys, new and interesting foods, time to explore outside their cage, etc. Providing them with a parrot friend also enriches their lives. The more entertained they are, the less likely they are to pluck.

If your bird does start to pluck, seek veterinary care as soon as possible. By taking quick action, you may be able to limit the damage. A good avian veterinarian should assess whether the plucking is due to a physical cause. An immediate remedial step may be to place a Victorian collar around the bird's neck. This physically prevents the bird from plucking. This collar is not a permanent solution and is awkward for the bird to manage. A slightly less awkward collar is a tube collar made from the foam pipe insulation that you can purchase a home supply store[14]. A tube collar works well to prevent breast and body plucking, but not very well if the bird is plucking its wings and tail. Once either collar is in place, be sure the bird is still able to eat and drink.

Several companies sell products for remedying feather plucking—none of which work well. The most noteworthy are feather sprays. The aloe and bitter sprays work to some extent, but you should avoid those containing lanolin or other moisturizers. A parrot's skin is naturally dry so you may actually cause more harm.

Unlike some parrot species that pluck out every feather, caiques usually only pluck or barber patches of feathers. Further, plucking usually only occurs during the molt period. If you fail to catch your caique plucking during one molt period, you have an opportunity to take remedial action at the beginning of the next molt period. For this, you need to be alert to when the molt begins. The molt usually begins shortly after the breeding season ends and you see spiky blood feathers poking through the skin. In the northern hemisphere, the molt usually begins at the end of June and continues through September. When you observe these new feathers coming in, it is time to put a collar on. If all goes well, you should be able to remove the collar after all the feathers have come in. Your bird will not pluck them again until the next molt period, but no one can guarantee this.

Behavior modification

After diet, the main topic of discussion among parrot owners is behavior modification. Usually people want to eliminate an unwanted behavior such as screaming, biting or plucking, but others just want to teach their bird to do a trick. I do not consider myself an expert on behavior modification, but there are many books devoted to this. If consultation of books does not help and your bird continues to exhibit a particularly troublesome behavior, you can consult a bird behaviorist.

Except for commenting on the problem of plucking and screaming, writers before the twentieth century did not dwell much on parrot behavioral problems. This does not mean there were no bird behaviorists. In the mid-nineteenth century, Henry Bates (17) used the services of an experienced native woman to tame what was probably a wild Illiger's macaw that almost literally fell into his hands. He wrote, "My friends in Aveyros said that this kind of parrot never became domesticated. After trying nearly a week, I was recommended to lend the intractable creature to an old Indian woman, living in the village, who was said to be a skillful bird-tamer. In two days she brought it back almost as tame as the familiar love-birds of our aviaries."

One can roughly divide the recommended methods used to modify parrot behavior into three

[14] To make a tube collar for a caique, purchase a piece of hot-water pipe insulation that has a 0.75 inch inner diameter. Cut off a piece 1.25 inch long. Bevel the inside of end of the tube to make it comfortable for the bird. Open the tube lengthwise and fit it around the bird's neck. Use tape to secure it in place.

approaches: Positive reinforcement, negative reinforcement and imitation. The most commonly applied approaches are positive reinforcement and negative reinforcement. B.F. Skinner first brought these two forms of operant conditioning to psychologists' attention. In this type of conditioning, an antecedent precipitates a behavior, which in turn leads to a consequence. Here is an example of positive reinforcement: You want your bird to step on a stick, you present the stick (the antecedent) and when the bird steps onto the stick (the behavior); you offer the bird a treat (the consequence). The treat can be a favorite food, effusive praise, or both. Offering the treat reinforces the bird's positive action and it realizes something good happens when it responds properly.

Negative reinforcement is similar to positive reinforcement except you punish your bird when it expresses an unwanted behavior instead of giving it a reward for a preferred response. An example of this is when you present your hand for the bird to mount (the antecedent) but the bird bites you instead of getting on (the behavior). You then punish the bird by placing it in a dark time-out box (the consequence).

All bird behaviorists agree that positive reinforcement works far better than negative reinforcement for curing bad behavior or for training your bird. What I have written here is clearly an oversimplification of these approaches. Discerning what antecedent is causing some unwanted behaviors can be complicated, and resolving it equally difficult. Some trainers incorporate clicker training into this approach as a way to give a quicker sign of your approval.

A method used less often to alter parrot behavior is imitation. In this approach, you playact the behavior you want from your bird. This can be with a person or with another bird that already responds properly to a stimulus. This "monkey see—monkey do" approach is what Irene Pepperberg (310) used to train some of her African grey parrots and is based on the earlier work of Todt (437). Your bird learns by example from watching another individual, human being or bird, already skilled in an activity. This is a powerful method that bird trainers under utilize; however, it is probably how young birds learn how to cope in the wild. Their main examples in the wild are their parents from whom they learn survival skills such as how to secure food and avoid dangerous situations. Indeed, chicks reared by their parents in captivity learn how to eat all the foods eaten by their parents within a week or so after they fledge.

In the wild, young birds note what their parents eat and how they break open seedpods, etc. They also probably note when and how their parents dive for cover when there is a threat from a predator. The susceptibility of chicks to imitation may explain why caiques reared in groups almost always wean much earlier than ones reared alone, suggesting they learn how to eat foods from each other. Another example of this is that a pet caique usually wants to taste the same foods you are eating and you can use this approach to teach it what to eat.

There are certain training techniques you need to avoid. You should not apply too severe a punishment when using the negative reinforcement approach, especially any that would cause bodily harm. These can cause your caique to become withdrawn or even more combative. Even more harmful may be the practice of response blocking or flooding (133). This is an enforced exposure to unpleasant situations. An example of this is wrapping the bird in a towel and handling it as a way to make it overcome its fear of people. A parrot's first response to an adverse situation is to flee. Forcing it to accept a situation in which it feels uncomfortable and has no choice but to submit can cause great trauma. While there may be a positive short-term response, positive reinforcement is far superior since it empowers a parrot to act on its own.

There are many excellent books on this topic, and despite my seemingly simple dissection of bird behavior modification into a few basic techniques, understanding bird behavior is far more complex than anyone has the ability to understand at this time. Caique behavior is one of the reasons people are fascinated with them. Their unique social skills, many of which mimic our own, endear them to us. The problems arise when their behaviors do not mesh with what we wish them to be, and often the problem is not the bird's behavior but our own.

Health concerns

Bird health and veterinarians

Nearly every reputable pet shop recommends you have your bird examined by a veterinarian familiar with avian medicine as soon as possible after its purchase. The time a shop allows varies from shop to shop, and some states have laws related to this. Whatever the time limit, the longer the better, because it takes time for the veterinarian to submit specimens to a laboratory and receive the results back. In the past, the post-purchase or new bird examination done by the vet was a cursory affair, and, unless the bird had obvious adverse clinical signs, the veterinarian usually found nothing wrong. This has changed within the past few years; diagnostic tests for several devastating bird diseases have become available. Be sure to ask the veterinarian about these; they may cost a bit, but if you have other birds, it may be wise to have these tests done before introducing a new bird into your existing flock. A trip to a veterinarian for these tests is especially important if you purchased the bird from a pet shop or other facility with a large turnover of birds where exposure to contagious diseases was possible.

Birds are not like people. They try to disguise their illness as long as possible, so when you first notice your bird is sick you must act promptly. If your bird develops adverse clinical signs, take it to a veterinarian as soon as possible. If the bird is part of a pair, take both birds with you—the other bird may be afflicted as well and having the mate nearby helps calm the sick bird. Most veterinarians are not knowledgeable enough to treat birds, so you must find a qualified avian veterinarian before you need one. The best approach for finding a veterinarian is to ask a local pet shop owner who deals in birds for the names of local avian veterinarians. Usually, you will discover that there are only a limited number of veterinarians in your area specializing in birds, and often you have to travel some distance to find one that suits you.

The second thing you need to know is where to take your bird in an emergency. My birds always seem to get sick or injured at nine o'clock in the evening on a major holiday when my veterinarian's office is closed. If an emergency does occur and you do not know how to obtain emergency care, call your regular veterinarian's phone number. You will very likely get a recorded message about where to find emergency care. In most cities, veterinarians have organized in a cooperative effort to deal with emergencies. It would save you time, however, if you already knew where to call or where to go. For example, in the New York City area, the Animal Medical Center at 510 East 62nd Street off Roosevelt on the East Side of Manhattan has a 24-hour walk-in emergency clinic for all animals.

Whenever you visit your veterinarian for the first time or for a healthy bird exam, you should discuss appropriate tests with him and if he recommends any vaccinations. These will vary with the veterinary standards of the area, the prevalence of disease, as well as the availability and reliability of tests and vaccines. Below are some of the routine tests.

1. Physical examination. This is an examination of the general appearance of the bird. It will be weighed, its general appearance noted, and its muscle mass felt, etc. The veterinarian also will use a stethoscope to auscultate for any unusual sounds of the vascular and respiratory systems.

2. Pathogen assays. There are a large number of assays for the presence of infectious organisms of parrots. The veterinarian will collect specimens such as blood, feces, swabs of the oral or the cloacal cavities, ocular exudates, etc. for these and submit some of them to an outside clinical testing laboratory. The following is a short list of the pathogens of greatest concern for which assays are available.

    a. Bacterial culture.

    b. *Chlamydophila psittaci.*

    c. Psittacine beak and feather virus.

    d. Avian polyoma virus.

3. Avian screen. This is a screen similar to the routine blood screen done for people. Veterinarians use this combination of tests to check for diabetes, malnutrition, liver disease, kidney disease, cancer, etc. It often includes a complete blood cell count that provides information regarding possible bacterial, viral, or parasitic infections.

4. Fecal exam. Veterinarians use a float test to detect parasites such as coccidia, capillaria, and tapeworms. They use a smear on a microscope slide to detect giardia and trichomonas.

5. X-ray. This is sometimes recommended to check on bone structure and for granulomas.

It is unlikely your veterinarian will order all the tests due to time and expense. He may suggest them only if there is a reason. He may suggest tests for infectious agents such as mycoplasma, aspirgillosis, Pacheco's virus, poxvirus, and Newcastle's virus. You should only order a complete panel of tests if you already have birds at home susceptible to contracting a disease from your new bird. If it is your first bird, or only bird, the veterinarian should be more selective about ordering the tests. Having the complete panel is expensive, so you must balance this against rational risks. For example, if you are sure the bird came from a closed flock and it is disease free, there may be little need for most tests. When a breeder says his flock is closed, it means that he has not added any new birds to his existing flock in several years. This greatly reduces the existence of disease in his flock. If the bird comes from an unknown source or a place where the bird was exposed to birds of questionable health, it may be very worthwhile to go for more tests.

Another recommendation that veterinarians now make is to determine the sex of your bird. The reason for this is that it may help him diagnosis and treat your bird should it fall ill. For example, a female may develop egg-binding or egg yolk peritonitis that might otherwise be overlooked. This is another reason you need to discuss with the veterinarian just what tests should be done.

You should have a well bird exam done on a regular basis. You should do this to confirm that your caique is free of problems and to catch minor problems before they become critical. It is also an opportunity to ask the veterinarian questions. The basic well bird exam should include 1.) a physical examination, 2.) choanal and fecal Gram stain, and 3.) a fecal parasite check. Depending on the situation, the veterinarian may order other tests such a blood cell count and serum chemistries. After your post-purchase visit, you should plan on at least one well bird check-up a year.

If your caique should die and its death is not due to an accident, you should have it necropsied. This is very important and you should have it done as soon as possible. Many bird diseases can only be identified in this manner. If your bird should die and you cannot take it to your veterinarian immediately, cool the body as rapidly as possible. To do this, soak the body in cool soapy water. The cooling will stop the decomposition process and the soap will allow the water to reach the skin. Then place the bird in a set of double plastic bags, squeeze out as much air as possible and place it in a refrigerator. Do not freeze it. Freezing damages the tissues making it more difficult to assess the pathology. Having the bird necropsied may be important to the health of the rest of your birds as well as the health of its human companions.

One of the good things about caiques is that they do not seem to be as prone to as many health problems as some other parrot species. Some believe caiques have an increased susceptibility to avian polyomavirus (315), but this has not been confirmed (350). Because of this, many veterinarians recommend that caiques be vaccinated shortly after weaning with the standard set of two

immunizations and then yearly thereafter. A sneeze now and then is OK. You should never attempt to medicate a bird without consulting a veterinarian. Using the over-the-counter antibiotics indiscriminately can lead to worse difficulties because the infectious organism can develop antibiotic resistance, or worse, disrupt the protective normal flora of the gut. Similarly, the bird sprays containing insecticides and the mite protectors are not only useless, but dangerous. Healthy parrots seldom have mites. For more on bird health care, read Bonnie Doane's book **The Parrot in Health and Illness** (112). It is well written and intended for the nonprofessional. Just remember, there is no substitute for a knowledgeable avian veterinarian.

Human health hazards of parrot ownership

As with all human activities, some health risks are associated with parrot ownership beyond your bird biting you. First, you can catch a disease from your bird. Such diseases are called zoonoses. Another hazard is the development of allergies to your bird or what your bird eats. Sometimes this can lead to a condition called bird fancier's lung. There have been attempts to link bird ownership during childhood to the development of rheumatoid arthritis, but there is a stronger linkage between cat ownership and this disease than for birds (34). Also of interest is that there seems to be no link between pet ownership, including that of birds, and asthma and rhinitis (323). There were a few small studies suggesting a link between pet bird ownership and cancer; however, a later scientific report (272) refuted this linkage. They found no additional risk of lung cancer associated with pet bird ownership even if the owner smokes, although there was a significant linkage with smoking. Thus, the two main human health hazards related to bird ownership are allergies and zoonoses.

Allergies are, perhaps, the most common health hazard. Worse, you can develop allergies not only to your parrot but also to what it eats. If it is a food allergy, you can just stop feeding that particular item to your bird. This is a particular problem for those who have an allergy to peanuts. Owners can also develop allergies to pine nuts (196) and sunflower seed dust (12, 266). Unfortunately, you can develop an unwanted immune response to dander and dust originating from the bird itself. Some bird owners develop an acute condition called hypersensitivity pneumonitis or chronic bird fancier's lung (288, 301). This appears to be an unwanted immune response to the inhalation of allergens. If you only suffer mild distress from the allergens produced by your bird, and remain committed to owning a parrot, make regular use of a wet mop to clean around the cage, purchase an air-cleaning device, and use a carpet sweeper with a HEPA filter. Several breeders have reported that these measures have allowed them to continue to keep their birds. If you buy an air cleaner, invest in a high volume machine that is both *effective* and *quiet*. Be advised, the better air cleaners are expensive, and all require frequent and proper maintenance.

Zoonoses are a more controversial topic. A zoonose is any infectious disease a person can catch from an animal. Almost every kind of pet can give you a zoonose. Rabies is perhaps the most notorious. You can catch cat scratch fever, hookworm, roundworm, staphylococcal and streptococcal infections from your dog or cat. Poultry are a common source of salmonella food poisoning, and you can contract this same organism from reptilian pets such as turtles, snakes and lizards.

In the case of birds, psittacosis is probably the most troubling (156). Veterinarians call this disease chlamydiosis, but the rest of the world calls it parrot fever. The microbe that causes this disease is a bacterium called *Chlamydophila psittaci* (formerly *Chlamydia psittaci*) and it can only proliferate within a living cell. It is one of the diseases your doctor must report to the government. There were 813 cases reported between 1988 and 1998 in the United States (200). This number is probably an underestimate of its true incidence. Complicating this is the recent discovery of a related organism, *C. pneumoniae* that infects people but not birds and shares antigenic markers with *C. psittaci*. This can lead to misdiagnosis in people. Still, you need to inform your physician you own a parrot. In people, the disease develops as a transient influenza-like disease with nausea, fever, vomiting, headaches, chills and malaise. Unfortunately, there is no vaccine for birds or people.

The publicity surrounding psittacosis led the United States and other countries to ban parrot importation in 1930 and later to the regulation of the import and sale of parrots (New York Times, Oct. 31, 1930 and June 2, 1938). It was only since the 1950's and the discovery that psittacosis was a treatable disease that governments relaxed their import bans. I know, because I always wanted a parrot when I was growing up in the 1950's, but the only parrots I could find were budgies, lovebirds and cockatiels. At that time, these were the only parrots that bred well in captivity. Gilbert Lee (219)

noted before the scare of 1929-1930, that there was little incentive to breed parrots. You could purchase an African grey, for example, for as little as $15 in New York. Afterwards, there were fewer imported parrots sale, and domestically bred ones were very rarely available because no one was very good at breeding the larger parrots yet.

Psittacosis is still with us, and presents a serious problem for bird owners. Fortunately, it responds to antibiotics. Both tetracycline and doxycycline are effective against this disease. Thus, this disease is no longer as dangerous as it once was. The main reason to fear this disease now is that it takes on so many insidious forms in birds that even experienced veterinarians often fail to diagnose it. I have a hand-reared female hawk-head parrot purchased directly from a breeder that I took to three different avian specialists before a veterinarian correctly diagnosed chlamydiosis. If you have other birds, it is often best to just assume any new bird, even a hand-reared one, has the disease before you bring it into your flock. This is one reason I recommend you have any new bird tested for *Chlamydophila* with one of the new assays (200) and isolate it from the rest of your flock for at least 45 days. This quarantine and observation period is important not just to prevent the introduction of chlamydiosis into your flock, but also to discover if the bird has other infectious diseases that might threaten your other birds.

If you suspect or know your bird has chlamydiosis, the Centers for Disease Control recommend contacting a qualified veterinarian and adhering to the following procedures (193):

- Protect the bird from stress and malnutrition.

- Observe the bird daily. Weigh it every few days to be sure it is not losing weight.

- Do not administer antibiotics through the drinking water and avoid feeding calcium or other divalent cations.

- Isolate the bird in an uncrowded cage away from your other birds.

- Clean up spilled food promptly and wash food and water containers daily.

- Provide fresh water and food daily.

- Be sure to continue the medication for the entire period.

There are other avian zoonoses. These include salmonella infections, which you can contract not only from birds but from almost any animal. Doctors diagnose tuberculosis due to *Mycobacterium avium* very infrequently in people, and when they do, it is usually in an immune impaired person. This organism, however, can be devastating for a flock of birds. Parrots, including caiques, may also be reservoirs of yeasts that cause opportunistic infections, again primarily of the immune impaired (240). A general rule is that most healthy people are not susceptible to these infections. However, infants, young children, the elderly and immune compromised persons such as AIDS patients are.

Traveling with or without your bird

Most caiques travel well as long as they have their roost box at night. When you travel, however, it is a good idea to have the bird's wings clipped. It is difficult to retrieve a frightened bird that has flown away, especially in a strange place. If you clip, you can take your pet bird out for an occasional short pleasure drive. One of my birds truly enjoys riding in the car. Sometimes I take her along when I go to a fast food joint with a drive-up window. She chortles with delight as she watches the scenery whiz by.

I have another pet, however, that inevitably gets carsick and regurgitates if the ride takes too long. However, if I put this bird into a carrier from which it cannot see, it usually tolerates the trip.

For longer overnight trips, you must pack a cage. This is one advantage of a small cage. Alternatively, there are collapsible cages especially manufactured for traveling. If you travel by car, take along the cage, making sure to dump out the water and replace it with plenty of fresh watery fruit as the source of liquid. Also, remember, if you leave any pet, including your bird, in a closed car during hot weather, it can have a heat stroke. If your trip requires a stop at a motel, be sure it allows pets in the room. Most do, but not all. You also must check on possible restrictions at any stops and at your destination. For example, you cannot take your caique with you to Hawaii—caiques are on that state's prohibited list.

If you travel by plane, you must check with the airline well before your departure on what restrictions they impose. They must comply with Federal regulations, particularly the Animal Welfare Act of 1966 and its amendments. Airlines must also comply with the International Air Transport Association (IATA) guidelines. Most allow you to carry small birds such as caiques on board with you in the cabin. If they permit you to carry on your caique, you need to buy one of the travel cages that fit under the seat. This meets the USDA container requirement that specifies that the animal must be able to stand upright and turn around. Most airlines require you to obtain a recent certificate of health from a veterinarian and having one is a good idea when traveling anywhere with a bird.

Black-headed caique (P. m. melanocephalus) at eight weeks of age. This chick is unusually colored. It has green feathers in a mutton-chop pattern on both sides of its beak. Chicks often exhibit aberrant colorations that disappear after they molt into adult plumage. (Photo by author.)

Prepare your bird for the flight by supplying it with plenty of seed or pellets, as well as plenty of fruit in place of water. Do not seal the carrier with tape or other fastener that may be difficult to remove, because security officials may ask you to open it for inspection. When you reach the airport, go to the ticket counter and inform them you are traveling with a bird. The airline usually charges an extra fee even though you carry the bird on yourself. Thereafter, just treat the bird and carrier as a piece of under-the-seat luggage. Of course, during the flight, you can pull it out from under the seat and play with your bird, but it is not a wise idea to remove the bird from its carrier. You may not realize it, but there are a few people, such as my sister, who have an extreme fear of birds. If your bird must travel in the hold, those who routinely travel with their pets recommend that you be a pest and tell every airline employee you see so that your pet gets added attention.

If you cannot accompany your bird, shipping a caique can be very challenging. First, it is illegal to ship any bird except fowl through the Unites States Postal Service. The easiest way to ship is to use one of the national pet shipping services. Of course, this is expensive. These shippers usually have listings in the Yellow pages. Otherwise, you need to contact the airline. Airlines vary in their rules for shipping birds. Some do not ship birds at all. Some require you to deliver your bird to the passenger counter, while for another you must find the freight office. Others require that you be a known shipper. All restrict shipping to larger planes with pressurized holds. Most restrict shipping by season. For example, for birds, each stop on the trip must be well above freezing, and still not be so hot as to result in heat prostration. Some airlines require you to have a veterinarian specify the limits of tolerable temperatures. Whenever possible, ship by the most direct route. Use a United States Department of Agriculture (USDA) approved shipping crate that you can fasten securely. In the post 9/11 environment, you should not seal the cage until the security inspectors have examined the crate and its contents. You must also designate the person receiving the bird at the destination along with their address and phone number. You will also be required to prepay for the shipment. Finally, do not use any dishes that could crash about inside the crate; instead place plenty of the bird's favorite foods and water-rich fruits and vegetables loose in the crate.

If you want to take your bird to Canada, Mexico or other foreign country before returning to the United States, traveling can be very complicated. In addition to the laws of the country where you take the bird, there are two different United States agencies you need to deal with when you return. These are the Animal and Plant Health Inspection Service (APHIS), an agency of the USDA, and the Fish and Wildlife Service (FWS), an agency of the Department of Interior. The mission of the USDA is to protect against the introduction of diseases that can devastate domestic fowl. For more information from the USDA, call (301) 436-5097. The Wild Bird Act of 1992 outlines the mission of the FWS. This act requires the FWS to protect wild bird populations in other countries by limiting the importation of endangered species. For more information, call (800) 358-2104 or (703) 358-2093. Both agencies have websites where you can find additional information.

Having to deal with two separate United States Federal government agencies clearly discourages traveling abroad with even one or two pet caiques. Maybe in the future, they will reinstitute a bird passport program similar to that allowed in the early twentieth century under the Lacey Act of 1900. However, I suspect this is too much to ask in the current political climate.

If you must travel without your bird, be sure to arrange for its care while you are away. I feel the best thing to do if your entire family has to be away for a short time is to have a trusted friend or commercial bird sitter visit once or twice a day. You should give them instructions to add or replace seed or pellets, refresh the water, and replace the old fruit with fresh. If your trip is only a day or two, you can prepare the food ahead of time. You should also provide a phone number and the location at where they can reach you if necessary. Also, be sure to leave the phone number of your local avian veterinarian and the local animal emergency clinic in case the bird should develop a health problem and they cannot contact you. You should also place a card in your wallet or purse with instructions in case you have an accident and cannot communicate with your bird's temporary caretaker.

If you cannot arrange for someone to come in, you may be able to arrange for a pet shop or veterinarian to sit your bird. They usually charge a fee for this service. Pet shops are normally reluctant to do this. Typically, they only offer this service to their established customers. There is a good reason they are reluctant—they are concerned about introducing diseases into their shop. For the same reason, you should try to avoid leaving your bird at a shop. There are two organizations of professional pet sitters in the United States. They are the National Association of Professional Pet Sitters (NAPPS) and Pet Sitters International (PSI), and you can contact them on the Internet. If you cannot find a bird sitter through these sources, you can try the care.com website.

The errant bird

Recapturing an escaped bird

As noted before, the most important reason to keep your bird's wings clipped is to prevent escape. Occasionally, however, we sometimes neglect this practice. This is not a major problem for tame birds kept indoors, but if you leave windows open or take the bird outdoors it may escape. For tame birds, this is usually the result of being frightened and the instinct to flee takes over. What should you do if this happens?

Most adult caiques are poor fliers and you can usually just run after your bird and pick it up off the ground. Yet, some caiques, particularly young ones, are very good fliers even when their wings are clipped. The single most important thing to do if your bird takes flight is to keep track of its location. If it lands on a high limb or perch where it cannot be reached, then, the bird's favorite person should call to it first to calm it and then to coax it down. It is important that the favorite person stay as near as possible to the bird to reassure and calm it. Then you have to follow one of two tactics.

As mentioned earlier, caiques usually have one thing they despise so much they lose their senses and attack it without abandon. While the bird's favorite person keeps track of the bird, a second person should bring out the object that inspires intense animosity in the bird. This will be different for each bird, so you must know what object e.g. scissors, to secure. Wave it about, but be sure to drop the object as soon as the caique starts flying toward you. If this fails, use Denise Cabral's approach (63) and prepare a picnic of the bird's favorite table foods. Then, while continuing to call the bird by its name, eat some of the food, making sure the bird is watching what you are doing. This approach may require greater persistence because the bird may be too frightened of flying to come down on its own.

If you lose track of the bird, it becomes more difficult to recover it. Still, there are a few things you can do. First, call the police and tell them the value of the bird, and then contact your local parrot club. The members of some clubs are veterans of parrot recovery, and can offer great assistance. Next, if you have a recording of your bird, play the recording near the last place you saw or heard it[15]. Bird watchers often use this to draw birds closer so they can see them. You can walk or cruise the neighborhood in your car looking and listening while using the recording to raise a response. If you do not recover the bird before nightfall, begin searching again shortly after sunrise when birds start to wake. You can put up posters offering an award. (Never give the amount.) You can place an ad in your local newspaper. Be sure to include information on how to contact you in the ad or on the poster. Then you have to hope all your efforts pay off.

If the bird is not tame but you have an idea where it is, you may have to resort to trapping. (You could do what some natives South America do and shoot a specially blunted arrow at the bird that knocks the bird senseless for a brief time, but I suspect most of us are not that skilled at archery.) To trap a bird, you need a special trap cage. Cabral (63) provides a description of how to build one of these. Trap cages usually consist of two cages—one on top of the other. The top cage has a large spring-

loaded door that you trigger manually. You set some of the bird's favorite food in this cage. In the cage below, you place a call bird, preferably the lost bird's mate or another bird of the same species. Trappers use call birds with great effectiveness to catch wild caiques in Guyana (162). Then, you wait and watch. With luck, you may be able to entice the escapee into the upper cage and spring the trap.

If your bird is stolen

Another hazard of keeping valuable birds is that they are an object of theft. If someone steals your bird, the first thing you should do is report the theft to the police. Then report your loss to local veterinarians and pet stores. You can also report your loss on one of the websites that list lost and stolen birds. If you belong to an email bird list, report it there, too. You may also place an ad in your local newspaper offering an award for its return. Then put up lots of posters (223).

The best way to deal with theft is to guard against it—be security conscious. Some people invest in a home security system to protect not only their birds but also themselves. This can be expensive and often people become lax and do not use the system to full advantage. Alternatively, you can buy a surveillance system that records all the happenings in your bird room, and has the added convenience of allowing you to snoop on your bird's behavior when you are not there.

Whether your bird is lost or stolen, you need to be able to prove ownership once it is found. This may not be easy because caiques of the same subspecies look similar to one another. If your bird has a closed band, be sure to record the information on it and keep it in a safe place. One can only place a closed band on the bird when it is about three weeks of age. Unfortunately, thieves can remove bands; one solution to this problem is to have a microchip inserted. A veterinarian can insert one of these chips within the bird's body and it will be undetectable without the proper instrument. Most veterinarians have the instruments that can read the encoded information on the chip. Thieves cannot remove chips as easily they can bands.

Another way of marking your bird is to stamp a wing with your name and phone number. This is a common practice of pigeon enthusiasts (160, 258). For this, you make a rubber stamp bearing the information. Then you stamp the information on one of the larger flight feathers, preferably the same feather on opposite wings. Be sure to use a non-toxic permanent ink. You will have to stamp all your birds each year after the

---

[15] If you do not have a recording of your bird, recordings of wild caiques are available from several sources including the Cornell Ornithology Laboratory.

feathers have molted. The main advantage of stamping is that should your bird escape or be stolen, the person who retrieves it can contact you immediately. If someone steals the bird, the thief will have to clip off both stamped feathers, but the missing feathers will provide additional evidence of his guilt.

For additional proof that a bird is yours make notes and take photographs of your bird. Individual caiques tend to have a few unique visual characteristics. Among the black-headed caiques, the feather pattern bordering the black portion of the head is usually distinctive. Some birds have more yellow on the tips of their tail feathers. Unfortunately, because the birds molt, these characteristics can change, so you should take new photos every year.

Check your bird for a tattoo. If a veterinarian determined the sex of your bird, he will tattoo under the upper bend of the right wing if it is a male and under the left wing if it is a female. Some of my birds have tattoos on both wings because a second veterinarian discovered that the first veterinarian did a poor job of surgical sexing.

Write down the physical and behavioral characteristics you think might allow you to distinguish your bird from other caiques. For example, does your caique have a slight deformity? Does it barber the feathers on only one area of its wing? To what commands does it respond? The most definitive way of proving a bird is yours is to have its DNA archived by one of the companies that also offers DNA sexing. The company can then compare the DNA from the recovered bird with the archived DNA to show that it is the same bird. Even if you do not have the bird's DNA archived, advances in DNA techniques now allow you to prove ownership in another way if you can secure DNA from your bird's parents or its chicks. This is because half the bird's DNA comes from each parent.

Upper or dorsal surface of wing of a black-headed caique showing the dark blue on the dorsal surface of the feathers of the primaries. The primary coverts above the primaries have more green on them. On the secondaries, only the outer half of the feather vane is green, but the secondary coverts are completely green. (Photo by author)

Young black-headed caique showing dark color of the ventral side of the secondary and primary flight feathers. (Photo by author)

Sammy, my pet female black-headed caique at age 14. Note the eye has two irises. The inner one is an olive color and the outer one is orange-red. These are pericyclic irises. The inner olive colored one controls the amount of light reaching the retina. The more colorful outer iris is aposematic and signals the emotional state of the bird. When this iris dilates, the eye becomes bright orange-red. Also, note the dark cast of the covert feathers covering the ear opening, i.e., where the black feathers of the head meet the apricot and yellow feathers. (Photo by author)

Pionites melanocephalus melanocephalus

From the German edition of **Histoire Naturelle des Oiseaux** by Comte Georges Louis Leclerc Buffon (1707-1788) (61) entitled **Herrn von Buffons Naturgeschichte der Vögel (60)**. Buffon gives the name of the black-headed caique as "Der Maipuri." The French still refer to it by this name or the alternative spelling "naipouri." Maipouri is the name for the tapir in Guiana, the largest mammal of Amazonia. The people of the region gave it this name because caiques make a sound similar to that of the tapir. (Courtesy of The Library of Congress, Washington, D.C.)

Le Perroquet Maïpouri mâle. Pl. 119.

Barraband pinx.ᵗ   De l'Imprimerie de Langlois

Pionites melanocephalus melanocephalus

Lithograph by Jacques Barraband from François le Vaillant's **Histoire Naturelle des Perroquets** published 1794 and 1805 (216). le Vaillant's narrative refers to this bird as a male. **Christopher Ludwig Brehm** published a nearly identical print with the bird facing in the opposite direction with some modifications of the tree limb in his **Monographie der Papageien** (38) suggesting he used Barraband's print to make a new lithograph, a process that requires making a mirror image. (Original in the possession of author.)

Pionites melanocephalus melanocephalus

A second lithograph by Jacques Barraband from François le Vaillant's **Histoire Naturelle des Perroquets**. le Valliant refers to this as a young bird which may explain the orange color on its breast. However, Barraband may have painted this bird from a skin of a wild specimen and it would likely have cosmetically tinged feathers on its breast from eating and leaf bathing. (Original in the possession of author.)

Part II. Breeding

The breeding of caiques has only become reliable within the last thirty years or so. This is primarily due to the development of the methods for sexual identification in the early 1980's. Additional reasons are that we better understand their husbandry, rely less on wild-caught stock, and may have unwittingly selected for birds that survive and breed better in captivity. Fortunately, we can apply the same approach to breeding both species. In this section, I combine my own experience with that of many early breeders to help guide those wishing to breed caiques.

Securing breeding stock

The biggest challenge to breeding caiques is securing breeding stock, especially if you plan to set up more than two or three pairs. Before the United Stated government imposed import restrictions in 1992, wild-caught caiques, particularly black-headed caiques, were regularly imported into the United States. Although the number of imported caiques was never large during any one period, there was a steady supply. At that time if you wanted to set up breeding pairs you contacted an importer and arranged the purchase of a few birds at a nominal price of $200 and often less per bird. The reason for the low price was that newly imported caiques did not make good pets and therefore did not go directly into the pet trade. Now though, breeders in the United States and places like Australia, where caiques are particularly rare and expensive, we must rely primarily on domestically bred birds as a source of breeding stock. Fortunately, early caique breeders in the United States and Europe had considerable success. Initially, the fecundity of the imported birds was quite low. For example, the 176 black-headed caiques kept by the breeders surveyed in 1991 produced only 27 chicks (199). Now there seems to be many more chicks available. Hopefully, the breeding of caiques is established well enough in the United States and other parts of the world that there will never again be a need to import large numbers of wild-caught stock.

Still, only two subspecies of caiques are well established in the United States—the black-headed (*P. m. melanocephalus*) and the yellow-thighed (*P. l. xanthomerius*). In Europe, Brazil and other parts of the world, aviculturalists frequently breed the green-thighed caique (*P. l. leucogaster*) and they are starting to breed them in the United States. There are some aviculturalists in Europe breeding the pallid caique (*P. m. pallidus*); however, the breeding of the yellow-tailed caique (*P. l. xanthurus*) has been limited to Brazil and a very small number of breeders in Europe. The breeding of these rarer subspecies is restricted by national government regulations, particularly those of Brazil, that restrict exporting and importing of birds. The era when you could easily import birds into the United States and Europe is over, but there still are wild-caught black-headed pairs producing chicks in the United States, while almost all the yellow-thighed pairs are now captive bred. I suspect all the subspecies will eventually be available from breeders, but it is going to be a while before you can buy a yellow-tailed, a pallid, or even a green-thighed as a pet in the Unted States.

Presently, nearly all of the available breeding stock in the United States is captive bred, obtained from the progeny of a breeder's own pairs or from other breeders. Even so, you should take great care when securing breeding stock. Occasionally, you see advertisements listing proven breeders for sale. The term "proven breeder" only means that the pair has laid a clutch of eggs sometime in the past. Therefore, when you see such an ad, you must ask yourself why anyone would sell birds that are producing two or more clutches of chicks a year worth thousands of dollars. If you elect to purchase them, you may be taking on someone else's problem. You need to ask many questions such as, do the birds destroy their eggs right after they are laid? Has the pair killed its newly hatched chicks? Are the birds getting so old that they are no longer suitable for breeding? Are they suffering from disease? Are they poor producers? Are they in good condition and of good quality? If you elect to purchase such birds, you need to assure yourself that the reason the seller is disposing of them is genuine. Still, sometimes you get a good deal and one regularly hears of the purchase of a previously unproductive pair that starts producing after they settle into their new regime and environment. You must realize, however, there are certain risks with acquiring adult pairs.

For those with patience, the best approach is to purchase young birds and pair them up yourself. No matter how the birds were reared, they can all be good breeders. The only proviso is that they should not be too closely related. Styles (419) reported that closely related macaws bred to the fourth generation start to lose egg and chick viability and this may be true for other parrot species. One way to set up pairs is to purchase birds at the prevailing retail rates. If you want to purchase two or more birds, you can often negotiate a better price when you purchase them directly from a breeder. If you can, buy from at least two different breeders so as not to perpetuate inbreeding. Always request as much information about each bird's heritage as possible. One suggestion that may save money is to buy parent-reared birds when available. Some breeders allow a few chicks to be parent-reared with the intention of using the birds as future breeding stock and they may have an excess of one sex. These do not usually make good pets, but this does not matter if you intend to breed them. Indeed, for some parrot species parent-reared birds are preferred for breeding. Because of this, there is a movement toward allowing parrots, especially the larger species, to rear their own chicks. For example, there is a linkage between the reproductive success of cockatiels and their early rearing experience (277). The disadvantage of purchasing young stock is that you have to wait two to three years before the birds reach sexual maturity and endure their first awkward breeding attempts before they settle into being reliable breeders.

You should also consider the quality of the birds. You obviously want to avoid defective birds. Most often, a bird's physical defect is not heritable, but you should not take that risk. One particular problem for caiques and parrots in general is a tendency toward psychogenic feather picking. As noted previously, this appears to be related to parental history and may be heritable, although we cannot rule out early rearing influences (138). Until we know more about this, it is best to avoid breeding birds that are plucking or barbering themselves.

After obtaining new breeding stock, it is very important to ascertain that the birds are in good health and unlikely to transmit disease to the rest of your flock. Therefore, it is very important for new birds to receive a veterinary health examination. As a rule, the more birds you already own, the more concerned you should be about introducing new birds. Do not accept the word of the seller no matter how reliable he seems; have your own examination done by an avian veterinary specialist. You also need to keep the birds quarantined from your other birds for at least 45 days while you await the results of veterinary assays and the emergence of possible diseases resulting from the stress of relocation.

Setting up new breeding pairs

There are three requirements for birds to breed: The birds must have reached sexual maturity, the pair must be comprised of birds of the opposite sex, and they must be compatible with one another. A strong recommendation is that the birds be unrelated. The reason for this recommendation is the need to retain the genetic vigor of the caique population, but you should put this aside if the goal is to increase the number of individuals bearing a desirable new mutation[16].

The generally accepted age when caiques reach sexual maturity is three years. Some domestically bred birds will breed at two years and the earliest reported age is eleven months (222), but do not expect those young caiques to be good parents (195). The onset of sexual maturity of female caiques is more obvious than for males. If you have other birds breeding in their vicinity, they often get irritable. If they are hand tame, they may inexplicably bite you. If they are not tame, they may become more aggressive when you go to refresh their food and water.

Although it seems obvious that the birds must be of opposite sex, the fact that caiques are monomorphic presents a challenge. Currently, the only reliable and reasonable methods for sexing caiques are by surgery or one of the DNA methods. Prior to the advent of surgical sexing, Tom Ireland (195) set up three pairs based on head and body shape, vent size, and compatibility. They failed to produce. After surgical sexing became available, he discovered that he only had two females and, by happenstance, had placed them in the same cage thinking they were a heterosexual pair. All the pairs he had set up were very compatible with each other. In the case of the female-female pair, one of the birds took on the role of the male and the other the female. Once he separated them and re-mated them with male birds, they both produced fertile eggs and chicks. Thus, do not make the mistake of thinking you can tell the sex of your birds based on their appearance or behavior. These days, I advise anyone wishing to set up pairs to have their birds

---

[16] If you find you have a mutant color form, you need to develop a breeding program designed to preserve the vigor of the lineage as well as the mutation. For this, you should set up a breeding program in consultation with an avian geneticist.

DNA sexed as soon as possible after obtaining them, even ones sexed before purchase. Reporting errors are uncommon, but they do occur. The cost is minimal and it may save you a barren breeding season.

The most difficult aspect of breeding is finding birds compatible with one another. Caiques, particularly black-headed caiques, can be very aggressive toward each other, and if you carelessly place them together they may fight ferociously even to the point of one killing the other. The best time to set up adult pairs is outside the breeding season, when they tend to be less aggressive.

The best way to match up pairs is to allow them to select each other. If you obtain a large number of birds at one time, Tom Ireland (195) recommended placing single birds in small cages and lining them up side-by-side with birds of opposite sex in alternate cages. Take care not to place clutch mates next to each other since they already have a mutual affinity. Then watch. Take note of how the birds relate to each other. If you see two birds sitting as closely as possible to each other in their respective cages, there is a good chance they will make a good pair. Continue to observe for a couple more days and when you feel confident, place them in the same cage. If they have bonded, they will perch next to each other and allopreen. Allow them to adjust a while longer, but watch them to be sure they are truly compatible. You can expect them to have occasional spats, but these should never reach the point where you think you have to separate them. Once you feel they are compatible, move them into a large breeder cage.

Breeding is more challenging if you plan to set up only one or two pairs, as is the case for most hobby breeders. As a hobby breeder, I have found it is easiest to begin with unrelated immature birds that are only one to two years old. Place them in separate cages next to each other well away from your other birds in a setting that is unfamiliar to them. If you acquire several new birds and you feel comfortable that they are healthy, you may do this during the quarantine period. I quarantine my birds with a friend who has no birds in order to avoid bringing disease into my flock. There, in the absence of the sight and sound of other parrots, the two birds are usually more amenable to forming an affinity with one another. If they do, you may allow them together for the rest of the quarantine period before finally placing them in the breeder cage.

You should introduce the two members of the pair to a breeding cage at the same time. This provides a neutral territory. If you keep one bird separately in the breeding cage for a long time, it may become aggressive toward the introduced bird. If both birds are naïve to the cage, neither will feel that the other is invading its territory. If you have a limited number of cages and must place one bird in the breeder cage before the other, it is usually best to place the hen in the breeder cage first (186). Then place the male as close to her cage as possible so that they can see and hear each other without allowing direct contact. If they seem attracted to one another, introduce the male. This order of introduction is important because males are usually more aggressive than females and will defend the cage more vigorously than a female will. Occasionally, though, the female is the more aggressive bird, and if this is the case then you have to reverse the introduction procedure (186). If all goes well, the birds will seek each other's company within a few days. Often, however, it takes weeks or even longer before the birds accept one another, but do not give up too soon. Still, some birds simply refuse to accept a mate no matter how many you offer. This is common for older hand-reared pet birds and seems unrelated to their sex.

Pairing up birds does not need to be for life. George Smith (399, 400) recommended changing mates after a pair has produced a few clutches as a way to maintain genetic diversity and he routinely re-mated his pairs. He separated original pairs and introduced them to new prospective mates in a cage new to both birds. He indicated that the cages should be arranged so that the birds cannot see and more importantly, not hear their former mates (397). Apart from the normal squabbling of caiques with their mates, he noted that they soon adjusted to each other and went on to produce clutches.

Caging of breeder pairs

Caiques are best set up one pair per cage. This is because most pairs are aggressive toward other birds during the breeding season. In the early history of captive breeding, because of the difficulty in determining their sex, aviculturalists in places like Busch Gardens tried setting caiques up in colony breeding situations. They found this only worked for the slightly less aggressive yellow-thighed caique (*P. l. xanthomerius*). From what I saw in the zoos of Brazil, colony breeding also works well for the green-thighed caique (*P. l. leucogaster*). Tom Ireland (243) used this approach in his early breeding attempts with some success, but he later recommended against it (195). The success of colony breeding, however, may depend on the size of the aviary. The Bristol Zoo in England set up several pairs of black-headed caiques in a very large aviary and they bred and reared chicks (395). This type of colonial breeding is encouraged by Reillo and McGovern (337) who feel captive breeding should occur in social groups. Brightsmith (42) has reported, that *P. l. xanthomerius* is a cooperative breeder in the wild and all members of a small flock assist the breeding pair. Nonetheless, I believe to achieve success in a small breeder operation, caiques are best set up one pair per cage. In confirmation of this, Paradise Park (10) in the United Kingdom kept a small flock together for 15 years and none of them ever went to nest. Only after they separated the birds into pairs did they produce chicks.

Breeding cages should be larger than the ones intended for pet birds, but they need not be too commodious. Smith (400) observed that he got better breeding from birds housed in smaller cages than in a large aviary. He attributes this to their habit of living within the tree canopy and smaller cages give them a sense of security similar to the dense foliage of their natural environment (395). However, recently Low (228) recommended a nine meter (29 foot) long cage. I have summarized the cage sizes used by various breeders in Appendix H. The minimum size successful breeders have used is 24 inches (60 cm) high, 24 inches (60 cm) wide and 48 (120 cm) inches long. I tend to believe that the larger the cage the better since it allows them more room to fly and provides the female more room to escape the male if he gets too aggressive.

Most breeders construct their cages out of galvanized wire mesh preferably galvanized after welding. If you cage the birds outside, you should use a small mesh size of 1 inch (2.5 cm) by ½ inch (1.25 cm). This small size mesh helps prevent vermin such as rats, mice and snakes from invading the cage.

If you are breeding caiques indoors on a small scale, you may use the same galvanized mesh wire cages, with large trays fabricated of (42) galvanized metal that slide in and out of the bottoms of the cages. Several companies, such as Corners Inc., fabricate these cages at a reasonable cost. Indoors, where there is less threat of vermin, a larger mesh size is acceptable, so I use a 2 inch (3 cm) by ½ inch (1.25 cm) mesh. You then line the trays with layers of newspaper or craft paper that can be removed one layer at a time for quick clean up, being sure to replace them completely at least once a week. Because caiques feel most secure on

high perches, set the cages as high as practical without compromising your capacity to service them, usually this is about five feet (1.5 m) off the ground.

The early literature indicated that caiques were very sensitive to cold, but this is not completely true. Once acclimated, caiques do very well outdoors in England (232) and as far north as the Carolinas in the United States. They should be kept indoors further north since caiques do not have enough down feathers to insulate them well (395). As a compromise, Jörg Asmus (13), a breeder in Germany, set up his cages so his birds could freely move between an outside cage and an inside cage. He maintained the temperature of the indoor cage at a 10°C (50°F) minimum, but his birds visited the outdoor cage even when the temperature fell below freezing. Further, caiques, if you give them a roost box and allow them to adapt, can endure frosts and snow without much stress. Payne (302), who lived in England, discovered this after he had a spate of forgetfulness and left a pair of green-thighed caiques outdoors.

The suspended cages pioneered by Ramon Noegel work well if you keep your birds outdoors. Construct the floors of these cages from the same or smaller mesh wire as the rest of the cage, and hang them from a support structure well above the ground—usually at or above eye-level. The wire mesh floor allows the feces and other debris to fall through the wire onto the ground, or preferably a cement pad, where it can be flushed away with a water hose. One can construct outdoor cages with earthen floors, but they are more difficult to clean and sometimes caiques take to excavating on a wheelbarrow load scale (27). If you build so the bird has access to the ground, you should use a gravel bed that you can easily clean with a pressure washer (13). Recently, outdoor bird breeders have taken to constructing large outer enclosures of regular home screening, such as those placed over swimming pools, and placing their breeding cages within them. This keeps out mosquitoes carrying the West Nile Virus as well as wasps and bees that can disrupt your birds' nesting and feeding (313).

Unlike Amazon pairs that need a privacy barrier so they are out of sight of other pairs during the breeding season, caiques are stimulated to breed when they see and hear another pair going to nest (241, 400). Those who have several pairs know that the same pair usually leads off the breeding season every year (195, 338). This suggests that the sight and sound of that pair's activity stimulates the other pairs (234, 242). For this reason, place your breeders' cages side-by-side, so they can see the other pairs.

You should space the cages a short distance away from each other so they cannot reach each other. Ralph Lima recommends the distance between cages be at least three inches (8 cm). While this distance is sufficient, it is not far enough to prevent fresh feces from reaching the adjacent cage. Some caiques defecate with considerable force and the fecal trajectory can reach the adjacent cage. Try to keep your cages at least one foot (30 cm) apart and, if practical, further.

A black-headed chick just beginning to get its feathers. Notice the beak is black close to the head where it is growing and light at the tip. When it is an adult, the beak will be completely black. (Photo by author)

The nest box

Caiques will accept almost any nest box as long as it is of sufficient size and situated well above the floor of the cage; however, if a pair is intent on breeding, even the box's location may not matter. Once, out of necessity, George Smith let a pair free in a small utility room and the pair was so earnest about going to nest they used a small box on the floor. Breeders have successfully used a number of designs and sizes of nest boxes (Appendix H). In the wild, caiques prefer cavities high in the trees of the forest canopy such as hollow limbs that are too small for the larger parrots (42). However, there is intense competition for suitable nesting cavities from other birds, animals and social insects, so often they do not have the luxury of staking a claim to an ideal cavity.

Nonetheless, there are several factors to consider when selecting a box. Perhaps the most important consideration is that at the beginning of

the breeding season, caiques continually work their nest boxes. They chew the box itself as well as rearrange and shove the bedding around and even out of the box. To prevent loss of bedding, you can use a slant, bi-level or inverted boot-shaped box in which the bedding is confined to the deepest part of the box. In horizontal boxes, caiques usually push the bedding to one side and often out of the entrance hole. Occasionally, a pair will not accept the box you have chosen for it. If this is the case, you need to experiment with other box designs until they finally settle in.

You may place nearly feathered chicks in plastic bins. There they will feather out completely and start exploring their world. This one is poking its head out because it knows it is feeding time. This one is nearly old enough to be in a cage. (Photo by author)

You can make the nest boxes out of a variety of materials. Wooden ones, especially those of plywood, are the most common, but some suppliers also offer boxes made of metal and opaque plastic. Since wooden boxes are cheap and widely available, sellers offer the greatest selection of size and design. Wooden boxes are easy to build yourself and sometimes you have to build your own if you need it to fit a particular cage. Be sure that the wood used in its construction was not chemically treated to prevent rot or termite infestations. The choice of construction material is more critical for outside breeding pairs. A metal or plastic box is probably better for outside use than wood. Wood tends to bow and the layers of plywood separate if you do not use plywood suitable for outdoor exposure. Another problem with wooden boxes is that the birds can chew their way out of them. On the other hand, metal boxes conduct heat and cold too well. So if you are using metal boxes, line their bottoms with a wood plank to provide some thermal insulation.

Most breeders use untreated pine shavings as the bedding. They also use fir chips (454), pine needles, coconut husks and eucalyptus chips. Early aviculturists sometimes added damp decaying vegetable matter as a way to increase humidity, but we now know you should never do this (432). As mentioned above, caiques continually work their boxes—they chew and shove the bedding around and in the process, it degrades or the bird tosses it out of the box. You should try to keep about three to five inches (8 to 12 cm) of bedding in the lowest level of the box. When the birds begin to breed, you need to monitor the bedding level almost daily and add bedding as needed until the hen lays the first egg. After the hen lays, stop adding any additional bedding because this may bury the eggs. Some parrot breeders "cork" the nest box. That is, they line the nest box with sheets of cork. The idea is that the birds will chew the cork in the same manner they would chew the interior of a cavity in the wild. George Smith (395) did not add any loose litter at all, but instead screwed large chinks of soft wood to the inside of the box and the birds whittled it away to make their own bedding. Some bird specialty stores sell coconut husks that you add to the nest box for the birds to chew. While this encourages some parrot species to breed, this is not necessary for caiques. Still, it is not a bad idea to toss a hunk of cork into their box occasionally. You can obtain sheets of clean rough cork intended for the mounting of orchids and bromeliads from plant supply companies, or you can buy unused corks from a vintners supply house. Other soft woods such as balsa, soft pine and the like will do as long as they are not painted or chemically treated.

While insect and mite infestations of the nest box are not usually a problem for indoor breeders, they can be if you keep your birds outside. Parasitic insects such as botflies are a major problem in the nests of wild parrots in the Amazon region (386) as are warble flies for the Puerto Rican parrot and other birds of South America (387). In North America, parasitic blow flies can be a problem while in Europe ticks of the species *Ixodes frontalis* sometimes kill nestlings (332). Further, some non-parasite insects such as fire ants and termites can invade a nest and kill nestlings. In addition to insects, Atyeo (15, 16) reports that there are several species of feather mites that afflict caiques in the wild. Thus, insect, tick, and lice infestations may be a matter for concern for some breeders.

To prevent infestations, Tom Ireland (195), who kept all his breeders outdoors in Florida, recommended mixing in a small amount of Sevin dust with the pine shaving bedding. While he gave a caution to use only the five percent commercial powder, he did not provide any guidance on the ratio of powder to shavings. A somewhat safer insecticidal dust, however, might be Permethrin dust. Some people use this on their cats and dogs. Alternatively, a somewhat less effective but perhaps even safer approach to limit ectoparasites is to add diatomaceous earth to the box (103). If mites are the only problem, mixing some cedar chips with the pine shavings may help.

Place the nest box as high as possible on the cage as convenient. Both Peter Them (432) and George Smith (394) recommend that you situate the box so that the entrance is in an area with low light. The caique's preference for darkness led a friend of the Danish aviculturalist Peter Them to paint the inside of the box black. He then noted that when given a choice they selected the painted box over the unpainted one. While it is not necessary to paint the inside of the box, obscuring the entrance to the box entrance from other birds in the vicinity often provides the pair with a feeling of greater security.

Because of the need to inspect the nest and remove eggs or chicks, all nest boxes should have an inspection door. The inspection door needs to be easily accessible from outside the cage and large enough for you to access all parts of the interior of the nest box.

Once the pair sleeps in the box, they are usually comfortable enough to nest in it. Occasionally a pair is reluctant to use a new box. Usually you can overcome this by catching the pair late in the evening before it becomes dark, placing them in the nest box, and sealing the entry hole so they cannot exit. Then, first thing in the morning unseal the hole. One night of enforced confinement in the box is usually enough for them to lose their fear (222). Sometimes you have to do this for two nights before they adapt, but from my experience, this approach is usually very effective.

Food and water for breeders

Breeding birds have different dietary needs than non-breeding birds. Shift them to a higher protein, fat and calcium diet when you first notice that the male making serious overtures to the female. This is particularly important for the hen as the laying of eggs requires calcium for shell formation and fat for yolk production (462). There are now formulated pellet diets specifically for breeding parrots. Prior to their introduction, one had to add protein, fat and calcium rich foods such as cheese, yogurt, cooked meat, and cooked egg to the breeder birds' diet. Supplementation with egg food has been a common practice in the breeding of smaller avian species such as canaries and you need to do this for parrots too. With the availability of formulated breeder diets, you can simply switch from the low protein, low fat maintenance pellets to the high protein, high fat breeder pellets. Switching is easiest if you use the same brand of maintenance and breeder pellets. Caiques have a definite preference for some brands over others so you do not want to disturb their eating pattern with too radical a diet change.

A recently weaned white-belly hiding in a cut off cereal box. Even when young, caiques are very curious about small dark cavities and take delight in exploring them. It is good to provide them a small box on the cage floor to escape to when you first introduce them to a cage. (Photo by author)

The hen usually becomes compulsive about chewing on mineral rich materials when the season begins. Cuttlebone is a one of the preferred calcium sources. Alternatively, you can make a calcium supplement block similar to those used at Loro Parque (420) (see Pet Section). While caiques tend to ignore the mineral blocks specifically sold for birds in pet stores, they often have a penchant for the plaster walls and brick mortar of your home. You need to keep a supply of cuttlebones on hand as a female caique can chew through them very quickly. After the hen chews one into crumbs, you need to replace it as soon as possible. Other than your plaster walls or the mortar in your brick walls, cuttlebones are nearly the only mineral source caiques crave.

The rest of the diet should remain the same. Continue to supply your caiques with fresh fruits and vegetables. If you offer a fortified safflower seed mix or other foods, continue to offer the same throughout the breeding season.

Finally, arrange the feeders and water containers so you can clean and change them without having to enter the cage too frequently.

When caiques breed, some pairs fiercely attack anyone foolish enough to put their hands in the cage. This does not seem to be as big a problem with domestically reared pairs habituated to their caretaker, but even they will attack strangers who haplessly put their hand in or near their cage. Provide each of your pairs with a bowl of water for both drinking and bathing. A continuous source of water is especially important in warm areas such as Florida. It is also important to monitor the water bowls and keep them filled as the birds often empty a bowl with their exuberant bathing. In large breeding operations, the automatic watering systems that flush and change the water on a regular schedule are a wise investment.

An "assistant" green-thigh allopreens the hen as a male treads on her. There were thirteen green-thighs in this cage. The cage was about 2 m (6.5 ft) wide, 3 m (10 ft) deep and extended about 3 m (10 ft) above an earthen floor. (Photo taken by author of birds in the São Paulo Zoo.)

Mating behavior

Once the members of a pair are comfortable with each other, you have to hope they mate. Day length seems to be an important factor for inducing breeding (395). Despite the fact that their natural habitat is at or near the equator, many tropical birds seem to be able to discern the very small seasonal differences in day length (167, 181). In the northern hemisphere caiques usually begin to breed in late November and continue through about June. In my experience, if you provide artificial light for longer than 13 hours a day it abrogates the seasonal cycle, and the pair will go to nest at anytime in the year. In the lull between breeding seasons, the birds are generally less aggressive toward you and other birds. An increase in aggressiveness usually heralds the new season and the male begins making overtures to the female. The characteristic courtship ritual consists of regurgitive feeding, mutual preening, and maintaining close proximity. Both birds spend a great deal of time sitting touching each other with their tails crossed (394). Dr. Smith also noted that a receptive female often keeps her beak slightly ajar even though she is capable of closing it completely. The male will try all sorts of devices to induce the female to mate with him. One tactic the male sometimes uses to elicit responsiveness is to take on the role of the female and try to squeeze under her in a sort of reversal of roles.

Pairs tend to be quarrelsome. They often fight over food, which one should sit on what perch, and other simple matters. This is normal behavior, but during the breeding season, an overly aggressive male is cause for concern. As the season progresses, the male usually becomes more and more aggressive toward the female, sometimes chasing her around the cage; this is one reason for providing a large cage. Males may try to feed the hen forcibly, causing damage in the hen's beak area (222). More commonly, the male will try to copulate with the hen forcibly. The male can be relentless in his pursuit. If this behavior becomes too violent, you must separate them as soon as possible. If left unchecked, a male caique may kill his mate (195, 222). Such males can be a problem. Tom Ireland was never able to rehabilitate any of his overly aggressive male caiques, but Ralph Lima claimed some success by pairing his up with new mates.

Once the female is receptive, copulation begins. Like all South American parrots, the male caique grips the perch with one foot and places the other on the female's back. This is called treading and is different from how old world parrots copulate in which the male stands with both feet on the female's back (407). Male caiques do not have a phallus or other organ that can deposit sperm into the female's cloaca. Rather, they do it by a sort of kissing of the cloacas of the two birds. Caiques are not shy about copulation and the act can last a quarter of an hour or longer. Caiques sometimes make a very distinctive sound during copulation, and this is an early indication that egg-laying will soon commence. The hen cannot store sperm, so for an egg to be fertile the hen must lay it within 48 hours of copulation (338). This may explain why the male is so obsessed with mating and tries to copulate with the female at every opportunity until the hen has laid all her eggs. Only after the female is busy incubating her eggs and less inclined to leave the nest box does he relent.

About Eggs and Egg laying

Several behaviors indicate the commencement of egg laying. As noted previously, one of the surest is that the hen starts chewing on the cuttlebone or your plaster or cement walls. The hen also begins to consume more water. Eggs require a lot of water. If you use a water bottle, the increase in consumption will be very evident (464). A hen's behavior will also change just before she lays an egg. The hen of my non-tame pair usually refuses to accept a treat from my hand that she would normally accept. Pet caiques stay closer to their box and work the bedding more intensely. They will push most of the bedding out of a shallow box and you may have to keep refilling it to prevent the egg from rolling around on the hard floor of the box. If the female is an unmated pet, she will want to be with you more at first, but later will want you to leave her alone.

When a caique becomes gravid, it develops a very distended abdomen. You need to monitor the health of the female more assiduously at this time because she may experience egg binding, and sometimes more serious maladies. On rare occasions, instead of making the proper descent of the oviduct the ovum develops in the abdomen. This happens when the infundibulum fails to catch the newly fertilized ovum and it falls into the abdomen. If the egg is not reabsorbed, this can lead to a life threatening infection called egg-yolk peritonitis. This results in a build-up of fluid in the hen's abdomen that makes her appear to be gravid. If the hen goes for more than several weeks in what appears to be an extreme gravid condition without laying an egg, and is in a decrepit condition she may be suffering from egg binding or peritonitis. You need to watch her closely. If she becomes wobbly on the perch or goes to the bottom of the cage, take her to a veterinarian immediately.

If you have multiple pairs, the same pair usually takes the lead in laying the first clutch of eggs every season (195, 338). Their mating and egg laying activity then sets off a chain reaction of mating and egg laying among the other pairs. Once egg laying commences, the hen usually lays an egg about every three days, but the interval between eggs can range from one to six days. The typical clutch size is three to four eggs. In some cases, a hen may lay only one or two. Clutches of five are not uncommon, and the largest clutch size reported is seven eggs (222). The hen does nearly all the incubation, but sitting usually does not begin in earnest until after the hen lays the second or third egg. Once the hen lays her complete clutch of eggs, the male becomes less aggressive toward her, and takes great interest in the nest, often visiting the box while the female is out eating.

Notice how distended the abdomen of this gravid black-headed caique female caique is. She will lay an egg shortly. (Photo by author)

Multiple clutching is common for caiques. Many healthy pairs produce two to three clutches and sometimes even four clutches a year. Usually a pair will go back to nest if all its chicks are pulled for hand rearing. If you pull the eggs instead of the chicks, the hen will usually lay another clutch. Dr. Smith (395) reported that when he removed the eggs as laid, one of his hens laid ten eggs before stopping. When he did this as a general practice, his pairs produced an average of 15 chicks a year and the most chicks he was able to produce in a year from a pair was 27. Smith later abandoned this approach but commercial aviaries often use it. Although this is a good way to build up a population, as a hobby breeder, I like my pairs to have the satisfaction of rearing their young; besides, I do not like to be tied down to the hand-rearing needs of so many chicks.

Nearly every hen will lay eggs at one point in her life whether or not she has a mate. Of course, birds without mates lay infertile eggs. Some females become aggressive, especially the first time, but most tame birds will allow you to look in on them while they are incubating their eggs. A pet bird may even allow you to pick her up and inspect her eggs while she is in the nest.

The size of a caique's eggs can vary from 3.1 to 3.3 cm long and from 2.2 to 2.6 cm wide (1.25 to 1.31 inches x 0.87 to 1.03 inches). Size appears to be related to the size of the hen, her health, her age, and the number of eggs in the

clutch. As is the case for parrotlets (59), the last egg in a clutch is usually smaller than the earlier ones. However, just as for parrotlets (59), there is no report of any correlation of egg size and the final bird size.

Co-parented chick peeking out of the nest box. This chick will soon fledge. (Photo by author)

Statistically, fertile caique eggs tend to be larger and heavier than infertile ones (338), but the scatter in the data renders this of little use to the average breeder. Further, eggs laid earlier in the season tend to be larger and more likely to be fertile than those laid later (338). Age also seems to be a factor in fertility. My oldest pair is now laying more infertile eggs than in the past. This pair has been together for sixteen years, and this hen's eggs are much smaller than those she laid earlier. Thus, parent age seems to be a factor in fertility.

If an egg is fertile, and the incubation goes well, a chick will usually hatch after 26 days, but it may hatch as early as 25 days or as late as 29 days. The length of the incubation depends on the temperature of the surroundings. Eggs require longer when it is cool because not all hens sit tightly and they sometimes spend long intervals away from the nest. The probable reason for this is that in the tropics, the days are quite warm, and there is less need to sit as tightly as in temperate zones. You can determine if the eggs are fertile by candling[17]. If you have good equipment, you can follow the development of the chick in the shell.

---

[17] Candling is the use of a very bright light capable of passing through the shell and egg as a way of observing the development of the embryo. Most poultry supply houses sell equipment for candling eggs.

Eventually, the egg will become opaque due to the development of the chick.

Do not clean or wash the eggs unless they are extremely dirty and avoid using soap or detergent if you do. The eggshell contains anti-bacterial proteins in its matrix that can wash away (265). As George Smith (404) noted, all naturally incubated parrot eggs take on a "patina of filth." If there is no noticeable increase in the opacity after a week, the egg is probably infertile. Even so, you should leave any infertile eggs with the hen for the length of time normally required for them to hatch. If no other eggs hatch, remove them. The hen will check the box a few times and toss out much of the bedding, and quickly revert to her original behavior as though she had never laid the eggs. If there are chicks that hatch, leave any eggs that have not hatched in the nest. They provide a reservoir of warm for the newly hatched chicks when the parents must leave the nest.

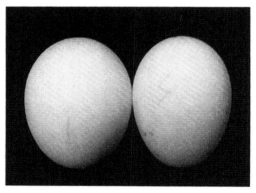

The same hen laid both of these eggs as part of a clutch of four. The first egg laid, marked "1" on the left, is noticeably greater in girth than the one marked "4" which was the fourth and last egg the hen laid. If you mark eggs, use a soft lead pencil. (Photo by author)

On rare occasions, a bird will lay an egg with a double yolk. This generally means that there are two embryos within. I am unaware of such an egg from a caique ever hatching. However, it is possible for two parrot chicks to hatch from a single egg. There is one report of this for a sun conure and both chicks survived. Surprisingly, upon DNA sexing, one was a female and the other a male (73). There is another report for a Barraband's parrot and again both survived (52).

If you need to store the eggs for a brief period, there is some data for this from a study of cockatiel eggs (94, 95). The best way is to place them in a sealed plastic bag at 55˚F (13˚C) and turn them at least once a day. The eggs should not be stored for more than four or five days. The researchers concluded the plastic bag reduced dehydration and prevented any pH change occurring from the loss of carbon dioxide. Before incubation, allow the eggs to come slowly to room temperature.

I have no real experience with the artificial incubation of caique eggs. For more information, consult Jordan's excellent book on parrot egg incubation (201). This is something a hobby breeder may have to do in an emergency, but most commercial breeders do it routinely. For this, you need an incubator that controls the temperature, humidity, and the turning of the eggs. A number of small incubators are commercially available, and they usually come with instructions. Low (233) recommends incubating parrot eggs between 98.5 and 99.5°F (36.9 and 37.5°C), but Dr. Smith (400), who routinely removed caique eggs for artificial incubation the day after they were laid, indicated that caique eggs should be incubated at a bit lower temperature than other parrot eggs, as low as 96°F. He also recommended not adding water to the incubator if you live in an area with moderate humidity such as the United Kingdom.

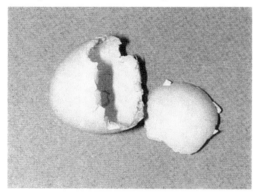

Remainder of shell after chick hatches. The process of hatching requires the chick to rotate in its shell while pressing its egg tooth against the shell to cut its way out. It does this with a powerful muscle in its neck called the muscularia complexus or pipping muscle. Notice that the chick shears off the large end of the egg. (Photo by author)

During the incubation process, the egg should draw-down. This draw-down, or loss of weight, is due to the loss of water and carbon dioxide during incubation. According to Smith (399), this should be between 18 and 19 percent just before hatching. Smith noted that the addition of water to the incubator seemed to prevent the normal draw down. He did not even add water during the hatching process, which most authors recommend, although he did recommend raising the temperature to 99°F (37.2°C) at hatching. Most breeders recommend that you use a mechanical turner rather then manually turning the eggs. If you must manually turn eggs, mark each egg with a dot or similar marking on one side with a soft lead pencil so that you can tell when you have turned it. It is a general rule that you should not handle the eggs too much during incubation, although you do need to check on their fertility from time to time. Finally, you must remember to turn off the mechanical turner when eggs are due to hatch.

Parent incubation

The female usually sits very tightly on her eggs and leaves the box only briefly to forage for food and defecate. In the wild, the male parent's duties appears to be to defend the nest cavity and drive raiders away (24). An unattended nest is very vulnerable to raids and egg destruction by other birds and predators. During daylight hours while the hen is in the nest sitting on the eggs, the male stays outside but nearby. Males exhibit their greatest interest in the nest when the hen leaves it and then they peek in to check that all is well. Should something happen to the hen, the male of some parrot species will take over the incubation and rearing (356, 469).

Toward the end of the incubation period, the hen sometimes bathes more frequently. This may be how she controls the moisture in the box (432). For this reason, the hen should have access to a shallow bowl of water. Smith suggests that if the female does not bathe very often and has a history of low hatch rate, you should add half cup of tepid water to the dry matrix in the box once a week but only for those birds kept indoors. If there is an inch or more of bedding, there should not be any problem with the water being absorbed. I have found, however, that this is not usually necessary.

During the incubation period, the hen "talks" to her eggs. If you were unaware that your hen was sitting on eggs, the distinctive sounds of a sitting hen will give you another message. Gilbert Gottlieb (151) has done some interesting studies with ducks and shown that this is important for the hatchlings to be able to recognize their own species. Oddly, in his studies, even the peeps made by other ducklings while still in the egg contribute to this capacity. In his experiments, he showed that when the parent duck incubated its own eggs or when he hatched a group of eggs in an incubator, the newly hatched ducklings were more attracted to a duck's sound than a chicken's sound. In contrast, if he harmlessly muted the ducklings several days before they hatched; they were attracted to both about equally. Whether this is important for caiques is a bit of a question, as they do not have an ear opening until a week or more after they hatch. Therefore, whether egg talking is important for preconditioning the chick to life after hatch or serves to stimulate her mate to be more solicitous remains a question.

The problem when a caique hen starts sitting on her eggs as soon as she has laid them is that the chicks hatch in the same order a few days apart. Ornithologists call this asynchronistic hatching as opposed to synchronistic hatching, when all the chicks hatch about the time as seen for chickens and ducks. This is a major problem if you expect all the chicks to survive. When the chicks hatch asynchronisticly, the oldest chick is often the only one to survive. This is because the chicks that hatch later may not be able to compete as effectively for food and attention (395). As is the case for crimson rosellas (*Platycercus elegans*), most deaths among later hatching caique chicks is within a few days of their hatch when the parents could easily provide enough food (210). Whatever the reason, in order to avoid the problem you must intervene and there are a number of ways to do this.

If you have a large number of pairs laying eggs, you can shift the eggs around so that eggs laid on one day are all set beneath one hen. Another way is to remove the first two eggs after the hen has laid them and replace them with artificial eggs (49). Then, after the hen has laid the third and usually last egg, replace the artificial ones with the real eggs. This usually results in all three eggs, the typical clutch size, hatching at about the same time. If you remove an egg, it may be stored at room temperature at about 75°F (23.9°C) for a day or so; for longer storage, see the section on egg storage above. Now, because the chicks all hatch at the same time, they compete at the same level for the attention of the parents and stand a much better chance for survival. Still another approach, and the one I now use, is to leave the eggs with the hen and allow the eggs to hatch in the same order they were laid. When the third egg hatches, I pull the oldest chick and hand-feed it. Then as subsequent chicks hatch, I pull the next oldest chick always leaving only the two youngest chicks for the parents to rear. Two chicks that hatch within a few days of each other seem to be the optimum number a pair can rear by themselves.

A problem seen with some pairs is egg breakage. This usually commences immediately after the hen lays its first egg. What appears to be happening is that the male and the hen fight over the egg. Unfortunately, you cannot remove the male because he has to fertilize any addition eggs the hen might lay. I have found the solution to this is to add an ersatz egg or two to the nest. You can add wooden eggs of about the same size as those laid by a caique. They do not have to be painted white. These are available at most craft stores. Alternatively, you can blow out the contents of an infertile egg and refill it with plaster of Paris. Adding the additional eggs provides both members of the pair with their own egg or eggs and they no longer fight for the possession of a single egg. After the hen has laid its full clutch, you can remove the ersatz eggs without fear the real eggs will be broken.

Black-headed caique chick at 13 days of age. The tiny white bump near the end of its maxilla is its egg tooth. Note the amniotic closure of the eye, ear and nasal openings. Also, note the sparseness of the down. An eye slit, a straight vertical line just to the upper left of the eye pupil, is just starting to form. It still has some food in its crop and will need a feeding in about an hour. (Photo by author)

Fostering eggs

Fostering is a term used by aviculturists to describe the use of a second hen to incubate and brood the eggs produced by another pair of birds. The birds do not need be the same species, although the egg size of the two should be comparable. I am unaware of any reports of caiques fostering the eggs of another pair or another species. However, one should consider fostering in situations when a pair habitually breaks their eggs; are poor parents; the hen refuses to sit; or the hen is incapacitated. Unfortunately, fostering is only possible if you have another hen sitting on eggs at the same time. One cannot simply place eggs in another pair's nest box. If you place an egg in the empty nest of a pair that does not already have eggs, the pair will destroy them just as parrots would do in the wild (24). Thus, you must either add or replace eggs

under a hen that is already sitting. Fortunately, the hen seems unable to count and will not realize that she is sitting on an extra egg or two.

Rearing the chick

There are four basic ways to rear caique chicks in captivity. They are:

- Let the parents rear them completely.

- Partial parent rearing in which the parents rear the chicks for several weeks after hatch and then they are removed and hand-fed.

- Completely hand-feeding the chicks from day one.

- A combination of the other methods called co-parenting. There are several forms of co-parenting.

Each of these rearing methods has a place in caique husbandry depending on the goal.

How well a caique socializes with people depends on how you rear it. With patience, wild-caught Amazons and African greys can become very agreeable pets. This is almost never the case for caiques. My experience, as well as that of others (232), is that wild-caught caiques and completely parent-reared caiques do not make good pets no matter how persistent you are at training them. Without human intervention, chicks left completely with their parents until after they fledge are best suited to be breeders. Some disagree with this. George Smith stated that you can remove them shortly after fledging and they still make good pets (400).

Caique parents usually do a good job of rearing only one or two chicks, but if there are more than two, the pair usually neglects the youngest or may even kill it. Further, novice parents that have never reared chicks before sometimes do not make a good transition from incubation to chick feeding. If you are not vigilant, none of the chicks will survive more than the few days it takes to deplete the nourishment in their residual yolk sac. Even the second clutch may present a challenge to these parents. After three or four clutches, though, they are usually experts. Yet, even experienced parent birds do not usually feed all their chicks. Because parrot chicks hatch asynchronously in the order in which the hen lays them, the last chicks to hatch have less chance for survival. This seems to be the case for both captive parrot pairs as well as those nesting in the wild (41, 398). They call the last chick to hatch a Benjamin for good reason. Like in the Biblical story of the older brothers selling Benjamin, the youngest brother, into slavery, older chicks want all the attention of their parents. In some bird species, the older chicks actually commit siblicide by pushing the younger ones out of the nest, but this is not in the case for caiques. Caique parents usually show more interest in feeding the larger and more vocal hatchlings. Chicks that hatch later are simply neglected and do not receive an adequate amount of food and warmth. This is the reason you need to monitor the chicks of all breeding pairs, especially novice pairs.

To monitor both the eggs and the chicks, you need an inspection door on the nest box. It is best to make inspections quickly while both parents are out of the box. If the parents are aggressive, you need to induce them to leave the nest. Inspection is usually easiest in the morning when the pair leaves the nest to feed. Otherwise, most pairs can be induced to leave their nest if some kind of commotion is made near their cage. Then, while they are distracted, you can make a quick peek before they return. If the pair is tame, they may let you do the inspection while the hen is still in the box, but not all tame pairs are amenable to this. Do not be afraid to handle even the smallest chicks. Contrary to popular myth, the parent will not destroy them afterwards. There are a number of things to note during the inspection. Here are some of them:

* Are the chicks and unhatched eggs in a huddle? Unless the environment is very warm, the chicks first huddle with the unhatched eggs and then with each other to keep warm when the parents leave the nest. Newly hatched parrot chicks are not capable of completely thermoregulating their bodies for the first week or so (163, 306). Usually the hen spends long hours in the box brooding the chicks, but not always. In their native tropics, daytime temperatures are quite warm and the chicks do not need continuous brooding. Possibly, because of this, some caique parents are less inclined to brood and supply the warmth needed in temperate areas. This seems to be more frequent for black-headed breeders. For this reason, the ambient temperature inside the box should be between 80 to 85°F (27-30°C) during the day. If a chick feels cool to the touch or is not huddling, it is a sign that it is not getting enough warmth and may be unable to digest food properly. You can provide additional heat by placing an electric heater beneath the box, taking care that it is far enough away it does not overheat the box's interior.

* Does the chick have food in its crop? Check the box an hour or two after the parents have had a chance to feed and return to nest. If you inspect the nest first thing in the morning, none of the chicks will have food in their crops because caiques do not feed their chicks during the night. If there is still no food in their crops after you have given the parents an opportunity to eat and return to the nest, the parents are neglecting the chicks.

* Examine the chick's toes and beak. When the parents do not to feed a chick, they sometimes chew on the chick's toes or beak. This is a sign they are not going to feed it.

In most of the situations above, you need to remove the chick immediately and hand-rear it.

Even for an experienced aviculturist, it is a difficult and troubling decision to remove a very young chick from its parents' care. It is usually the youngest chick that you must remove, and if its parents have neglected it awhile before you discover it, you will need patience to restore it to normal growth.

Clutch of black-headed caique chicks that have just been fed. Notice how full the crop on the chick at the right is. (Photo by the author)

If the parents are killing the chicks in the nest, the male is usually responsible. If this is happening, you must immediately remove the male to a separate cage, preferably one close to the hen's cage. The hen does not need the male to rear the chicks and usually does a good job by herself. You can return the male to the cage once all the chicks eyes have openned.

Artificial brooding. When you remove a young chick still in pinfeathers for hand-rearing, you must provide warmth. Because newly hatched parrot chicks are pliothermic and cannot regulate their body temperatures (306), you must keep them warm in a brooder that maintains a temperature between 95°F (35°C) and 98°F (37°C). This is warmer than for some other parrot species. It is important that the brooder not be set at too high a temperature. Howard Voren (448) recommends setting the brooder at 97°F (36.1°C) as brooders tend to fluctuate and you must avoid spikes over 100°F (37.8°C). If you lack a brooder with good temperature control, you can temporarily keep the chick in an incubator intended for hatching eggs. If the incubator has a fan, be sure to keep adding water to maintain humidity.

Unless you are very experienced, you should avoid pulling day-one hatchlings. It is easier to care for a chick that the parents have fed for even two or three days than a day-one chick. If you can, leave the chicks with the parents until about the time their eyes open at about three weeks, although some breeders routinely pull the chicks earlier at seven to ten days (454).

The main reason for pulling chicks at an early age is to ensure they imprint on people after they open their eyes the first time—at least this is the dogma. Interacting with people is important if the chick is to become a good pet. The three-week-old chicks are also able to regulate their body temperature better, and do not need to be kept quite as warm as new hatchlings. However, you still need to keep them in a brooder because they lose heat rapidly due to their small size and lack of heavy down. You should keep chicks of this age in a brooder at about 90°F (32°C) until the chick starts to develop feathers. It is crucial that the brooder not be too warm. When featheration nears completion, move the chicks into plastic bins at room temperature. If allowed to rear their own chicks, the parents spend far less time in the box with the chick after the first two or three weeks. One Florida breeder, Tom Ireland (195), did not recommend providing any heat for chicks three weeks or older and kept all his chicks at room temperature. I compromise because the parents still spend the nights in the box with their chicks so they are receiving some brooding during the cold of the night. During the brooding period, keep the brooder and bins dark to emulate what the chicks would experience in a nest cavity in the wild by covering them with a dark towel, or other dark material.

As I gained more knowledge about breeding caiques, I realized that most caique pairs are only able to rear two chicks at a time. Now I remove all but two youngest chicks as I described previously and hand-feed the older ones. It is far easier to feed a five or six day old chick than a day one chick. Even people experienced in feeding

other species of parrots from day one find that day one caiques are one of the most difficult to feed.

The time to start the chick's socialization is when the chick's eyes open. You will notice the chick staring at you. Let it look at you by bringing it up to your face where it can gaze at your face. You should hold and talk to it. At about six weeks, the chicks first pin feathers push through the skin. The feathering process seems to irritate the chick. Helping it break the feather casings offers you another chance to interact with the chick, but you must not break any of its blood-filled feathers. If you can, try to handle and talk to each bird individually a little every day or more often.

Hand-feeding chicks

We are now fortunate to have several manufacturers of avian hand-feeding formulae. Before these were available, every breeder had to prepare his own formula and most were not ideal (80, 173). Commercial hand-feeding formulae provide adequate nutrition for caiques, but they do vary from manufacturer to manufacturer and sometimes from batch to batch even from the same manufacturer. When selecting a commercial formula, there are a number of considerations. One is gelation time. This is the length of time the formula requires to thicken. This varies considerably from one manufacturer to the next. Select one with a gelation time of only a minute or two. Some formulae require up three minutes to set up and you have to keep adding more water to thin it. This is important because a formula that is too viscous is difficult to deliver into the beak of the chick.

The most important concern, however, is nutrient content. An examination of eleven commercial products by Wolf and Kamphues (467) indicates that while they usually contain sufficient and sometimes more than sufficient amounts of most nutrients, a few were low in specific amino acids. In particular, they lacked the sulfur-containing amino acids methionine and cystine. The availability of these amino acids is especially critical when the chick begins to grow feathers. Unfortunately, most manufacturers do not supply this information as part of the package information. Overall, though, the quality of manufactured formulae far exceeds the formulae early aviculturalists had to compound themselves. Even so, some aviculturalists continue to supplement the commercial formulae by adding strained human baby food, lory nectar, vitamins, minerals, et cetera. There is no need for this when you feed formula. Just follow the manufacturer's instructions.

64

Take great care when feeding chicks less than a week in age. As noted previously, Some aviculturists find caique chicks more difficult to feed than other parrot chicks (470). Very young chicks need a dilute formula at first and you increase its concentration gradually over the first five days or so. These chicks rely on the remainder of their yolk sac to survive the first few days after they hatch. At this early age, they need liquids more than food to avoid dehydration. Some breeders prepare their formula with Pedialyte®, but you should never do this. The main reason to avoid diluting the formula with Pedialyte is that very young chicks can develop opisthontonos, a condition in which the body takes on an unusual rigidity with the head held so far back it almost touches its shoulders and its legs stretch out straight behind (405). The exact cause of this problem is unknown but it may be a mild form of salt-poisoning, although Smith speculates that it may be not be salt per se, but the richness of a full strength formula diet. Having too rich a diet may overload a young chick while it is still using up the very rich nutrient supply of its yolk.

Prepare formula fresh at each feeding and take great care to keep your equipment disinfected and clean. Disinfecting the equipment is particularly important if you are feeding chicks from more than one clutch. For this, use a mild disinfectant such as a quaternary ammonium compound or stabilized chlorine dioxide. (See Appendix E). Because of potential bacterial growth, I find it convenient to prepare formula in disposable plastic cups and throw them away after each use.

The temperature of the formula is very critical and you must monitor it with a good thermometer. For very young chicks, the formula must be almost exactly 105°F (39.5°C). Any higher and you risk burning the chick's tiny crop; any lower and the food will not be accepted. To keep the food warm, place the cup in a bath of warm water at the same temperature during the feeding. For very young chicks, a one-milliliter tuberculin syringe without a needle works best. It allows better control of delivery than an eyedropper or a plastic pipette. Feeding of chicks at this age is easiest for right-handed people. To feed them, hold the chick in your left hand with it facing away from you, and then apply the end of the syringe to the right side of the chick's beak. Then squeeze out some of the formula near the beak and let the chick take it in on its own. At this age, do not force the syringe into the beak. Feed very young chicks only a few drops of dilute formula at a time for the first few days. At this age, their air sacs are not well developed, so

they cannot breathe well when taking food (403). It is better to underfeed than overfeed. The best guide is the visual examination of the chick's crop—it should look full but not overly distended.

Other breeders recommend feeding from the left, placing the tip of the syringe into the beak and delivering the food more forcefully. For the majority of chicks, the entrance of the esophagus is on the right side of the chick's oral cavity and the trachea on the left. One must take great care to avoid getting food into the trachea. When a chick aspirates into its trachea and lungs, the chick will die almost immediately from suffocation.

Let the chick dictate when to feed it by watching its crop. In the wild, some Amazons only feed their chicks twice a day (121, 343). However, you should not let this dictate your feeding schedule for captive caiques, as we are not up against the pressures on wild birds that must limit their visits to the nest because of the need to spend time gleaning food and avoiding attracting predators to the nest site. For younger chicks, this will be about every two to three hours during the day, but you should stretch the interval as the chick ages. You do not have to wait until the chick is completely empty to feed it if this is inconvenient for your personal schedule. Chicks are somewhat flexible in this regard. Further, it is important to allow the chick to empty completely at least once every 24 hours. Competent parent birds do not feed their chicks during the night, so you need not either. I usually feed them just before I go to bed at about eleven o'clock in the evening and make sure I get a good night's rest myself. Other hobby breeders recommend this as well (113, 403).

In the morning, the first thing you should do is weigh the chick to monitor its growth[18]. Then immediately afterwards, give the chick its first feeding of the day and return it to the brooder. Its weight should increase steadily, but do not worry too much should the chick not increase in weight every day. You may even see a drop of a gram or so when it is a few weeks old. However, you should become very concerned if there is a drop in weight for three or more consecutive days. A time when you should expect a slight dip in growth rate is when the feathers first break through the skin.

There is much discussion among aviculturalists about the advantages of hand-rearing versus parent-rearing of parrots. There are several

---

[18]They sell a number of scales for this. Select one that weighs in grams in order to be consistent with how most veterinarians record bird weights.

issues related to this. First, most parent-reared parrot chicks grow more rapidly than hand-fed birds (78). The second is that parent-reared birds make better breeder stock. I have not noticed either of these problems for hand-reared caiques. Indeed, since the development of high quality hand-feeding formulae, the rate of growth of my hand-fed caique chicks has been significantly faster than those I allow my pairs to co-parent. It usually takes about one additional week for parent-fed chicks to reach their final weight than chicks I hand-feed. Neither do parent-reared birds make for better breeding stock. If anything, hand-reared birds make better breeding stock as long as you let them socialize with other caiques while they are young.

This young black-headed chick has a half of a seedless green grape inserted into its beak to emphasize the soft pads at the corners of the beak. Touching them stimulates the chick to pump for food. (Photo by author)

Young chick seeking attention from male yellow-thighed parent. The author co-parented this chick. (Photo by author)

It is not difficult to feed a healthy chick at three weeks of age. They naturally pump in the food when you touch the soft pads on each side of the beak. It is only a matter of delivering the food in a convenient manner. Most large breeding operations feed their chicks with syringes. Some use gavage needles or tubes to deliver the food directly into the crop. These methods are rapid and much less wasteful than some of the other methods I describe. You can also monitor food intake better, but you need proper training to do this. Another method is spoon-feeding pioneered by Gilbert Lee (219) and advocated by Rosemary Low (231). For this, you feed the bird with a spoon that has had its sides folded up to form a sort of narrow sluice. A stainless steel baby spoon works best for caiques. This is very effective but slow and messy. Being slower has an advantage. It allows more time for you to socialize the chick and breeders think this results in a better pet.

The last way to feed the chick is the flexible disposable plastic cup method. When you use this method, you prepare the food in a plastic cup, and then you compress the sides of the cup to form a 'V.' If the formula is just thin enough, it flows down the 'V' into the chick's beak. This method allows the container to make better contact with the soft pads at the corners of the beak than any other method, causing the chick to pump vigorously. The chick will often consume its full portion in a single continuous feeding. The collapsible five or seven ounce non-colored plastic cups work well and they are less brittle and do not crack when you pinch their sides. When you use this method, the formula may be prepared in the same container used to feed the chick. Further, these cups are inexpensive and you may discard them along with unconsumed formula when you are done. Of course, after feeding you will have to clean up the chick and spilt food with a warm damp clean cloth or paper towel. Having three different feeding methods is useful when a chick is recalcitrant about eating with one.

There is another way for a person to feed a chick. It is probably one of the oldest ways, but I cannot recommend it. Some natives of South America premasticate the food they feed parrot chicks. Schneebaum (370) wrote about how a native Amazonian fed parrot chicks: "He took up the birds and held them both on a finger, securing them there with a thumb. He put a piece of yucca in his mouth, chewed it, puckered out his lips, opened the beak of one parrot with his other hand and stuffed some of the softened yucca into it with his tongue." I suppose you could do this in a pinch; however, you run the risk of transferring unwanted pathogenic organisms to your chick.

At some point during the hand-feeding phase, nearly every chick regurgitates a portion of the formula immediately after you feed it. Usually you do not observe this until week four or later. Do not be alarmed. This regurgitation is most frequent after the first feeding early in the day. Sometimes the chick spews out nearly everything it swallowed. When this happens, be patient and try to get a small amount into the chick by feeding it more slowly. Then, about an hour later, feed the chick again. Usually, it will take the food more readily then and regurgitate less.

You will find that the appetite of a growing chick in its mid-growth spurt can be prodigious. Beginning between three and four weeks of age, a chick consumes much more than an adult bird. Chicks can take between one and two tablespoons (17.5 and 36.5 ml) into their crop at each feeding and swallow it as quickly as you can shovel it in. At about six weeks, there is a transition. The chick starts to be fussier about taking formula and its intake starts to decline as its weight approaches that of an adult. At this point, it is good to be skilled in feeding the chick by several different methods in order to coax it to eat.

At about six weeks, it is also time to start the weaning process. When you notice the chick is picking at things in the brooder, provide it with a few solid foods. Add some cold dry breakfast food such as a few Cheerios, a sliced grape and a small piece of spray millet to its bin or brooder. Once you see that the chick is eating these, start adding other foods. At this age, the chick will not be able to hold these in its foot, but will chew them and begin to hold them in its beak. As the chicks grow older, it is amusing to see their frustration when they try to hold food in their feet. With a few weeks practice though, they eventually develop good motor skills with their prehensile feet and hold their food. They especially like grapes and the softer fruit such as

kiwi and orange from which they can extract the juices. They prefer seeds, but by limiting the amount of seed, you can usually wean them onto pellets.

Unlike some parrot species, caique chicks usually wean rather easily. I have had chicks suddenly refuse to accept formula, but others that wanted fed for weeks after they could cope on their own. Chicks reared alone usually take the longest. Caiques wean by simply taking smaller and smaller amounts of the formula until they finally just accept only a swallow or two. By this time, they are usually eating an adult diet and can do without. Surprisingly, many year-old birds remember their days as a chick, and if they see you feeding a younger chick, they beg for a taste of the hand-feeding formula.

Keep hand-reared chicks clean. Even caique parents seem to clean up after their chicks. When you check a nest of chicks, you almost never see evidence of droppings until fledging time. When they are very young, keep the chicks of nearly the same age in small disposable plastic bowls such as soft margarine bowls lined with soft white tissue (toilet or nasal), not paper towels. The reason for using white tissue is to watch the appearance of the chick's droppings. It is always a great comfort to see that the chick's digestive system is functioning, especially when it is very young. The droppings will be tiny, but should have the same appearance as those of an adult bird. Using a soft tissue paper is important at this age because the chick's skin is very thin and even a paper towel can be rough enough to abrade it. This is a particular problem for squirming caique chicks. Abraded skin is evident when you see blood on the tissue paper and scrapes on the bird's feet. If you see this on the tissue, apply an antibiotic ointment to the abraded skin, switch to lining the dish with waxed paper, and keep a close watch. As the chick grows, you can move it into progressively larger bowls and at about two and a half weeks start using a paper towel as a liner instead of the soft tissue.

There are a number of reasons for rearing chicks in groups in the same bowl and brooder if they are nearly the same size. One is that they provide each other with warmth until they are capable of maintaining body temperature on their own. Another reason is that the bones of young chicks remain soft and incompletely calcified until shortly before they fledge (163). When parrot chicks huddle in the nest or in their bowl, they are also providing each other with mutual support in standing. Raising single chicks seems to be associated with a high incidence of osterodystrophy in the larger parrots. For this same reason, you should do the feeding as quickly as possible so the chick does not have to stand by itself too long. Raising caiques in a group also provides them with a better capacity to learn and socialize. As noted above, single chicks do not wean as rapidly as those reared in a group nor do they wish to explore their surroundings as much. Sometimes, you have no choice but to rear a chick alone, but avoid it if you can.

Once chicks reach a certain size a simple lined bowl will no longer suffice. The chicks will roam the whole area available within their bin or brooder. This requires a new approach to keeping the chicks clean and there are a number of methods. Perhaps the most common is to place a layer of absorbent material in the brooder. Most people use wood chips; others use non-medicated horse pellets because they fear the chicks may ingest the wood chips. For a hobby breeder who can devote lots of time to the chicks, I line the brooder first with a cloth baby diaper and then place a paper towel on top. The diaper serves to absorb the moisture from the droppings, and the paper towel catches the solid portions. To clean, replace the diaper with a clean one and toss the paper towel. Also, place a soft toy such a small teddy bear with the chick; this seems to be especially soothing for single chicks. The arrangements for keeping the chick clean, however, are really a matter of personal preference.

As fledging time approaches, the chick should become familiar with a cage. A standard commercial cockatiel cage with a roost box attached will suffice. The acclimatization should not begin until the chick is proficient at perching steadily on your finger and is capable of standing fully upright on a perch. At first, one of the perches in the cage should be set low and within reach of the chick from the cage floor. The chick, however, will soon learn how to climb and will use higher perches. Until it can climb well, the chick usually appreciates a small cardboard box, such a half of a cold cereal box, laid on its side on the floor of the cage that it can scurry into and hide. For the first day or two, remove the chick back to the familiar confines of its brooder for the night. Once it seems comfortable with the cage, allow it to remain in the cage overnight. Most chicks will have explored the roost box by then and will take to sleeping in it, but you may need to confine the chick to the box by blocking the entrance for the first night or two. Once it gets used to the roost box, the chick will prefer sleeping in one the rest of its life. At first, you will need to line the roost box with a paper towel. Young birds do not quite understand that they are not supposed to defecate inside when first introduced to the roost box. Therefore, you will need to change this paper towel every day until the chick learns bowel control. After the chick has learned this, you may switch to using wood chips in the box. It usually takes only a few days for the young bird to acclimatize to a cage and roost box.

If you are hand-rearing other parrot species or more than one clutch of caiques, you should take care to segregate your older caique chicks from them. Caiques, even young chicks, will terrorize any other chicks you might be rearing (412). Soon after their pinfeathers appear, caiques start to roam and if they can reach another clutch that you are hand-rearing they will harass them unmercifully. Thus, you should consider this when setting up your brooding area.

Co-parenting chicks.

There are also ways to produce hand-tame chicks that does not require their total removal from the parents for hand-rearing. This may seem contrary to the dogma that a bird imprints on the first living thing it sees when it opens its eyes, but like many other dogmas, people often oversimplify a kernel of truth. In reality, things are more complex. Birds have the capacity to imprint on more than one kind of living being and that being need not be present at the precise moment the chick opens its eyes. Since 1994, I have been rearing hand-tame caiques using an approach I call co-parenting. Co-parenting is in its infancy as an avicultural practice, and we still need to work out some of its parameters. Further, the practice of co-parenting seems to be one of degree. For example, Casky (68) adopted the practice of assisting his macaw pairs in feeding their chicks to be sure they received a more nutritious diet. As a by-product, he discovered that the chicks were more people-friendly. A group at the University of California at Davis (2, 84, 264) investigated the co-parenting of orange-winged Amazons. They found that if they handled the chicks for 20 minutes or so a day, the chicks suffered far less stress and, indeed, became quite tame toward their human handlers. Leaving the chicks with the parents as long as possible has also been shown to be beneficial for African grey parrots (368). One reason for this may be that the chicks have a chance to learn the subsong of its male parent which is the case for the Meyer's parrot (*Poicephalus meyeri*) (247) and the galah cockatoo (*Cacatua roseicapilla*) (360). You should note that co-parenting may not be suitable for all parrots, particularly pairs that react poorly to nest inspection. In some cases, the parents may harm a chick if they are aware that you are entering their nest box. You need to make a judgment about whether a pair will accept daily inspections without undue stress.

I have used two approaches to co-parenting caiques. In one, I leave the chick with the parents for the entire rearing period. However, this only works if there is only one chick with the parents. In the other, I rotate all the chicks of a clutch in and out of the pair's nest so they only have one with them at any one time. This only works well if there are three or more chicks in the clutch. In either case, I do not begin the co-parenting until the chicks' eyes start to open at about three weeks of age.

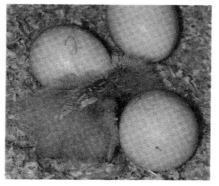

Chick huddling with eggs to keep warm while parents are away from nest. (Photo by author)

In the first approach, I start a regime of handling the chick left in the nest twice a day. In the morning, you only need to handle the chicks for few minutes. If the handling of the chick is timed just after the parents emerge from the nest box, the chicks' crops will be empty, and you can use this time to feed them a bit of formula. Just do not give them a complete feeding, since the parents will be forcing food on them later. In the late afternoon, handle the chick again for 10 to 15 minutes. By handling, I mean nuzzling, talking and clucking to it and keeping it warm in your cupped hand. As it gets older, handle it longer at each session and offer it a half of a sliced grape or other soft fruit warmed by dropping it into hot water. When holding the chick, position it so it can look into your face. Indeed, this may be of critical importance. You want the chick to focus its attention on you. You can then tell if you are succeeding when it stares back at you rather than averting its eyes. You should also spend time gently scratching it, particularly about its head. Scratching it during the feathering process helps remove the feather casings

and this later leads to the acceptance of your preening efforts. Finally, cradle the bird gently in the palm of your hand close to your chest. When you rest quietly together, the chick will vibrate almost imperceptibly, similar to the purr of a happy cat. Like a cat, the bird's vibration is a sign of a happy chick. This vibration appears to be due to muscle vibration. At two and three weeks of age, you can feel the vibration by touching the pipping muscle or muscularia complexus, which remains disproportionately large at this age. Later, as the muscularia complexus decreases in size, the whole chick will seem to vibrate. I suspect this may be a mechanism for creating warmth.

Some chicks take to sleeping on their backs like this yellow-thighed that is sharing a bin with a black-headed chick. People rearing caique chicks are sometimes shocked to see this and think the chick is dead. This, however, is normal behavior. The sliced red grapes are a weaning food. (Photo by author)

As part of the handling, you can help the chick learn to perch. At first, the chick's feet will lack the natural tendency to clamp onto your finger, but a week or so after it has completely feathered out, it will start to develop its perching skills. Prior to this time, the chick seems incapable of gripping with its feet and the toes do not automatically clamp, but remain extended when you try to place the chick on a perch. When the chick begins to perch, its tail end will hang low and you will have to balance it carefully, but in a week or so, it should be able to perch comfortably on your finger. Once it has mastered perching, you can move on to teaching the "up" command. To do this, you start with the chick perching on one hand and then offer it the chance to climb onto your other hand. Offer the chick your thumb as a balance point onto which it can hitch its beak and then gently encourage it to move its feet onto the first finger of the same hand. Repeat the lessons as a way of bonding with the chick.

In this form of co-parenting, it is best to handle the chicks when the parents are away from the nest box, preferably out of sight in a completely different room. This works well if the parents are hand-tame and part of their routine is to spend time away from their cage anyway. The reason for this is that some parent caiques seem to get jealous of you handling their chick and compensate by over preening it after you return them to the box. In some cases, the parents over preen to such an extent that they barber or puck the chick's feathers. Fox and Millam (130) report this for the orange-winged Amazons (*Amazona amazonica*) they co-parented. Not every pair caique does this, but if they do, it is usually a problem if you co-parent subsequent chicks from that same pair again. I have achieved mixed results using this approach, and not all the chicks become human friendly.

In the other form of co-parenting, I do not spend so much time handling chicks as the first approach requires. This has become my preferred method. However, you cannot use it unless there are at least three chicks in the clutch. For some reason, doing this with only two chicks in the clutch does not produce uniformly tame chicks. The co-parenting starts when the eyes of the chicks begin to open. First, I reduce the number of chicks in the nest to only one. Then once a day, I replace the chick with one of its clutch mates starting with the oldest, then replace it with the next oldest until each of the chicks in the clutch have spent 24 hours in the parents' nest box. Then I start the cycle over again with the oldest chick. Of course you must hand-feed the chicks that are not with the parents, but you would have to do this anyway. You continue rotating the chicks until they start to wean. In this way, every chick in the clutch is exposed to both rearing by its parents and the person hand-feeding it. When they begin weaning and fledging, you can place all the chicks back in the cage with their parents. There the parents greatly speed the weaning process by teaching them to eat adult bird foods. Surprisingly, the parents accept all the chicks and they all sleep together in the parents' nest box.

The final step in early chick development is fledging. Fledging occurs when the chick leaves the nest and makes its first flight. This is the day you walk into the aviary and find the chick sitting on a perch outside the nest box. The same applies to hand-reared chicks. A chick's flying capacity is quite limited at first and its landings are less than graceful. Within a week, though, it usually becomes adept. If it is co-parented, you should leave it with its parents during this learning process. One problem, however, is that it may become less willing to leave the cage during this time. Therefore, between one and two weeks after

fledging, you should remove the co-parented chick to a cage of its own, or to one containing other young chicks of about the same age. After you separate a co-parented chick from its parents, it takes only a day or so to adjust, but it usually adapts quickly and develops a strong attachment to people.

Disturbances

People who breed parrots usually try to prevent outside disturbances of their aviary during the breeding, incubation and early rearing periods. This is less of a problem with domestically bred stock that is habituated to people, but it was a problem for aviculturists in earlier years when only wild-caught stock was available (242). Some pairs, particularly in public aviaries, are so inured to people they will go to nest even when there is a general hubbub of activity outside their cages. Most pairs in private hands are not accustomed to too much commotion, and the female feels compelled to pop out and see what is happening every time she hears a strange person or animal come near the cage.

Minor disturbances do not bother most pairs, particularly if they occur as a part of the daily routine. Still, inspecting their boxes is stressful for some pairs, and it is best to wait until the hen has left the nest before opening the inspection door. The best opportunity for this is in the morning when both the hen and cock are out of the box for their morning feeding. Even then, try to be stealthy. In the wild, their eggs and chicks are very vulnerable at this time, and an anxious pair will not go too far from the nest. If the parent birds are stick tame, take them into another room out of sight of their nest and cage and give them a treat and some juice on a stand as a way to emulate foraging. Then return and inspect the nest. The disturbances that bother them most, however, are unexpected visits by too many strange people, and unknown animals such as cats and dogs. Perhaps the most disruptive thing is the introduction of a strange caique or other parrot into the aviary during the breeding season (13). In general, if you avoid changing the daily routine, particularly their feeding schedule (242), during the breeding period the birds usually remain content and produce chicks year after year.

Physical development problems

While rearing chicks, you should pay close attention to their development (117). There are four common developmental problems you can correct if caught early. These are spraddleleg, misdirected toes, constricted toes, and beak misalignments. You cannot correct these as easily once the birds are adults. It is important, therefore, that you deal with the problems as soon as possible after you notice them. With experience, you will learn to correct some of these yourself, but the first time you encounter them you should consult an avian veterinarian.

Spraddleleg, also known as splayleg, is one of the most common developmental problems. It is also one of the easiest to correct if detected before the chick's bones have completely calcified. Spraddleleg is a deformity in which a bird's leg splays laterally out from the body at the hip. In extreme cases, birds with this condition are not able to stand erect. Usually, you first notice spraddleleg while hand-feeding the chick. It tends to have more difficulty standing than the other chicks in a clutch and if you look closely, you will notice that its leg is not aligned directly under its body, but extends outward at an odd angle. If the chick is very young, place it in a small deep dish and pack tissue around it to help it stay upright. If it is a mild case in a bit older chick, start using a piece of rubberized mesh such as that used under carpets to prevent skidding or in drawers to prevent pottery chipping. Place the mesh on top of a paper towel liner as a way of providing the chick better purchase on the floor of the brooder and enable it to stand better. You can easily rinse the droppings from these mesh pads in hot water and they air dry quickly.

For an older chick with a more severe case, you can make a hobble that forces the leg into the correct position. One way to hobble the chick is to use tape to bind the spraddled lower leg to the correctly positioned lower leg in order to bring it back into alignment. The cloth elastic medical tapes work well for this. The hobble should allow ¼ to ½ inch (about 1 cm) distance between the legs depending on the age of the chick. You will need to adjust the hobble as the bird grows. Another way to correct spraddleleg is to cut two holes into a thin piece of soft foam rubber sponge at the correct distance of 0.5 inch (about 1 cm) or so depending on the chick's age and gently push the legs through holes. If you use this approach, be sure to position the sponge as closely to the body as possible. You then need to keep the chick in a small bowl in order to keep it upright during the rest of the development process.

A similar developmental problem arises when the outer toe of the chick does not migrate into its correct position. One of the defining characteristics of parrots is that they are zygodactyl l, that is they have two toes pointing forward and two pointing backwards. When a parrot chick first hatches, however, they have three toes pointing forward and only one pointing to the rear. Within the first week or so after hatch, the outer toe rotates so that it points to the rear. Occasionally, the toe fails to rotate properly. The chick's foot reaches nearly full size at about four weeks after hatch. Therefore, as soon as you notice this abnormality, you should take action because correcting this problem is very easy. When the toe is just large enough to manipulate, tape the misaligned toe side-by-side to the other rear-pointing toe. Because at this age the toes are growing very rapidly, you need to remove and replace the taping frequently so that growth is not restricted.

Another common developmental problem is constricted toe. This occurs when a narrow band of tissue forms a sort of tourniquet around the toe and prevents proper blood circulation. This only requires minor surgery to correct. If you do not correct this promptly, however, the distal portion of the toe may swell and develop into a necrotic lesion. This can result in the loss of the toe. The surgery consists of cutting through the constricting band and suturing the lesion back together. A qualified veterinarian should do this procedure.

Beak misalignments are another developmental problem that you can often correct while the bird is still a chick. Fortunately, these seem to be uncommon for caiques. There are three common beak deformities of parrot chicks: Scissor bill, under bite and mandible compression. Scissor bill is the lateral deviation of the two mandibles in which the upper mandible slides past the lower to the right or left. Under bite (or mandibular prognathism) is when the lower mandible outgrows the upper mandible. When this happens, the cutting edge of the lower mandible cannot make proper contact with the upper mandible. Mandible compression is a disproportionate narrowing of the upper mandible. Some believe this deformity results from an improper hand-feeding technique in which the feeder holds the still soft beak between his or her fingers during the feeding process. If you notice that a chick's beak is not developing properly, take it to a qualified veterinarian immediately. There are a number of methods to correct beak problems, but the appropriate one depends on the nature of the deformity. If you do not treat the bird, it is not life threatening. Parrots usually adapt well to malformed beaks and learn how to overcome their handicaps, but, if you treat young chicks promptly, the repairs are usually not noticeable when they get older and they need less beak grooming later in life.

Expectations

Breeding any animal is fraught with unexpected circumstances, and we are still in the early era of caique breeding so there is still much to learn. You must steel yourself for the fact that not every chick is going to survive. Hobby breeders who allow their pairs to hatch and rear their chicks are almost certain to experience a chick dying. While most pairs readily take to the task of rearing their chicks, some never seem to get the hang of it. When a pair takes to breaking their own eggs and killing their own chicks, you can get frustrated. I have written here about my approach to solving some of these problems. Yet, sometimes, you find yourself in such a new situation you are baffled about just what action to take.

If things do not go well, do not beat up on yourself. You must realize that not all eggs are going to hatch nor are all chicks equipped to survive after they hatch. The cause is often difficult to determine. It may be due to bad husbandry, but it can also be due to a lethal mutation. Aviculturalists do not usually discuss their failures, but I think they ought to be more open about them. One of the reasons I wrote this book is to teach what I have learned from my own bitter experiences. It is my hope that I can prevent my fellow breeders from having to relearn some of these lessons.

Pionites leucogaster leucogaster

Edward Lear lithograph from 1832. This is the first known image of this subspecies. Lear labeled this illustration *Psittacus badiceps* or "Bay-Headed Parrot." We know Lear better for his nonsense verse such as "The Owl and the Pussycat." (Courtesy Ewell Sale Stewart Library, The Academy of Natural Sciences of Philadelphia.)

Pionites leucogaster xanthomerius.

Joseph Smit chromolithograph published in the **Proceedings of the Zoological Society of London,** 1879 (378). It accompanied an article by P.L. Sclater entitled "Remarks on some parrots living in the Society's gardens." Sclater had earlier described this as a new subspecies (377). (Original print in possession of the author.)

Pionites melanocephalus melanocephalus (left)
and *Pionites leucogaster leucogaster* (right)

William T. Cooper painted this image of the two nominate species of caique for Joseph M. Forshaw's **Parrots of the World** published in 1973. The original watercolor is in the possession of the National Library of Australia. (Reproduced with the approval of the artist and the permission of the National Library of Australia.)

77

Part III. Some Natural History

Species and subspecies descriptions

Pionites melanocephalus melanocephalus Linné 1758

Pionites melanocephalus was the first species of caique named using Linnæus' binomial naming system (224). The reason for this is that Linnæus invented the system, so he got to name it. He was also the first to describe the criteria that all parrots must meet. The following, from his **Systema naturae** (Vol. 1, page 96), is the description he applied to all parrots. Of course, he wrote in Latin.

> **"44. PSITTACUS <u>Rostrum</u> aduncum: mandibula periore mobili cera instructa**
>
> **<u>Lingua</u> carnosa, obtuse, intega**
>
> **<u>Pedum</u> digiti antici 2, posticique 2."**

After giving the requirements of birds belonging in the parrot group he placed them all in the genus *Psittacus*. He then went on to describe the different species within this group including the black-headed caique, which he describes thusly:

> **"melanocephalus 33. P. brachiurus viridis subtus luteus, pileo nigro, pectore albo. Mus. Ad. Fr. 2. p.**
>
> **Psittacus coccineus, ventre albo. Edw. Av. 169. t. 169. habitat in Mexico."**

He almost got it right. One has to wonder where the red ('coccineus') came from. He cites George Edwards (118), but he obviously did not examine Edwards' lithograph or narrative very closely. He also stated that black-headed caiques were indigenous to Mexico, an error repeated in the works of others who slavishly copied Linnæus. Nonetheless, this description earned Linnæus' authorship for the species *P. melanocephalus*, which eventually became the subspecies *P. m. melanocephalus* despite the fact that Edwards was the first European to recognize it as a species and did a better job of describing it.

Here is a more up to date description of the adult nominate subspecies. The upper surfaces of the back, wings and tail are green; the crown of the head is black; the abdomen is white; the sides of the body, legs and under-tail coverts are yellow; the under surfaces of wings are black; the undersides of the tail feathers are brownish. Older black-headed caiques sometimes develop a few orange feathers in their black crown (399). Some birds have green highlights on the edges of their thigh feathers; this trait is very pronounced on a specimen from French Guiana in the Carnegie Museum. There is a line of green feathers under each eye. Beneath the green line, there is often a wash of whitish feathers. The nape is an apricot color that fluoresces bright yellow under near ultraviolet light (black light). Most specimens also exhibit fluorescence of a narrow, approximately one-centimeter (0.5 inch) wide band of feathers extending from beneath the lower mandible to where the white feathers of the breast begin. The apricot colored feathers under the wing and on the upper thigh also fluoresce. The coverts over the ears, within the apricot colored portion of the head, are darker than the surrounding feathers. The feathers at the sides of the throat and on the sides of neck are yellow to orange but do not fluoresce. The outer primaries of the wing are blue on the upper surface and black beneath. Under some lighting conditions, the undersides of the outermost primaries exhibit a rusty redness along the vane parallel to the shaft. The secondaries are green on the outer upper surface and black on the inner lower surface. The bill and feet are usually black. On most birds, the periopthalmic skin is black but on some birds it is light gray to nearly white. The light coloration of the periopthalmic skin may be sex-linked, and seems to occur more frequently on female birds. It is about 22 cm (nine inches) from its beak to the end of its tail.

Immature birds exhibit several distinguishing characteristics. The universal characteristic of all young caiques is that their eyes appear to be almost black. On close examination, however, the iris is a deep brown. As the bird matures, the iris develops an aposematic orange-red color that the bird uses to signal its emotional state. The breasts of most immature birds, but not all, are suffused with yellow to orange feathers. In contrast, on adult captive birds, these feathers are white. Very young chicks usually have a horn colored bill that changes to black as it grows. Finally, the bare periopthalmic skin around the eye of young birds usually progresses from a flesh color to black. Less noticeable differences from adult birds are green tinged feathers on the head and slightly narrower tails.

This subspecies' range includes eastern Venezuela, the Guianas, Brazil (north of the

Amazon River), and Southern Columbia. From Southern Columbia and Southern Venezuela into the northeastern most part of Peru, there is a broad clinal zone[19] that grades into the range of the pallid subspecies *P. m. pallidus* (229, 286).

Pionites melanocephalus pallidus Berlepsch 1889

Heinrich von Berlepsch (26) was the first to note that this form was different from *P. m. melanocephalus* in having lemon yellow instead of orange thighs, flanks and under-tail coverts. He first published this observation in 1889 in the **Journal für Ornithologie** giving him authorship for this subspecies[20]. Below is his German text.

"**122.** *Caica melanocephala* **(Linn.). (cf. antea p. 291.***)*

Ein Exemplar von Yurimaguas in der Sammlung des Herrn Nehrkorn, welches ich nicht gesehen habe.

NB- Die Vögel von Ost-Pern und Ost-Ecuador unterscheiden sich von denen aus Trinidad (welche wahrscheinlich als Typen zu betrachten sind) und aus Guiana durch viel hellere, fast citronengelbe Färbung der Hypochondrien und Tibien, welche Theile bei den Vögeln aus Trinidad und Guiana stets mehr oder weniger orangeroth resp. lachsfarben überlaufen sind. Auch die Kehle und Kopfseiten und die Unterschwanzdeckfedern sind bei den Vögeln vom oberen Amazonas heller gelb gefärbt. Dieselben sind vielleicht als *C. melanocephala pallida* Berl. zu sondern."

Aside from the incorrect assertion that caiques occur on Trinidad, Berlepsch's description is accurate. For the most part, the description of *P. m. pallidus* is the same as for *P. m. melanocephalus*. The primary difference is that *P. m. pallidus* has lemon yellow thighs and *P. m. melanocephalus* has orange thighs. There is a gradation between the ranges of the two and some museum specimens of *P. m. pallidus* have hints of orange on their thighs. The nape on both species is an apricot color that fluoresces under a black light, as do some of the feathers beneath the beak, on the upper thigh and upper sides. The under surfaces of the tail feathers are brownish, while the under tail coverts are yellow. There is controversy among aviculturalists as to whether *P. m. pallidus* is a separate subspecies. There is a clear gradient from the northeast coast of South America to southern Peru in thigh color from orange to the lemon yellow of this subspecies (229).

Pet pallid black-headed caique (P. m. pallidus) at the La Mission Hotel, Coca, Ecuador in 2000. (Photo by author.)

We know little about the immature form of *P. m. pallidus*. It seems likely that they exhibit both the dark eye color and a suffusion of yellow feathers in their breasts like the nominate form. An immature specimen in the Carnegie Museum exhibits a significant number of green feathers on

---

[19] A cline, clinal belt, or clinal zone is a geographical region lying between the ranges of two species or sub-species capable of inter-breeding. This often results in a gradient in the physical features across the zone due to interbreeding.

[20] Rough English translation. "122. Caica melanocephala (Linn.). (cf. antea p. 291.)

There is a specimen from Yurimaguas in the collection of Mr. Nehrkorn, that I have not seen.

NB- The birds of east Peru and east Ecuador differ from those of Trinidad (which may be regarded as the type form) as well as from those of Guiana by being much brighter, having nearly citron yellow colored sides and thighs. These parts on the birds from Trinidad and Guiana are almost always an orange to salmon color. Further, the throat and sides of the head and the under tail feathers of the birds from the upper Amazon are a more bright yellow. Perhaps this form should be separated as *C. melanocephala pallida* Berl."

its thighs, which we do not usually see for *P. m. melanocephalus*. Whether this is a permanent trait limited to only a few birds or lost in adulthood as is the case for *P. l. xanthomerius* is unknown.

The range of *P. m. pallidus* is primarily east of the Andes Mountains in eastern Ecuador, northern Peru extending well south along the Huallaga and Ucayali River valleys as well as along the eastern edge of the Andean foothills north into Columbia (71). Specimens have been collected as far east as Tonantins on the Solimões River (Carnegie Museum). North and east of the Solimões-Amazon River there is a broad clinal zone with *P. m. melanocephalus* extending into southeastern Columbia and southern Venezuela into Brazil. Traylor (438) noted that birds from Sarayacu, Ecuador were almost "exactly intermediate" between *P. m. melanocephalus* and *P.m. pallidus*. Ridgely (346) noted there were individual birds similar to *P. m. melanocephalus* in the vicinity of Imuyacocha, Ecuador, but the rest were *P. m. pallidus*. To the east and southeast of the Ucayali River, an uplands known as the Sierra Contamana near the border with Brazil separates it from the range of *P. l. xanthomerius*, the yellow-thighed caique (159). One may see hybrids with *P. l. xanthomerius* along a narrow clinal band where their ranges meet (159).

Pionites leucogaster leucogaster Kuhl 1820

This is the nominate form of the white-bellied caique, *Pionites leucogaster* that we presently break into three subspecies. The one described here is the green-thighed caique. Heinrich Kuhl (212) was the first to describe it in the scientific literature in his **Conspectus Psittacorum**. Like Linnæus, he wrote in the scientific language of the time—Latin.

"121. Psittacus leucogaster *Illiger.*

In Brasilia rarus.

Cauda, alis, dorso tibiisque viridibus; pectore abdomineque albis; crisso, genis gulaque flavis; capite ochraceo, hic et illic nigrescente; rostro magno, albo; capite magno; corpore crasso. – Ps. Melanocephali, cui proximus, figura et magnitudine.

In Museo *Berolinensi, Principis Maximiliani, Temminkiano.*"

In his description, he recognized its close relationship to *P. melanocephalus*, and *P. leucogaster* appears immediately before it in his monograph. It is also noteworthy that at this early stage in taxonomy, all parrots were in the *Psittacus* genus.

A more complete English description follows: The upper surfaces of the back, wings and tail are green; the abdomen is white; the flanks of the body and legs are green; the under surfaces of the wings are black. The nape and top of the head are an apricot color. These apricot feathers fluoresce yellow when illuminated with near ultraviolet light. The feathers under the throat and on sides of neck are yellow. The outer primaries of the wing are blue on the upper surface and black beneath. The under tail coverts are yellow. The inner primaries are green on the outer upper surface and black on the inner upper surface. The bill and bare skin around the eye is flesh colored. It is about 22 cm (nine inches) in length. Their feet are typically a gray color, although some retain the flesh color of the immature bird.

Immature birds of the *P. leucogaster* species usually have a significant number of black feathers in their crowns that are absent on adult birds. The breast of immature birds, like *P. melanocephalus*, is usually suffused with yellow.

It is native to the state of Para in eastern Brazil but only south of the Amazon River. There is a very broad clinal zone with *P. l. xanthurus* extending from the western border of Para to the state of Amazonas. It also extends into northeastern Mato Grosso

Pionites leucogaster xanthomerius Sclater 1857

The common English name for this subspecies is the yellow-thighed caique. Phillip Lutley Sclater (377) was the first to describe and name this subspecies. The type specimen, collected by Henry Bates and purchased by Stevens, is in the Natural History Museum at Tring, England. Here is the narrative for specimen 65 from Sclater's report in the Proceedings of the Zoological Society of London from 1857 in which he establishes his precedence for this name.

"Mr. S. Stevens has lately received a small but interesting collection of birds from Mr. H.W. Bates, now resident at Ega on the Upper Amazon. Although many travelers and collectors have passed through this country, we are still without any detailed information concerning the general character of its ornithology. Those into whose hands collections from new localities come, are in general too prone to pick out single objects and describe them as new, instead of what is much more important in a scientific point of view, giving an accurately determined catalogue of the whole of the species. Such accounts are always useful—in the first place increasing our knowledge of the facts of geographical distributions, and secondly, giving great assistance to future investigators who are studying collections from the same quarter. The species transmitted by Mr. Bates are the following. They are mostly from Ega or from the Rio Javarri, the frontier stream of Peru and Brazil, but the exact locality is in every case affixed."

"65. Caica xanthomeria, G.R. Gray in Mus. Brit.

The apparently new species, of which the only two specimens sent have passed into the collection of the British Museum, closely resembles *C. leucogaster*, Kuhl (*badiceps*, Lear), but has the flanks and thighs yellow instead of green, and exhibits some minor variations in shades of colouring."

The appearance of mature members of this subspecies is similar to *P. l. leucogaster* except its thighs and flanks are a lemon yellow instead of green. Another difference is that the bare periopthalmic skin ranges in shade from a flesh color to black. The upper surface of the tail feathers is green but the underside is brownish similar to those of *P. m. pallidus*. The under tail coverts are yellow. For most adults, the beak is flesh colored, although an occasional specimen has black variegation (395).

The most noticeable difference between the immature and the adult birds is black feathers on the head. Nearly all young birds have dark feathers in their crown, although some chicks never develop these black feathers. On some chicks there are so many black feathers they can be confused for

P. m. pallidus. Like immature *P. melanocephalus*, their breasts are usually flecked with yellow. A small number of immature birds exhibit green frosting on their thighs and a green band under their eyes similar to that on *P. melanocephalus*. This usually disappears in the adult. Like all caiques, immature birds have dark eyes that undergo a change to nearly the same red-orange color seen for all caiques. Their feet are usually a gray to flesh color.

The range of this subspecies is southern Peru, northern Bolivia extending into western Brazil south of the Solimões-Amazon River. East of this region, there may be a clinal zone with *P. l. xanthurus*. As noted above, there is a narrow hybridization zone along its northwestern range with *P. m. pallidus* where the two species come into contact.

Pionites leucogaster xanthurus Todd 1925

This subspecies is similar to the *P. l. xanthomerius*. Like that subspecies, it has yellow flanks and thighs. What distinguishes them from that subspecies are their lemon yellow tail feathers. Below is Clyde Todd's (436) original description:

"Pilem, sides of the head (down to and including the auriculars), hind-neck, and sides of the neck dull apricot orange; back, rump, upper tail-coverts, upper wing-coverts, and secondaries externally bright parrot green; tail deep chrome to primuline yellow, some of the rectricies with a basal area of parrot green, concealed except on the middle pair; primaries and their coverts with their inner webs black, and the outer webs Berlin blue with a narrow outer webs Berlin blue with a narrow outer margin of green; under wing-coverts parrot green, the carpel edge mixed with yellow; white, with a wash of pale yellow in fresh plumage, the sides shaded with

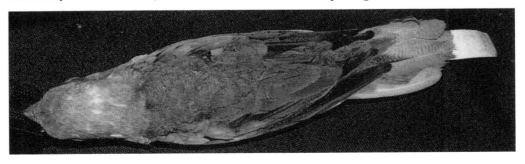

Yellow-tailed caique (P. l. xanthurus) specimen in the Carnegie Museum, Pittsburgh, Pa. (Photo taken by author with permission of Robin Panza, Collection Manager.)

light salmon orange; tibiae and under tail-coverts empire yellow; 'iris cadmium yellow; eyelids white; feet flesh white; bill bone white.' Wing (type) 141; tail, 79, bill, 25; tarsus, 16."

I can add little to this description, except to say that the yellow color of the tail is the most distinctive difference from the other subspecies of the caiques. The tail feathers are not completely yellow; the base of the feather near the body is green but sharply breaks to yellow for most of the length. The undersides of the tail feathers and the under tail coverts are both yellow (286). Its fluorescence pattern is similar to the other subspecies of *P. leucogaster*. Samuel M. Klages first collected this subspecies on July 18, 1922 at Nova Olinda, Brazil. The type specimen is in the Carnegie Museum, Pittsburgh, Pennsylvania. We know little about the immature form of this subspecies.

The exact range of this subspecies remains elusive. It is seldom reported by birding enthusiasts, most likely because its range is in what is even today one of the least visited regions of Amazonia. Todd's specimens were collected at Hyutanahan and Nova Olinda in western Brazil. Haffer (159) reports them from along the Rio Teffe, Rio Purús and upper Rio Madeira. I was fortunate to see birds matching this description during my visit to the Rio Cristalino Lodge near Alta Floresta, Brazil. These observations are consistent with the general range indicated by Fernando Novaes (286). To the east, south of the Amazon River, Novaes indicates there is a broad but poorly characterized clinal zone with *P. l. leucogaster*. Von Pelzeln (308) noted that Johann Natterer, who collected more bird specimens than anyone before or since and visited Brazil in the years from 1817 to 1835, collected two birds with yellow tails, but provided no indication where they came from. Unfortunately, most of Natterer's notes were destroyed in a fire in 1848. Another early report of the yellow-tailed form was made by Hellmayr in 1907 (176). We assume there is a clinal belt with *P. l. xanthomerius* to the west and southwest.

Fry's intermediate form

As a part of the Royal Society and Royal Geographical Society Expedition of 1967-1969 (392), Hilary Fry (136) discovered an unexpected form of caique in northeastern Mato Grosso along the Serra do Ronador, a narrow ridge separating the upper Rio Araguaia from the upper Rio Xingu. He noted that it "differs from described races in the colour of the thighs and retricies; it was nearest to *P. l. xanthomerius*." This was surprising because he discovered this bird a considerable distance from the range of *P. l. xanthomerius*. The range of the *P. l. xanthurus* subspecies separates its range from that of *P. l. xanthomerius*. Confirming Fry's report, Novaes (286) refers to this group as an "intermediate" form between *P. l. xanthurus* and *P. l. leucogaster*. There is some question as to whether these birds qualify as a subspecies, or are simply part of a broad southerly clinal zone between *P. l. leucogaster* and *P. l. xanthurus*. I have taken the liberty of calling this form "Fry's caique" after the first person to describe them.

Fry collected his specimen in the canopy of a dry forest in the northeast section of Mato Grosso between the Rio Araguaia and the Rio Suiá-Missu, a tributary of the Xingu. Novaes (286) collected another three birds of the same description in Mato Grosso on the east bank of Rio Teles Pires and I have seen photographs of a green-thighed form of the yellow-tailed taken in the Rio Cristalino Reserve where I personally observed only the yellow-tailed form.

The taxonomy of caiques

The Englishman John Ray (1627-1705) was the first person to use the term species to group like organisms together and he initiated the use of Latin for naming them. However, we owe Carl Linnæus (1707-1778), a Swedish botanist, a debt for developing the binomial system of naming and classifying all species that scientists use today. The binomial system is a cataloging system in which scientists give every species a two-word Latinized name that we call its scientific name. The first part of the name is the genus name shared by closely related species, while the second part is unique to the species. Under taxonomic rules, the genus name is a Latin noun and the species name is a Latinized adjective or modifying noun. Often it is descriptive. For example, *Pionites melanocephalus* means it is a black-headed member of the genus *Pionites*, while *Pionites leucogaster* means a white-bellied member of the same genus. *Pionites* itself means "fat, plump and sleek" (321) which may explain why in some parts of the world it is known as the "little fatty." Most early naturalists quickly adopted Linnæus' system for naming species because it was simple, allowed a convenient way of grouping similar species, and, perhaps most important of all, replaced a confusion of vernacular names that varied not just from country to country but often within the same country.

After developing his system, Linnæus went into a frenzy of naming all the known species of plants and animals before anyone else could. His reason was to avoid a muddle of names if too many people took part in the naming process, although a huge ego was also a factor. He went about this task by ransacking all the published natural histories he could lay his hands on, and, in the process, lumped all the parrots together under a single genus name: *Psittacus*. When he came across the caique in George Edwards' **A Natural History of Uncommon Birds** (118) he took one look and gave it the Latinized name *Psittacus melanocephalus*. When he was done, he published their new names in his opus Systema Naturae. There were many editions, but most taxonomists consider the 10th edition, published between 1758 and 1759, to be his most authoritative. In it, you can find the taxonomic scheme for the black-headed caique, the only caique known to Linnæus:

Class: Aves

Genus: *Psittacus*

Species: *melanocephalus*

There are some differences in how we treat scientific names now. Linnæus did not use italics in his original publication, but it is now accepted practice. Further, in the arcane ways of taxonomy an author is now included. The author is the first person to recognize and publish a binomial name of a new species. Thus, because Linnæus was the first to publish the scientific name for the black-headed caique under his protocol, he is the author. The present full scientific name is *Pionites melanocephalus* Linné 1758. In this case, we use Linné as the author because Linnæus took the name Carl von Linné after the Swedish King made him a noble in 1762. The date at the end of the name is the year Linnæus published the edition of **Systema Naturae** in which he first named it. In scientific publications, scientists usually add the author and sometimes the publication date after the full binomial name when first used in a scientific paper and abbreviate it to just the first letter of the genus plus the species name when mentioned

later, thus *P. melanocephalus*. It is of note that when taxonomists changed the genus name from *Psittacus* to *Pionites*, they retained Linnæus' original species name and preserved his species authorship.

An important aspect of taxonomy is that it attempts to group similar organisms together as a way of showing their potential relatedness. This has resulted in a hierarchical system. In this system, taxonomists place the most closely related species into a group called a genus, which in turn they place within an even larger group known as a family, and so on. At each higher step in the hierarchy, the relation of one species to another becomes ever broader until eventually it includes all life forms. I do not pretend to understand all the arcane rules of taxonomy, but as noted above, the scheme originally used by Linnæus was quite simple. Later authorities such as De Schauensee (109), Forshaw (127), Alderton (5), and Juniper and Parr (204) have continued to use his taxonomic hierarchical scheme to classify caiques but they expanded it and it now appears more like the one in the box on the next page.

One result of the development of the Linnaean system was a race across the world to discover and name every animal and plant on the planet. Expeditions explored every nook and cranny of the world collecting specimens of every sort. With all the specimens being shipped back to Europe, wealthy nineteenth century gentlemen, such as the Baron von Berlepsch and the Dutchman Coenraad Temmick, accumulated extensive collections of butterflies, bird skins, and the like. Capitalizing on this, less wealthy but more earnest natural scientists, such as Henry Bates and Alfred Wallace, were able to support their own collection efforts by selling rare specimens to wealthy patrons and organizations such as the London Zoological Society. As these collections grew and their owners tried to organize them, they not only realized that many of their new acquisitions represented not just new species, but that their taxonomic organization was more complex than Linnæus anticipated.

In particular, they realized they had to separate the parrot family into subfamilies, each with its own set of defining characteristics. The lories and lorikeets are quite different from the cockatoos that in turn are quite different from the Neotropical parrots. Still, the basis of the separation of parrots into superfamilies, families, subfamilies and tribes of the Psittaciformes has proven a difficult task leading to a high degree of arbitrariness. A number of treatises describe how to divide the parrots into families and genera, but George Smith's 1975 article (407) on the "Systematics of Parrots" provides one of the more rational approaches. He divided all the parrots into four large subfamilies. These were the Platycercinae that includes species such as the cockatoos, keas, grass-parakeets; the Loriinae that includes species such as lories, Indian ring-necks; the Arinae that includes all the New World parrots; and the Psittacinae that includes mostly African species such as the grey and Senegal. The origin of Smith's use of the subfamily name Arini to which caiques belong has roots in the work of others. Verheyen (441) used the term Arinae and von Boetticher (32) the term Araini. Yet, there is still no complete agreement as to how to organize the different families of parrots. At about the same time Smith published his view, Wolters (468) included the *Pionites* as a monotypic form within the family Pionitinae. There have been many attempts to organize the taxonomy of the parrots, and one could write a whole treatise on this.

Even at the lower taxonomic level, in the late nineteenth century, there was considerable controversy over the genus name before taxonomists finally accepted *Pionites*. I have included a list of the various genus names, authors who used them, and the dates of their usage to give an idea of how one replaced another. *Psittacus* was the first genus name. As noted above, this was the genus name given by Linnæus to all parrots. In that early period, the taxonomists of Europe rarely encountered

parrots, let alone caiques, so they continued using it as the genus for caiques into the early nineteenth century. By the mid-nineteenth century, when taxonomists began reclassifying parrots into multiple genera, most people dealing with caiques applied the genus name *Caica* or *Caïca*. They did this based on the perception that René Primevère Lesson (221) had been the first to use it to distinguish caiques from the other genera of parrots. I suspect Lesson adapted this name from one of the Caribe languages spoken in northern South America. In the Caribe language of Apalai, spoken in the Guianas, the word for some parrots is "çaroque," while in Witoto, a dialect of Caribe spoken further west in Columbia, it is "uique." Many authors used *Caica* as the genus name into the latter half of the nineteenth century and a corruption of this appears to be the origin of "caique." This name was used frequently enough in 1914 that Hopkinson (190) indicated that caique should be its proper English name. There was considerable controversy about abandoning *Caica* as the genus name. Count Tommaso Salvadori (366) argued strongly for its retention and wrote in a footnote in volume 20 of the **Catalog of Birds in the British Museum**:

The generic name *Caica*, commonly attributed to Lesson, was not used by him; he only made use of the French name *Les Caicas* for a group (or *race*, as he calls it) of Parrots (Tr. D'Orn. p. 198, 1831), and Psittacus*"pileatus*, Gm., was looked upon as the type by him (Compl. De Buff. ix. P. 212, 1837): later on Lesson (Rev. Zool. 1842, p. 135; Descr. Mamm. Et Ois. p. 197, 1847) incidentally used the name Caica as a

```
Kingdom: Animalia
    Phylum: Chordata
        Subphylum: Vertebrata
            Class: Aves
                Superorder: Neognathae
                    Order: Psittaciformes
                        Family: Psittacidae
                            Subfamily: Arini
                                Genus: Pionites Heine 1890
                                    Species: melanocephalus Linné 1758
                                        Subspecies: melanocephalus Linné 1758
                                                    pallidus Berlepsch 1889
                                    Species: leucogaster Kuhl 1820
                                        Subspecies: leucogaster Kuhl 1820
                                                    xanthomerius Sclater 1857
                                                    xanthurus Todd 1925
```

subgenus, while he was describing *Psittacus* (*Caica*) *chrysopogon*, which is a *Brotogeris*. Bonaparte was the first to use the generic name Caica; he regarded *P. melanocephalus*, Linn., as the type, but he included in it also *P. pileatus*, Gm. Although the name Caica evidently refers to P. caica, Lath. (= *pileatus*, Gm.), which belongs to another genus, I do not think we should be justified in not using it here."

Richard Sharpe (381), however, was unconvinced stating:

"It is not often that I have had occasion to differ from the conclusions of Count Salvadori, whose judgement on vexed question of nomenclature I have been able to follow in the majority of cases, but his argument for the adoption of the genus Caica seems to me to be the best that could have been employed to secure the rejections of the names."

Count Salvadori (365) finally conceded this and wrote in 1888:

"My reasons for using the generic name *Caica* Bp. (nee Less.) in preference to *Pionites* have not been accepted by Dr. Sharpe ('Handlist,' ii. p. 25) nor by Mr. Hellmayr (Nov. Zool. Xii. P. 302); and I submit to their verdict, although it appears to me that the reasons for so doing are not quite satisfactory."

Thereafter, *Pionites* replaced *Caica* conferring on Ferdinand Heine first authorship of the genus (175). Peters (314) made the most succinct argument for this change when he wrote:

"Pionites Heine is a substitute name for 'Caïca Lesson 1831,' which however was then employed only in the vernacular sense, 'Les Caïcas,' for a group of four species viz— *Psittacus pileatus* Gmelin, *Psittacus vulturinus* Kuhl, *Psittacus melanocephalus* Linné and *Psittacus leucogaster* Kuhl. Lesson did not use Caïca in a nomenclatural sense until 1842, and when he did so it was for a species quite different from any of the foregoing."

Thus, taxonomists abandoned Caica in favor of Pionites. In the meantime, some German taxonomists applied another genus name. They gave the genus name *Pionias*, but this passed out of usage rapidly once *Pionites* was accepted.

Usage of different genus names over time.

Psittacus.

Linnæus, 1758 (224); Latham, 1790 (215); Miller, 1796; Shaw, 1809-12 (382); Kuhl, 1820 (212); Latham, 1821 (214); Spix, 1824-25 (413); Lear, 1832 (218); Saint-Hilaire, 1837; Brehm , 1842 (38).

Caica or *Caïca*.

1831, Lesson (221); Sclater, 1857 (377); Sclater, 1862 (375); Garrod 1873 (141); Newton, 1877 (282); Sclater, 1879 (378); Taczanowski (1884-86) (422); W.L. Sclater, 1887 (379); Berlepsch (1889) (26); Salvadori , 1891 (366); Lloyd, 1895 (225); Mitchell, 1911 (267).

Pionias.

Finsch, 1868 (125); Pelzeln, 1873 (307).

Pionites.

Heine, 1882-90 (175); Reichenow, 1883 (336); Salvadori, 1906 (365); Penard, 1908-10 (309); Brabourne, 1912 (36); Dawson, 1915 (102); Chubb, 1916 (72); Todd, 1925 (436); Peters, 1937 (314); Olivera Pinto, 1938-44 (290); Haverschmidt, 1948 (169); Smith, 1975 (407); Wolters, 1975 (468); Sick, 1993 (386); De Schauensee, 1966 (109); Hilty, 1986 (183); Hoyo, 1992 (192); Rodner, 2000 (353).

One of the consequences of this name switching was confusion about the proper endings of the scientific names of the species and subspecies of caiques. Because Latin is the basis of the name, they are subject to gender rules. The species and subspecies names are modifiers of the genus name and so should agree in gender. Thus, when Linnæus named the black-headed caique *Psittacus melanocephalus* he made sure that the gender of the adjective *melanocephalus* matched the masculine genus name *Psittacus*. Then, during the short time when taxonomists applied the name *Caica* as the genus name, they modified the name to *melanocephala* to be consistent with the switch to the feminine gender of the new genus name. However, when the genus name *Pionites* was finally accepted, gender confusion set in. This was corrected by David and Gosselin (98) who state, "**A compound genus-group name ending in the suffix ites, oides, ides, odes, or istes is to be treated as masculine unless the author, when establishing its name, stated that it had another gender...**" They further noted, "***Pionites* Heine 1890 was first established in combination with** the Latinized masculine adjective *melanocephalus*, and is thus masculine." Many authors mistakenly continue to use the feminine ending. Just to be clear, the correct name is *Pionites melanocephalus*. Further, the subspecies name must also be masculine and so the correct name of the nominate black-headed caique is *P. m. melanocephalus* and for the pallid form *P. m. pallidus*. *P. leucogaster* remains unaffected, but the subspecies name for the yellow-thighed caique is *P. l. xanthomerius* and the yellow-tailed *P. l. xanthurus*. Thus, I use the masculine Latin species and subspecies names throughout this book except when quoting another source.

Specimen of *P. l. xanthomerius* in the Academy of Sciences, Philadelphia showing the typical staining of the breast of wild caiques. (Photo by author.)

There is also controversy over whether *P. melanocephalus* and *P. leucogaster* are separate species, a single species or a superspecies. Both Smith (398) and Wolters (468) believe they are one species. In particular, Smith believes that the present *P. leucogaster* species should be a subspecies of *Pionites melanocephalus* due to the precedence of the name. *Pionites leucogaster leucogaster* would become *Pionites*

melanocephalus leucogaster in his scheme. Others, however, such as Haffer (159) and Novaes (286) believe they are separate species within a superspecies. It is a generally accepted concept that a species ought not to be able to interbreed with another species when their ranges overlap. The only place where the ranges of two accepted species meet is in the western limits of their respective ranges where Haffer (159) notes they are capable of hybridizing. This suggests that speciation is not complete and the two accepted species are not truly separate. This may not be the end of the argument. Within the Psittacidae, there is a great capacity to hybridize. Everyone agrees the macaws occur in several well-differentiated species. Nonetheless, in captivity blue and golds, scarlets, green-wings, military and other macaws frequently hybridize with one another (434). In the case of caiques, there is a report of a hybrid resulting from the mating of a caique with an Illiger's macaw (*Propyrrhura maracana*) that everyone agrees is a completely different species from the caique (386). Especially astounding is a report that a many-colored parakeet native to Australia has hybridized with a yellow-headed kakariki native to New Zealand (104). This makes it clear that classifying animals, especially parrots, into separate genera and species is a matter of human convention.

Before leaving this topic, one should note that there is a movement afoot to reorganize the taxonomy of caiques once again. Early on, a number of naturalists lumped caiques with other genera of Neotropical parrots. Otto Finsch (125) and August von Pelzeln (308) included the presently accepted genera *Pionopsitta* and *Pionus* in the same genus with the caiques and gave this grouping the genus name *Pionias*. In their recent **Checklist of the Birds of Northern South America**, Rodner, Lentino and Restall (353) expanded the Pionites genus to include species usually placed in the *Pionopsitta* genus. In addition to *P. melanocephalus*, they would include the brown-headed parrot, the rose-faced parrot, the orange-cheeked parrot, the saffron-headed parrot, and the caica parrot in the *Pionites* genus. Below is how they would arrange the species. (They did not include *P. leucogaster*, because they only focused on birds of northern South America.)

Genus: *Pionites* Heine

    Species: *melanocephalus* Linné

    Species: *haematotis* Sclatter and Salvin

    Species: *pulchra* Berlepsch

    Species: *barrabandi* Kuhl

Species: *pyrilia* Bonaparte

Species: *caica* Latham

This would be a reversion to the earlier classification scheme of Sclater (376), and is contrary to what others believe. For example, Hans Wolters (468) took great pain to clearly separate caiques from the *Pionopsitta* genus and other short-tailed Neotropical parrots.

Regardless of whether or not taxonomists accept this new ordering, there will likely be more changes in the taxonomy of caiques. When new approaches and technologies are applied, we often find that taxonomic schemes need to be changed. The earliest taxonomists, beginning with Linnæus, based their classifications on the general appearance of a species. George Gray (155) placed all the parrots along with the other birds with zygodactyl feet such as toucans and woodpeckers into a superorder he called "Scansores." Garrod (141), Mudge (274), Smith (407), applying anatomical methods to parrots, suggested other ways of organizing the taxonomy of parrots. More recently, Birt (29) and Francisco (132) and others have applied cytological and protein analysis techniques.

A recent karyotype study indicates there are three main groups of parrots in the Americas (67). In this case, caiques are included with the macaws and conures (238), a second group is comprised of the Amazons, and a third group contains the pionus parrots. Soon, however, researchers will be able to apply powerful genomic DNA based technologies to the problem of sorting the relationships among species. From the known nuclear and mitochrondrial DNA sequences, the most closed related parrot genus is the hawk-headed parrot (*Deroptyus accipitrinus*) (425). My guess is that when scientists acquire enough genomic data, they will be able to apply even better methods to bird taxonomy, and reduce taxonomy to a mathematical function; however, it may still require human judgment to define when two closely related groups should be separate species.

Biogeography

I described the current ranges of the different subspecies in the first part of this section. Now, we consider how caiques came to occupy those ranges. The *Pionites* as a genus is restricted in its natural distribution to the tropical area of South American called Amazonia, which, in this case, includes the interconnected Orinoco River basin as

well. The Atlantic Ocean is the boundary on the east and northeast. The Andes Mountain range forms the boundary on the west. It restricts the caique's range from Bolivia in the south, through Peru, Ecuador, and Columbia, to coastal Venezuela in the north. A broad cerrado/campo area forms the southern boundary of their range, and the Brazilian highlands that parallel the Atlantic Ocean in the southeast part of its range provide a barrier to it moving into the easterly parts of Brazil. This restricted range seems somewhat surprising, since caiques would seem well suited for survival on the western slope of the Andes, in the Pantanal, and in the Atlantic rainforest just beyond those barriers.

Within this range, though, the genus has differentiated into the five subspecies. The most salient feature related to the distribution of caiques is the sharp separation of the two species *P. melanocephalus* and *P. leucogaster* by the Solimões/Amazon River that is most pronounced in the lower Amazon (159). Most believe this is due to a combination of the great width of this river, which is indeed impressive, and the caique's poor flying ability. This separation breaks down in western Amazonia where the black-headed form occurs south of the main Amazon trunk in the Huallago and Ucayali River valleys (157). Their limited flight capacity may be the reason, but it is not very convincing if you have seen them fly. While caiques may not be the best of fliers, they can fly a considerable distance in the wild. I suspect the great separation is due more to their great reluctance to venture far from forested areas than due to a lack in flight capacity. Haffer (159) holds a similar view. Perhaps this also explains their failure to colonize the Pantanal and Atlantic forest areas. To invade those areas would require flight over wide areas of grass and scrubby growth with few trees—very unlike the tropical rainforests caiques prefer.

The distribution of the two species and their subspecies within their range has attracted the attention of scientists. Jürgen Haffer (158) set forth a widely accepted but controversial hypothesis to explain the great richness of fauna in the Amazon region. Based on the present day distributions of a number of bird species, he proposed that a sequence of epochal events led to the evolution of the two species and the five subspecies of caiques. In Haffer's view, these events in the Amazon basin track back to the Quaternary epoch with its succession of ice ages in the northern hemisphere that in tropical zones likely took the form of alternating wet and dry periods (248). However, some believe their evolution extends further back

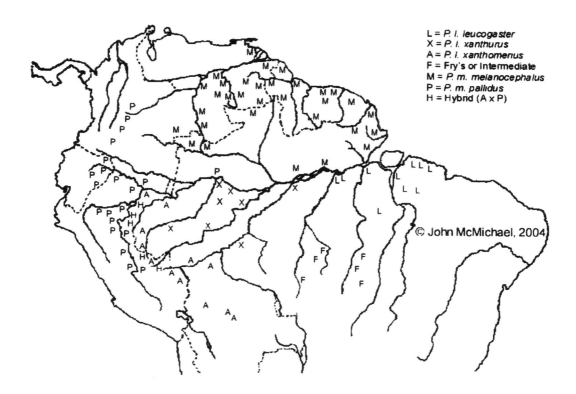

Distribution of species and subspecies of the *Pionites* genus. This graphic is based on the distribution diagram of Novaes (286), modified to include information from Traylor (438), Fry (136), Haffer (159), Todd (436), Desenne (110), Wheatley (458), Rodner (353), Ridgely (346), Chapman (71) and tag data on museum specimens.

into the Cenozoic (91, 329, 361). Haffer's hypothesis is derived from the thinking of ErnstMayr who first put forth the idea that genetic isolation is a major engine of evolution, Haffer(158) speculated there were at least six "endemic islands" he called "refugias" within the Amazon basin into which the rainforest retreated during dry periods. Haffer delineated his refuge zones based on the observation of the ranges of several species in Amazonia and scientists are in general agreement with the location of these endemic islands (89, 329).

In a variation of Haffer's theory, Nores (285) speculates that the oceans rose more than 100 m (330 ft) in Amazonia and formed actual islands. However they formed, these refuges were separated enough from one another for long enough that the fauna could differentiate independently leading to

the development of new species. Several cycles of this appear to have led to the species richness we associate with Amazonia. This theme of alternating isolation into refugias and re-expansion after their isolation seems to explain much of the evolution of the species and subspecies of *Pionites*.

We are unable to match the evolution of the various forms of caiques with the climatic cycles with confidence; however, Fernando Novaes (286) and Haffer (159) offer some scenarios. Based primarily of the schemes of Novaes and Haffer with consideration of other studies (89-91, 329), I offer the following evolutionary scheme:

1. The original range of the *Pionites* protospecies lay near the present day mouth of the Amazon River, possibly in what Racheli calls the Guyanan endemic

area (329). This protospecies was probably similar to our present day *P. melanocephalus*.

2. The uplifting of the Andes Mountains forced all the rivers east of them first to flow north into the Caribbean Sea. Later, after the northeastern Andes in Columbia and Venezuela rose and blocked that route, the Amazon was forced to flow toward the Atlantic Ocean. This resulted in the formation of the Amazon River we know today (189), and the split of the original protospecies' range. An alternative view is that the rise and fall of the oceans may have been the cause of the split. During an ice age, the river would be narrow; however, during the wet period, the Amazon would rise somewhere between 40 to 100 m (130 to 330 ft) and become a long, wide extension of the Atlantic Ocean into the heart of the Amazon basin. Whatever the cause, the split of the protospecies' range resulted in the population north of the river retaining its black head, while the population south of the river evolved an apricot head and eventually became *P. leucogaster*. Scientists refer to the development of separate species resulting from a physical splitting of the protospecies range, a "vicariant event" and the evolutionary process "allopatric evolution." A consideration supporting evolution of *P. leucogaster* from a prototypic *P. melanocephalus* is that juvenile white-bellied caiques almost invariably have a few black feathers on their heads as an atavistic trait.

3. With the course of Amazon River well established and with a subsequent wet period, the two populations extended their respective ranges westward—*P. melanocephalus* north of the river and *P. leucogaster* south of the river.

4. When a long dry period set in, one not sufficient to dry the Amazon River itself, the fauna became isolated into endemic islands once again. South of the river, the expansion of dry areas split the *P. leucogaster* population into two or three refuges in another vicariant event. One refuge was in the proximity of the present Brazilian state of Para near present day Belém. Another was further west near the Purus and Tefé Rivers. During the separation, the eastern population evolved to become the *P. l. leucogaster* subspecies while the western population evolved to become *P. l. xanthurus*. Novaes, however, suggests that north of the river this dry period was not sufficiently strong as to result in well-defined refuges, rather the extremely large east-west expanse of its range led to phenotypic divergence by a parapatric mechanism. In this evolutionary mechanism, two species arise as a result genetic differentiation of individuals at the two geographic extremes of a large species range. Even today, the *P. m. pallidus* subspecies may still be in the process of differentiating itself from the nominate *P. m. melanocephalus* subspecies. Supporting this is the fact that over the wide clinal zone separating the two "pure" forms of *P. melanocephalus*, there is a gradient in phenotype between the two subspecies (229). In Haffer's view, however, the nominate form continued developing in the Guiana refuge while the *P. pallidus* form evolved in the Napo River area after they became separated by a grassland that extended from the Venezuelan llanos to the Amazon itself (181). One can make a similar argument for both types of evolutionary mechanisms for the subspeciation of *P. leucogaster* south of the Amazon.

5. Finally, a wet period set in, and, based on the pollen record (252), the evergreen rainforest has been expanding over the past 3000 years and today it may be at its greatest extent ever. This expansion of the rain forest correlates well with the increase in insolation, the quantity of sunshine per unit area, received by Amazonia during this same period of time (28, 248).

   a. In this latest period, *P. l. xanthurus* has expanded its range westward to where it meets the range of *P. m. pallidus*. In Novaes' view, the hybridization of these two subspecies resulted in the *P. l. xanthomerius* subspecies. In Haffer's view, however, there has only been a limited degree of hybridization between *P. l. xanthomerius* and *P. m. pallidus* and they have only recently been in contact with each other. Instead, he proposes *P. l. xanthomerius* evolved from yet another population isolated in another refuge, the east Peruvian refuge, during the last major dry period.

b. During this recent wet period, *P. l. xanthurus* extended its range back toward the east through southern Pará and northern Mato Grosso where it met a westward expansion of the *P. l. leucogaster* range. This resulted in the hybridization of the two subspecies and the development of the intermediate form first described by Fry (136). If the current wet period continues, the range of caiques may break though into the Pantanal area and maybe into other areas previously uninhabited by caiques.

One feature of the current distribution of caiques is that the two species do not significantly overlap in their distributions. Haffer (159) made this clear when he refuted assertions made by De Schauensee (108) and Forshaw (127) that they did. There is, however, a contact zone between the two species in eastern Peru at the headwaters of the Amazon where the two hybridize, but the degree of hybridization is not extensive. At this point though, I must provide some cautions regarding Haffer's hybrid observations. Immature *P. leucogaster* almost invariably have black feathers on their heads and, therefore, can resemble *P melanocephalus*. Unfortunately, Haffer failed to note the age of the wild birds he inspected. Nonetheless, during my visit to the Tambopata Research Center, which lies within the range of *P. l. xanthomerius*, I saw one bird with a significant amount of black on its head that appeared to have the eye coloration of an adult although this was difficult to assess through binoculars. This Research Center is located just a mountain ridge away from the gallery forest along the northern Ucayali River (304, 347) the southern most part of the range of *P. melanocephalus*. Haffer regards the sporadic nature of their hybridization in the area where they are in contact as evidence that *P. melanocephalus* and *P. leucogaster* are separate species. But he did not mention that local natives sometimes carry birds from one range into the other and that this might facilitate hybridization (344). However, he along with Smith noted there is also a case for considering the two species as two allospecies within a superspecies.

Caique ecology

There are plenty of publications on the ecology of macaws, cockatoos and Amazons, but none focuses on the ecology of caiques. McLoughlin (257) published some notes on caiques in the wild, but they are very brief. Thus to provide some concept of their life in the wild, I have had to patch together information from a variety of sources and make inferences from the studies of other parrots in the wild.

All reports agree that caiques seldom stray from the low elevation humid forests of the Amazon and Orinoco River basins. A large number of reports indicate (100, 109, 299, 339, 345, 353) that caiques occur in the rainforest only up to an elevation of 1000 to 1100 m (approximately 3600 ft). Within the tropical evergreen rain forest, however, there is a stratification of ecologies based on distance from the ground. You can roughly divide these into the ground and low undergrowth zone, the mid-level zone, the canopy zone, and the zone above the canopy. Caiques tend to prefer the canopy or just above it (142, 304, 305, 460). Walther (451, 452) noted they like to perch on exposed leafy limbs to catch some sunlight rather than perch close to the tree's trunk. The most important reason for their preference for the canopy is probably the fact that most trees bear their fruit in this zone. While caiques prefer the canopy, they do visit the lower mid-forest zone (100) and descend even lower at the forest edge (109, 345, 346).

Most authors report that they prefer *terra firma* or dry forests (333), but others note that they visit both forms of flooded forest[21]. The guides I have worked with in Amazonia indicate that caiques like to be near water, preferably running water in a slightly hilly or upland area. *P. l. leucogaster* will breed at the edges of igapó forest near Belém (292) and *P. m. pallidus* in the Maurita-palm swamps of eastern Peru (149). Ridgely (345, 346) and Prum (325) indicated that both species may be found foraging in the várzea, while Gilardi

---

[21] The Amazonian rainforest is comprised of a complex set of forests. The *terra firma* forests are seldom if ever flooded. However, much of the rest of Amazonia is flooded at one time or another. The river can rise as much as 40 m (130 ft) and if you are in a boat or canoe, you find yourself floating among the trees. The várzea forests are seasonally flooded forests in the flood plain of "white water rivers." Although called white water rivers, they are usually a muddy brown from all the silt they carry. These rivers usually rise in the Andes. The igapó forests are the seasonally flooded forest of "black water rivers." These rivers usually drain lower elevations of the Amazon basin where water leaches out tannins from fallen leaves causing the water to have a deep black tea color.

and Munn reported that the *P. l. xanthomerius* in Peru prefers "transitional forests" between the seldom flooded forests and upland forests. Fry (136) stated that the intermediate form of the caique he observed in Mato Grosso was the only parrot species definitely feeding within the dry forest of the area. Haverschmidt (170) noted that they were found "in forests of the sand ridges, in savanna, and forests of the interior" of Surinam, but he did not observe them in the adjacent open savannas areas. However, there are reliable reports that *P. m. melanocephalus* do frequent the savannas north of the Amazon (74). These conflicting reports indicate we know little about where caiques choose to inhabit and forage. Further, there are large areas in Amazonia where one would expect to find them, but they are absent. For example, Naka (279) reported no sightings of the black-headed caique near Manaus, Brazil. Similarly, I was unable to observe any caiques near Humaitá, Brazil, a town in the heart of Amazonia on the Madeira River, where even life long residents indicated they had never seen one when presented with a photograph of a pair of yellow-thighed caiques.

Caiques usually move about in small noisy flocks. Gilardi and Munn (142) noted that *P. l. xanthomerius*, while often seen as single birds, tended to be more social than other parrots and formed flocks of four to six and occasionally ten birds. Rasmussen reported that *P. melanocephalus* flocks in the Parque Nacional Yasuni of Ecuador had a mean size of 5.3 ± 3.3 forming larger flocks than all other parrot species of the area except members of the *Brotogeris* species. Brightsmith noted that *P. l. xanthomerius* goes about in flocks of four to eight birds, while Hilty and Brown (183) wrote that the black-headed occurred in flocks of three to ten in Columbia. Whitney agrees and notes that both species travel in pairs or groups up to as many as eight. Unlike some parrot species such as the Amazon parrots (88) and blue and yellow macaws (342), they do not roost in large communal flocks but in the same sized flock as seen during the day, preferably in cavities (459). We suspect that caiques are monogamous, and a breeding pair forms the basis of at least some flocks. However, given the size of their flocks, the social relationships among it members are probably more complex than we now appreciate (414).

In the rainforest, you usually hear caiques rather than see them (257)[22]. They like to vocalize among the leafy branches, and occasionally on bare limbs (459). Many birds, have absolute pitch perception (455), and caiques may be among them. This may allow them to communicate with each other. Further, the pitch of their call seems well suited for piercing the obstructions of the canopy permitting communication even when out of sight of one another (273). This may explain the similarity of its voice to that of the Rock parakeet (*Pyrrhura rupicola*) that inhabits the same dense foliage of the canopy (298, 299). The common French name for the caique is the Perroquet Maipourí, which means tapir parakeet. The settlers in French Guiana gave it this name because it makes a sound like a tapir. Naturalists describe their sound in various ways. Penard (309) writing in Dutch described it as a "kere kere kere" while McLoughlin wrote that when disturbed they made a repeated "keeya-keeya" call. He notes that their banter ranges from whistles to what he likens to a rusty gate. The sound made by the black-headed was described as a "Loud musical call, also a whistled toot" by De Schauensee (109). Hilty and Brown (181) described the sound of the black-headed caique of Columbia as a high pitched "cleeeooo-cleeooo," and when perched various whistles and a piping, almost electronic sound that is not very parrot-like. Whitney (459) noted that they deliver an "inventive variety of more musical notes and phrases" while perched in the canopy. McLoughlin wrote that the black-headed pairs often participated in long duets lasting over thirty minutes in which participants alternate singing performances similar to that of hawkhead parrots (personal observation) and yellow-naped Amazons (472). Finally, there is a report by Bradley Davis, a guide at the Cristalino Jungle Lodge, that caiques imitated the Bright-Rumped Attila (*Attila spadiceus*) a bird species whose song carries long distances. The one call though that all parrots, not just caiques, seem to recognize is the alarm call, at least this is the case among captive reared birds. Only one bird need sound it, and all parrots regardless of species take off in confusion.

Whitney (459) describes their flight as rapid and direct, usually for only short distances above the canopy. Their flight has a "whirring sound" and steady wing beats accompanies it flight. In addition to making different sounds while flying they also vocalize more frequently (37). Their vocalization while in flight consists of "high-pitched squeals and screams." Having experienced seeing them in flight, I can attest that you can hear them at some distance.

Many birds in the tropics exhibit a migratory pattern, not the long distance migratory

---

[22] A recording of both species' vocalizations is available from the Cornell Ornithology Laboratory.

pattern seen for birds that visit temperate climes, but one based on following food resources. Mealy Amazons (*Amazona farinosa*) exhibit this type of migratory behavior (181). The observation of a seasonal pattern for scarlet macaws in Costa Rica suggests this as well (440). Since the number of caiques seen in any season at any one place are about the same throughout the year (257), it seems unlikely that caiques migrate like those species. Instead, they must survive by changing food sources as the season progresses. A list of foods they forage on is included in Appendix C. It is long, but probably represents only a small fraction of what they eat. Such flexibility in food sources presumably allows them to switch food sources rather than migrate. A further reason to believe they do not migrate is that they seldom fly any higher above the ground than about 400 m (1300 ft) (346) something they would likely do if they migrated longer distances.

Most authors indicate caiques prefer sweet foods[23]. Penard noted in 1908 (309) that they ate fruit and nectar-containing flowers, and nearly every report since confirms this. In a conversation with Dr. Brightsmith, he noted that one way to find the white bellied caiques while walking through the jungle is to look for flowers on the ground. The yellow-thigh caiques drop them after biting into the base and extracting the nectar. McLoughlin (257) also noted that black-headed caiques dropped intact flowers with their bases clipped beneath the trees in which they are feeding. Cotton (87) identified one of the flowers as *Erythrina fusca*, and noted that they ate the anthers of the flower as well. One of the common features of these flowers is that they are brightly colored orange, pink or red. Birds can perceive colors, while most insects and possibly even monkeys cannot (211). Pearson (305) noted that he often saw them feeding in mixed flocks with other frugivorous birds. One of the attributes of the rainforest is that the trees and plants producing edible fruits, seeds and flowers are not only seasonal but also geographically scattered. Parrots of the rain forest probably forage tens of kilometers every day (335). Thus, caiques need flexibility in their foraging and sometimes cannot be too fussy regarding what fruits and seeds they consume. This may be especially critical at the end of the dry season when fewer plants bloom or set fruit or seed.

Winkler (463) suggests that for non-migratory birds, a flexible feeding behavior solves the need to migrate. At the end of the dry season, relatively fewer trees produce the fruits and seeds needed by caiques and other frugivores (341). Scientists call these keystone plants because in certain seasons they are the only foods standing between an animal surviving or dying. This may be the case for caiques in certain areas of Amazonia (312).

Many animals develop a mutualistic relationship with plants in a way that they both benefit. For birds, this usually takes the form of distributing their seeds or performing pollination. Most scientists consider Caiques, like other parrots, to be seed predators. That is, when they eat the seed they destroy it. While this is probably true for most seeds that caiques eat, it may not be true for all. There is nothing published on the stomach contents of the caiques collected in the wild, but there is a note attached to a specimen of a male *P. m. melanocephalus* collected in Guyana in the collection at the Academy of Sciences in Philadelphia. It lists the stomach as containing "small seeds and vegetable pulp." Unfortunately, it does not state whether the seeds were intact or not. I have never known a healthy pet caique to pass an intact seed, so it seems unlikely that caiques distribute seeds in this way. Nonetheless, tame caiques have a great penchant for the tiny seeds of commercial figs and one or two of these may slip through. Another way a caique may distribute seeds is when seeds occlude to the outside of the bird's beak. Anyone who has had a pet caique knows that when they eat sticky foods some of the masticated pulp sticks to the outside of the upper mandible. In the case of figs, this includes its seeds. The caiques clean their beaks by rubbing their beaks against the branches and limbs on which they perch. By doing this, the caique could place the seed in a spot where it can thrive. This would seem a good way for epiphytes and plants such as strangler figs to get their seeds transported to suitable new locations.

A better-documented case for a mutualistic relationship for caiques is the pollination of the flower of *Platonia insignis* (250). This tree produces bacuri, an economically important fruit in Amazonia. This tree has a cup shaped flower with nectar located at the base. To reach the nectar, the bird has to put its head into the cup and in doing this, anthers located on the flower's rim deposit pollen on the bird's head. When the bird drinks the nectar of the next flower, it pollinates it.

Wild caiques sometimes compete with people for commercially grown grains and fruits.

---

[23] During my visit to Humaitá, Brazil, I met an older man from one of the reserves on the Preto River. He claimed that his people call the white-bellied caiques the cocoa parrot because of its fondness for the sweet pulp in the wild cocoa pod (*Theobroma cacao*). When I visited the settlement of these natives along the Transamazonian Highway, however, the natives claimed to have never seen a white-bellied caique.

Smith (400) noted that caiques raid rice fields and eat the unripe grain heads. When they do this after a heavy dew, their feathers can become so wet they cannot get airborne. The local villagers can then catch them and they often end up in the cook pot. Caiques raid other fruits that people use for food as well. Schomburgk (371) noted in British Guiana that they would settle on "the trees of the provision fields." He neglected, however, to say specifically what they were eating. There are several cultivated fruits that caiques will take if given the opportunity. The black-headed caiques of Guiana consume poixdoux (*Inga* spp.) and guava (*Psidium guajava*) (257). In the eastern Amazon region of Para, the inhabitants have developed an important trade in the fruit of the açaí palm (*Euterpe oleracea*) and cultivate large groves of them (3, 330). Caiques and other parrots eat the seasonally available dark grape-sized fruit of this palm (268, 269). The locals prepare a purple liquid from this fruit that they thicken with farinha made from manioc. There is always a concern when wild animals or birds take to eating commercially important plants because there is a tendency to consider them pests and subject to eradication. Moegenburg's studies noted that if the fruit of the açaí were not completely harvested, frugivores, including caiques, are still able to thrive and the locals should be encouraged to leave behind a small amount of fruit. We hope the locals do not persecute the few caiques and the other birds that feed on their commercial crops (56).

An interesting foraging method used by caiques in French Guiana is as followers of the red-throated caracara (*Daptrius americanus*) (203). This species of caracara is a predator of wasp nests. A variety of other frugivorous canopy birds follow the caracaras, but the report indicates that these birds feed on different foods than the caracaras. However, knowing our captive caiques' penchant for insect larvae, it is difficult to believe they are not partaking of some of the insects disturbed by the caracaras.

Almost no naturalist has paid much attention to the caiques' great craving for animal-based foods. However, it is clear to pet caique owners that they very much enjoy eating animal flesh. When offered a chicken bone, a tame caique will jealously defend it and eat at it until they have taken their fill. McLoughlin (257) is one of the few to suggest that the caique's diet in the wild includes non-plant origin foods. He noticed that his captive caiques were very fond of termites, grasshoppers, and small caterpillars. The need for a source of animal proteins rich in the sulfur-based amino acids would be especially important when rearing chicks. Plants are notoriously lacking in the amino acids critical for a chick to build muscle and develop feathers. Thus, it is likely that they also take insects, small snails, crustaceans and other small animal forms as food.

There has been no systematic study of the weights of wild caiques; however, naturalists occasionally record their weights and I note some of them in the accompanying table. The weights of these birds are within the weight range of captive reared birds. To confirm a statistical difference, we would need a larger sample. However, I would not be surprised if they had a lower weight than captive reared birds since they are much more active and the need to fly requires they remain slim. Slimness is consistent with comments on the tags attached to the birds in The Academy of Sciences where the person preparing the skins noted little or no fat on the specimens.

An unusual behavior of caiques and other parrot species is that they gather at salty clay licks known as colpas in Peru and barreiros in Brazil where they consume clay (43, 387). Scientists call this geophagy. So far, there are only reports of this for the yellow-thighed caiques in Peru. Sick (386) reported geophagy for parrots in Brazil but did not specifically note this for caiques. At the Tambopata Research Center in Peru, large flocks of 15 or more caiques gather at the colpas in the morning hours where they appear to take turns going to a bank of soil exposed by river erosion. If the morning is foggy or rainy, they tend not to visit, although they relish visiting the day following a rain (43). They are selective in the clay they eat, taking it only from one layer of the exposed bank. They do not do this to obtain grit since parrots do not require grit nor is the soil they consume high in sand of suitable size (43). One theory why parrots eat the clay is that it is rich in kaolin that neutralizes plant toxins allowing parrots to broaden the range of plants they can forage on (143). An alternative theory is that it is important for acquiring mineral nutrients. The latter is consistent with Brightsmith's (44) report that parrots use colpas more frequently at nesting time particularly after their chicks hatch. We also see a seasonal craving for minerals among captive female caiques prior to egg laying when they take to chewing a cuttlebone, plaster walls, and other mineral components like the walls of one's household that are ignored the rest of the year. Both wild and captive birds need calcium and other minerals to produce eggs and feed their growing chicks. Whether the reason for geophagy is toxin neutralization, the acquisition of minerals, or just a craving for salt remains unresolved. They may partake of the clay for all of these reasons.

Wild caiques exhibit a seasonal cycle. While there are places within the caique's range where there is little seasonal change in temperature or precipitation, such as Limonocoha, Ecuador (304); most of Amazonia experiences seasonal changes in precipitation. There is a significant drop in rainfall in the summer months at Yarmacocha, Peru and Tumi Chucua, Bolivia (304). In northern South America, there are two rainy seasons. For Guyana, one is from May to June and the other from December to January. At Tambopata near Yarmacocha, my guides, and Lepperhoff (220) confirmed, that the yellow-thighed caiques start to breed at the beginning of the rainy season in December and the chicks fledge in March and April. My guide during my visit to the Rio Cristalino Lodge near Alta Floresta, Brazil, also noted that the yellow-tailed caiques began breeding in December at the beginning of the rainy season. This coordination with rainy season, however, does not seem to be universal. In the Belém area, *P. l. leucogaster* explore nest holes in April and have young in the nest by late November suggesting they breed and rear their chicks in the drier part of the year. Similarly, Jan Ribot (Webpage 2002) noted that the breeding season for the black-headed caique in Surinam was from September through November—coinciding with the main dry season. Yet, in the neighboring nation of Guyana, McLoughlin (257) reports fledging in the month of May suggesting that the caiques began to breed at the beginning of the winter rainy season.

Hilty and Brown (183) report that the black-headed caiques of Columbia breed in the spring months of April and May. Complicating this is our experience with indoor breeding of captive caiques that have never experienced a cycle of temperature, rain or food variation. Captive caiques are very sensitive to artificial day length, and when they are exposed to longer periods of daylight of more than 14 hr per day, they will breed nearly anytime of the year. That wild caiques north of the equator tend to go to nest in the spring and those south of the equator tend go to nest in the fall may be consistent with this. Day length may only be one factor since the availability of food is important for chick growth and in the tropics this depends on the seasonality of rain. In some years, the plants and trees produce less fruit. When less food is available during the breeding season, the number of chicks parrots rear, their growth rate and their final chick size is usually smaller (340).

Caiques nest in natural cavities in trees. Brightsmith (46) reports that in southeastern Peru, they and other parrots of the region prefer cavities in trees of the *Dipteryx micratha* species. This species of tree offers a hard wood difficult for predators to break through, does not decay too rapidly and its flaky bark prevents vines and epiphytes from taking hold. This may also make them more difficult for snakes to climb. The most critical criteria, however, appears to be height above the ground. Oniki and Willis (292) reported on three nest cavities for *P. l. leucogaster* that were 22 m (72 ft), 25 m (82 ft), and 16 m (52 ft) above the forest floor. Novaes (286) noted that near Belém, Brazil, the *P. leucogaster* nest cavities were between 16 and 30 m (98 ft) above the forest floor. During my visit to the Posada Amazonas near Puerto Maldonado, Peru, I observed the same tree cavity as Lepperhoff (220) who reported a pair of *P. l. xanthomerius* had used it as a nest. It was also of great distance from the ground. The black-headed caique also nests in holes high up in the trunks of trees. McLoughlin reports a nest

Species/subspecies	Location	Sex	Weight (g)	Reference
P. m. melanocephalus	Surinam	M	152	Haverschmidt (169)
		F	148	
		F	130	
		M	161	Fawcett,
		F	155	Acad. Sci. Phila.*
P. m. pallidus	Yarinacocha, Peru		149	Pearson (305)
	Sucumbios, Ecuador		138	Gerwin,
			157	Acad. Sci. Phila.*
			156	
P. leucogaster			155	Terbough (430)
P. leucogaster (Fry's)	Brazil		158	Fry (136)

*Data on tag attached to specimens collected by John Gerwin and Robert Fawcett in collection of the Academy of Sciences, Philadelphia

at 17 m (55 ft) and Lloyd (225) writing in 1895 about the parrots of British Guiana, noted the nests were so high people were almost never able to get to their eggs. The reason for their great height is probably predation and Renton (343) noted that the greater the height of a parrot's nest the less nest predation.

Despite their distance from the ground, nest predation remains a hazard all cavity nesters must endure. For the most part, parrots do not excavate their own cavities, although some parrots, but not caiques, excavate cavities in aerial termiteria (45). Caiques are cavity adopters and must content themselves with existing cavities. Once caiques occupy one, they spend a great deal of time enlarging it by chewing away at the soft or rotten portions inside the cavity. There are a number of problems with reusing an existing cavity. Over time, predators learn of the cavity's location and, realizing it may contain eggs or defenseless chicks, make frequent visits. Predators include mammals such as monkeys, opossums, raccoons, rats, tayras, and kinkajous; other birds such as toucans, toucanets and araçaris; snakes; and insects such as botflies (235) and hornets (439). While at the Posadas Amazonas on the Tambopata River, the guide related that he suspected that in the previous year, toucanets had raided the caique nest hole easily seen from the tower. The result was that the caiques did not use that cavity the next year.

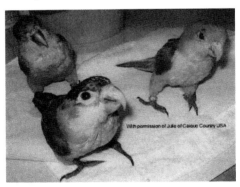

Atavistic expression of black head feathers and green feathers under eye by a yellow-thighed caique chick. The chick on right is from a different pair and is more typical. Most yellow-thighed chicks do not express any green feathers under their eye. Both the black head feathers and green under-eye feathers molt and are not seen on the adult. (With permission of Julie of Caique Country, USA.)

Another problem is that parasitic mite and insect infestations do not always clear from one usage to the next (235). Thus, it is not surprising that the fewer times a bird uses a cavity, the less prone it is to predation or parasitism (45) and the

birds have greater success in producing young. This may be one reason wild caiques always seem to be exploring new cavities.

Although we do not know for caiques, the mainland parrots of the *Amazona* genus limit their visitation of their nest cavity. Most only visit and feed their chicks twice a day in the early morning and late afternoon (122, 343). They also keep their feeding time brief. They may avoid feeding in midday due to heat that can be very intense in the tropics as well as to avoid drawing the attention of predators. I expect caiques do the same. However, while Amazon parrots do not roost in the cavity with their chicks, caiques do.

Even adult caiques must also keep on the look out for daytime predators. Aside from people, raptors and snakes are probably the most important of these. During my visit to Tambopata colpa, the passage of a roadside hawk (*Buteo magnirostris*) sent all the parrots, including the yellow-thighs, into flight. McLoughlin observed several adult black-headed caiques fleeing in different directions to escape a hawk. Nestlings and recent fledglings are at greatest risk of predation.

We know little about the caique's daily activities and how they vary from season to season. One of my correspondents, who lived in southern Venezuela[24], indicates that they tend to follow the same routine every day. She noted that the same flock of 20 to 30 black-headed caiques would fly by their dwelling twice a day at about the some time, once in one direction and later in the opposite direction. The following is an attempt to describe their daily routine when they are not breeding. After first light in the morning, they awaken and emerge from their roost cavity which they will territorially defend (407). They probably behave like captive birds and never defecate in their roost cavity (397). So one would expect the first order of business is to defecate although they may hold their feces for up to an hour after leaving their nest (Smith, 1975). Shortly afterwards, they begin the first activity of the day—call time. Once the flock has gathered, depending on the season and weather, they may move to the local colpa where they eat the clay (43, 44). The next activity is foraging for food during the cool morning hours. Because trees bear flowers and fruits at different times during the

---

[24] In Venezuela and the Spanish speaking areas of northern South America, they call the black-headed caique the "siete colore" or seven colored parrot. Six of the colors can be easily identified, but the seventh one is a question. It may be the brick-red color on the outer primaries visible under some lighting conditions.

season and are widely spaced within the forest, caiques need to move about many miles in or just above the canopy. This requires a commuting to different parts of the forest. They are usually quiet while foraging (182). They may also spend some time working "chew holes" or cavities in trees possibly in search of moisture or grubs (106). During the heat of the midday, most birds of the canopy, move to a lower position in the canopy away from direct sun exposure (451) and become quiescent and even more difficult to observe (181). In this way, they reduce their exposure to the heat of the sun, avoid expending energy, and are less prone to attack by raptors. Toward evening, they start their second major call time of the day and once again forage for food. Like captive birds, they probably like to settle into their roost cavities well before sunset when nocturnal predators such as owls, the vampire bat (*Desmodus rotundus*) and false vampire bat (*Vampyrum spectrum*) start to forage (128, 439). The vampire bat is as stealthy about approaching and bleeding birds as it is mammals. The large false vampire bat stalks and eats birds roosting on limbs at night, and parrots are among its favorite prey. Once settled into their roost cavity, caiques have bouts of activity often accompanied by loud noises. Smith (394) suspects they spend some of the night gnawing at the inside of cavity. At day light, they emerge and begin a new day.

Caique conservation

Preservation of wild populations

Conservationists concerned with species preservation in the Amazon do not regard caiques as an endangered species (83, 345), nor are they listed as threatened or endangered in the large online Avibase listing. This, however, does not prevent them being listed in Appendix II of Convention on International Trade in Endangered Species (CITES) and subject to import/export restrictions. Naturalists consider caiques of both species to be common within their ranges (287, 304). Still, Brazil has long imposed restrictions on the possession and export of its fauna and most other South American countries do the same. Guyana and Suriname are the only countries where one may legally export wild-caught caiques. In 2003, CITES permitted Guyana to export 600 caiques and Suriname 1378 caiques. Their export has not had much of an impact on their population in the wild and they remain moderately common there (162). The main threats they face are local

harvesting for pets, as food, and habitat destruction. Some harvesting of caiques for pets may deplete a population in localized areas, but it does not pose a universal threat (287, 444, 473). In contrast, poaching of the larger and more valuable parrots such as the Amazons and hyacinth macaw has had a major effect on their population despite the CITES trade restrictions (435). While harvesting for the pet trade is a minor threat to caiques, deforestation and fires are far more menacing. This seems to be a particular problem in the southern range of *P. leucogaster* in Brazil (345). To this end, there has been an effort to set aside reserves or parks as a way to preserve biodiversity. Initial reports indicate that this approach helps prevent clearing and logging; however, much more needs to be done such as increasing the number and size of the preserves and controlling hunting within them (55). Thiollay (433) reported that unregulated logging and hunting can do great harm and caiques disappear from the areas in French Guiana where these practices are prevalent. However, Johns (197) suggests that small-scale logging and agricultural operations have little effect on the frequency of *P. leucogaster* visitation to the areas near those operations. In another study, black-headed caiques seemed unaffected by the presence of large oil field operations (64, 65). Thus, what may affect them most are the large clear cuts needed to establish cattle ranches and large scale agricultural crops. Historically, large-scale attempts at agriculture in Amazonia were short lived. The lushness of the rainforest is deceptive. The persistent rains leach away most of the minerals needed for commercial crops, and farmers can only harvest one or two crops from the land using the traditional slash and burn practices. On a small scale, the rainforest recovers quickly from this form of agriculture. In the case of large cattle ranches, recovery may be more problematic. Ranchers in some areas of Amazonia have introduced tolerant grasses for their cattle to graze (207). It is unknown if this will prevent the usual inexorable return of the jungle. So far, agriculture has not seriously threatened caiques in the heart of Amazonia, but along its edges particularly in the south and east where it meets the cerrado is another matter. In that region of Brazil, farmers raise huge quantities of soybeans, corn and other field crops. There, the farmers are rapidly clearing land even in the face of government regulations against it. In the dry burning season, the farmers set huge fires to clear their land of trees. The immensity of these fires is such that the smoke from them forms large gray clouds that waft thickly over the land including the gallery forests along the rivers that penetrate into the cerrado where caiques typically reside. This is the case for the Cristalino Reserve, where the birds remain motionless and prefer not to fly. Further, as part of this new practice, the farmers need to fertilize to keep up production and these nutrients leach in the rivers. The overall effect of these agricultural practices on the survival of caiques and other Amazonian species in these regions is unknown and bears close monitoring.

A danger that does not receive much attention is that indigenous peoples continue to hunt them. When I traveled along the Transamazonian Highway and passed close to a couple of the reserves set aside for indigenous natives in Brazil, I spoke with some of their members. Only one native spoke freely with us and that was well away from the reserve. What he told us was alarming. He said that natives do not hunt parrots to sell as pets but for feathers and to eat. All parrots are hunted, not just the large ones. The reason they hunt them is that they remain very poor despite government assistance programs and have to secure protein rich foods where they can. My informant noted that they hunt one day a week and fish the rest of the week. Particularly disturbing were the number of children on these reserves. During my visit, there seemed to be far more children than adults. If this is the case on other Brazilian Indian reserves, there soon will be an even greater demand for protein rich foods and this does not bode well not just for parrots but all the fauna on these reserves.

Since the implementation of the Wild Bird Conservation Act (WBCA) of 1992, almost no wild-caught parrots have been imported into the United States. However, Europe and Asia still import large numbers of birds. In recent years, some breeders have imported a few green-thighed caiques into the United States from Brazil and Europe. Those from Brazil are required to be second-generation captive bred birds and may not be taken from the wild. Those from Europe must be captive bred too. Even before the import ban, the number of caiques imported into the United States was modest. For example, 7,576 grey-cheeked parakeets (*Brotogeris pyrrhopterus*) were imported in the period between October 1979 and June 1980. In the same period, only 425 black-headed caiques and eight white-bellied caiques were imported (354). While 168 black-headed and only ten white-bellied were imported into the United Kingdom between 1981 and 1984 (48). Bolivia exported almost all of the white-bellied caiques, i.e., *P. l. xanthomerius* (345). Fortunately, there has been great interest in breeding caiques. A TRAFFIC survey of private breeders in 1991 found nineteen

breeders were keeping *P. leucogaster* and fifty keeping *P. melanocephalus* (199). In contrast, the grey-cheeked parakeet nearly disappeared from American aviculture and aviculturalists, struggling to preserve the remaining captive population (166), are only now starting to produce any numbers. *P. l. xanthomerius* seems to be faring particularly well in captivity. This illustrates a phenomenon peculiar to the people who breed imported birds. They devote much more attention to breeding rarer birds than the more common and, therefore, cheaper birds. In a way, we are fortunate that they only imported caiques in modest numbers, enough to peak the interest of aviculturalists, but not so few as to command the prices of the larger, showier parrots. One of the curious phenomena related to the parrot market is that many of the parrots, particularly the larger parrots such as the macaws, that originally were very expensive have declined in price fulfilling the avicultural market model of Robinson (352).

In the last decade or so, the purveyors of parrots within the countries that formerly exported wild-caught birds are working to reduce their reliance on wild-caught birds. A few exporters in the Guianas now breed black-headed caiques (293) hoping to make them a renewable resource. However, with the cost of a wild-caught black-headed caique from a trapper in Guyana being less than two dollars, one wonders why they make the effort (162). Another renewable resource approach that would have worked well for the countries that export parrots, was a concept called parrot ranching (23, 275). Parrot ranching is a sustainable form of harvesting of parrots from the wild. How this works is that the local landowner collects the chicks from a nest but leaves behind at least one chick for the wild parrot parents to rear. This makes great sense since only one or two chicks usually fledge from each nest because the youngest ones usually die. The chicks reared by the parents would sustain the wild population and the harvested chicks sold. The promise of a yearly income would also have given the owner an incentive to protect the nests, which are usually in old growth trees, and thus protect the rainforest itself. The owner might even put up nest boxes to encourage more parrots to breed. Unfortunately, this approach was not viable because unethical exporters would have surely subverted it to export illegal wild-caught birds. With the passage of the WBCA in the United States, however, nearly all importation of parrots whether wild-caught, ranched, or captive reared ceased.

In summary, the status of caiques in the wild is good. In the protected areas, such as Manu National Park in Peru, *P. l. xanthomerius* is abundant (142). Hilty and Brown (183) noted that caiques are still common in Columbia. Hoyo et al (192) noted that international market forces did not threaten them, but locals commonly keep them as pets in Venezuela and other Amazonia nations despite restrictions against this. This is because most South American peoples hold that while selling a native pet bird is a crime, owning one is not (153). There are still quite a few imported caiques in the United States from before the imposition of the import ban in 1992, but nearly all caiques now sold in the United States are domestically bred. Parrot nestlings are still harvested for the pet trade including some caiques (237). Fortunately, caiques are not among the more frequently collected species (149).

Lack of escapee populations

Another aspect of conservation is the consequences of birds escaping or people releasing them into new ecological situations. This is an inherent problem when people keep exotic birds in captivity. In Florida, there are several populations of cockatiels, budgerigars and other parrots (389, 456). (It is ironic that you are now more likely to see "wild" budgerigars in Florida than in Australia.) It seems clear that unwanted introductions will affect some localities more severely than others. Alien bird species such as European starlings and English house sparrows have already changed the spectrum of avian species in most of the United States. Except for the Quaker parakeet and other cold tolerant parrots, most parrots are not likely to survive long in the northern climes of the United States. However, warmer areas, such as California and Florida (129), are amenable to the establishment of tropical species. Still, the lessons learned from the attempts to re-establish rare parrot species such as the thick-billed parrot (*Rhynchopsitta pachyrhyncha*) in New Mexico, prove how unsatisfactory captive bred stock is for repopulating the wild. Aviary reared birds seem to be incapable of surviving in the face of predators. Thus, the occasional escape of a captive bred caique would not be expected to form the basis of a feral population. Most of the feral populations of large parrots in the United States are the result of the accidental release of imported wild birds already well versed in how to survive in the wild. There has been a sighting of a single black-headed caique in south Florida near the Miami airport (319), but no others, and there are no reports of a breeding population. Since most of the caiques now sold are captive bred, it would seem unlikely that they are capable of breeding in the wild—at least if we continue to breed them in low numbers. There is almost no chance of this happening in areas subject to severe winters or areas with unsuitable ecological circumstances such as the deserts, grasslands and the mountains of the American West. Most captive bred caiques simply do not know how to cope in the wild.

Tropical islands, however, are one habitat of special concern since they have extensive rainforest-like environments. Since caiques are not very fussy about the foods they eat, lush tropical islands with abundant fruit crops might prove an ideal habitat for this frugivorous bird. Further, island ecologies tend to be missing or have less skilled predators such as the hawks and snakes found on large continents. Hawaii is an example of such an island ecology, and that state has banned the import and keeping of caiques.

Mutants, hybrids and color variants

There are several ways caiques can express atypical colored featheration. Aside from unethical people dying or bleaching birds to make them appear to be a rarer species in order to fetch a higher price, people can manipulate the color of a parrot's feathers to a limited degree. The methods they use include changing the bird's diet, hybridization of the different subspecies, and possibly a little known method involving treatment of the feather follicle. In addition, wild caiques themselves may cosmetically alter their own feathers. Aviculturalists, however, consider the breeding of mutant forms the most interesting way of altering bird color. Although, I am aware of possible caique mutations, no one has confirmed them as heritable in breeding experiments. For some parrot species, there is a plethora of mutant color mutants. If this were a book on budgies, grass parakeets, or cockatiels, there would be a whole chapter on the genetics of coloration. However, we know so little about caique coloration all the available information can be included in this one short section.

The basis of feather coloration

Before proceeding, it is important to understand the origin of feather coloration. Feather coloration is the result of two very different properties of feathers. One is pigmentation and the other is feather structure. The final color of a feather is usually an amalgam of the two. Feathers, like our fingernails, are not composed of living tissue, so the feather follicle must incorporate pigment at the time of the feather's formation. There may be others, but two main sets of pigments occur in parrot feathers. These are the psittacofulvins (255, 256) and the melanins (331). I refer to these pigments as sets because neither of these pigments represents a single shade of color, but rather a range of shades depending on the molecular modification of their core structures. The psittacofulvins represent a range of colors from yellow to red, while the melanins represent a range from red-brown to black. Thus, for caiques, the yellow and orange colors are due to the incorporation of psittacofulvins into the feather. Parrots differ from most other orders of birds in that they do not incorporate dietary derived carotenoids (331, 445), but synthesize their own yellow/red pigments, although this has yet to be ruled out for the iris of their eyes (289). The black seen in the head feathers of the black-headed caique, in the wing primaries, and periorbital skin and feet is due to melanins.

Pigments may serve other functions in addition to providing coloration. Melanins may protect against feather degradation by bacteria. Shawkey (383) suggests that this may explain Gloger's Rule about why feathers of birds inhabiting warm wet climates where micro-organisms grow more easily, such as the jungle, are usually darker than birds from cooler, drier climates. The psittacofulvins may inhibit lipoperoxidation and thus protect against adverse reactions to things like exposure to ultraviolet radiation (316). Thus, the pigments may have evolutionary advantages beyond mere coloration.

The blue color of feathers is due to structure (116, 280) and an optical phenomenon called coherent scattering (324). The form of coherent scattering seen in feathers is similar to the reflection of light from thin layers such as an oil film floating on water on top of black asphalt. When light enters the film, only those wavelengths of light with an integral number of wavelengths corresponding to thickness of the film reflect back to your eye. The asphalt absorbs the rest of the light. In feathers though, the "film" is a set of small nanometer sized vacuole-like structures of relatively uniform size often in a quasi-organized array. If there is an underlying layer of dark melanin, the feather is dark blue, if there is no melanin or other pigment, the feather is white. In combination with a yellow pigment and the background of melanin, the feather structure gives rise to the green feathers seen on most parrots.

First reported for caiques by Völker in 1937 (447), the fluorescence of some pigments of parrot feathers has been rediscovered (11, 33). One can see this for yourself if you illuminate your caique with a black light. Upon learning of these reports, I arranged for UV fluorescence photography of a pair of my white-bellied caiques by Prof. Davidhazy at the Rochester Institute of Technology and you can see these results in an accompanying picture. On white-bellied caiques, the entire top of the head and nape fluoresces a bright yellow. On black-headed caiques, only the nape fluoresces. The location of the fluorescent feathers at the caique's nape may be significant. On the golden conure (*Guaruba guarouba*), a predominantly yellow parrot, a small patch of feathers located in the same position fluoresces (33). Arnold (11) suggests that the fluorescent patches, in the gular area and on the crown of budgerigars are sexual signals for that species. I was not able to discern any difference in the fluorescent pigment patterns of the male and female caique. However, our limited experience with fluorescence photography means we still cannot rule this out.

The reason for not ruling this out is that caiques see the world very differently from us. In contrast to people, who have only two light detection cell types in their retinas, parrots have three cell types in their retina one of which is thought to detect long wave UV light. Further, to facilitate UV light detection, their lenses are clear without the yellow tint of the mammalian lens that blocks UV light (152). In addition, parrots have four different detection pigments known as opsins in their light detection cells while people only have three (146, 174). The understanding of bird vision is made even more complicated by the presence of pigmented cone oil droplets that probably act as optical filters (146, 147). Thus, parrots probably have greater richness of visual perception than people do. As a way of understanding this, consider people with the dichromatic form of human color-blindness. People with this form of color-blindness lack one of the cone cell opsins, and they do not have the range of color perception of people without this malady. Further, things such as UV reflectance (25, 124) or other visual cues may allow birds to discern colors that we cannot (93, 147, 168, 194, 303). Santos (367) now claims she is able to discern sexual dimorphism of blue-fronted Amazons (*Amazona aestiva*). We consider this parrot monomorphic because we cannot tell their sex by visual inspection. Santos used multiple-angle spectroscopy, a method that tries to take into account our human failure to see all the wavelengths of light that a parrot can. Perhaps when we fully appreciate bird vision, we may find new approaches to understanding our own visual perceptions.

Effect of diet on color

People have long known that diet affects the color of canaries and flamingos and this has also been shown to be true for American goldfinches (*Carduelis tristis*) and northern cardinals (*Cardinalis cardinalis*) (254). By selective breeding and crossing canaries with red siskins (*Carduelis cucullata*), canary breeders have produced birds that range from a clear yellow to a vibrant red. Their color, however, is not the result of breeding alone, since these birds only express their best coloration when they are color fed. Some owners feed their canaries natural products containing carotenoids such as paprika, cayenne, or other red peppers. Most feed a commercial diet containing a mixture of canthaxathin and β-carotene. Owners can even achieve different shades of red in their canary's feathers by varying the amounts of the different foods and supplements. Similarly, flamingos are white when not feeding on their natural diet of small crustaceans. Most zoos feed their flamingos a special diet to bring out the color. Some use beet juice, but like canary owners, most feed a commercial food containing a commercial mixture of canthaxathin and β-carotene. People have tried to color feed African grey parrots the same canthaxathin and β-carotene mixture to enhance the red color of their tails. From our recent knowledge, this should not work since the yellow, orange and red colors of parrots are the result of psittacofulvins not carotenoids. Thus, feeding carotenoids to a parrot probably has little effect on the color of its feathers.

There are, however, diets that do influence parrot coloration but these are not benign. Caiques develop a coloration called localized melanistic leucism (57) from eating a diet too rich in fats, especially nuts and sunflower seed. Birds with this condition express a pied-like coloration and have yellow feathers on their backs intermixed with the green ones. I first encountered this condition when I purchased a bird thinking it was a pied mutation. This bird had dull splotchy yellow feathers intermixed with the green ones on the bird's back and wings. After I placed the bird on the same diet as the rest of my other birds ate, its feathers grew in a glossy green once the annual molt was complete. Breeders have had similar experiences with other parrot species particularly Senegal parrots. This condition may be similar to what happens to cockatiels on a diet deficient in either choline or riboflavin. These birds develop yellow flight feathers lacking melanin (154).

In line with the view that certain metabolic alterations can affect coloration, some native inhabitants of South America deliberately feed a diet too rich in fat and this alters the parrot's feather coloration. Before there was a trade in valuable parrots, the natives did this to make the parrots produce more flamboyantly colored feather to use in making body decorations. They usually feed oil or a fish fat. The oil they feed is dendé or red palm oil (386). Helmut Sick reports that these birds grow bright yellow feathers. Alfred Russel Wallace (450), co-discoverer of the concept of evolution, witnessed natives feeding parrots the fat of a large catfish, and Mrs. Agassiz wrote during her husband's expedition up the Amazon in 1865 (3) that the Indians fed parrots the yellow fat of the Pirarara fish. Both of these reports noted that the fish fats caused the feathers to develop only a yellow tinge. Even the very early aviculturalists in Europe may have unwittingly done this. le Vaillant included illustrations of completely yellow parrots and other abnormally colored parrots in his **Histoire Naturelle des Perroquets** (216, 217). Usually these illustrations were of captive birds, so one must suspect diet was a cause. For example, Watson (453) writing in 1890 ascribed the appearance of several bright yellow feathers on a red-faced lovebird (*Agapornis pullaria*) to it eating the cayenne biscuits provided to other birds in an aviary. When they fed the biscuits to other lovebirds in the same aviary, they all died! Thus, the yellow color comes at a cost—most likely liver disease. One sometimes sees a similar phenomenon in cockatiels fed a diet too rich in fats. They, as well as other parrots, develop a "fatty liver disease" known as hepatic lipidosis (465). Thus, while you can use diet to influence feather color, the methods that work for parrots are at best unhealthy and at worst devastating to the bird's health.

Tapiragem

One can also be able to manipulate the color of individual feathers on parrots. Helmut Sick (386) reported that some indigenous peoples of South America use a method called tapiragem to change the color of selected feathers on parrots. While expressing doubt, le Vaillant (217) noted that other naturalists had reported that the "savages" of Guiana rubbed the blood of a frog into the skin and new feathers grew out with a different color. Other reliable sources, however, have confirmed the existence of this practice (428). Sparks and Soper (411) reported on this technique and Alfred Wallace (450) gave one of the better descriptions of the process in 1853 when he related how the Indians made their headdresses:

"The feathers are entirely from the shoulder of the great red macaw, but they are not those that the bird naturally possesses, for these Indians have a curious art by which they change the colours of the feathers of many birds.

They pluck out those they wish to paint and in the fresh wound inoculate with the milky secretion from the skin of a small frog or toad. When the feathers grow again they are of brilliant yellow or orange colour, without any mixture of blue or green, as in the original state of the bird; on the new plumage being again plucked out, it is said always to come of the same colour without any fresh operation. The feathers are renewed but slowly, and it requires a great number of them to make a coronet, so we see the reason why the owner esteems it so highly, and only in the greatest necessity part with it."

Yellow-thighed caique with black peri-ophalmic skin. On most of the subspecies, this skin is flesh colored. (Photo courtesy of Gloria Balaban.)

Scientists have not replicated this technique in a convincing manner (427, 445), but the many descriptions of tapiragem are good starting point for this. Each native group practicing this technique uses a different concoction. While Wallace reported using an extract from a frog, other natives use the fat from the river dolphin, turtles, and various fish. Whatever the preparation, the treated feathers usually grow in yellow or orange.

The underlying cause for tapiragem appears to be some sort of damage to the feather follicle that prevents incorporation of the black pigment melanin (428). If this is the case, there may be situations in which such damage can occur fortuitously and not from tapiragem. I have seen a green-thighed caique with a single white primary flight feather in the São Paulo Zoo, and an aviculturist in Germany informed me he had a bird with several white primaries. A possible cause of this may be feather follicle damage similar to that induced by tapiragem. The reason a caique flight feather grows in white or a pale yellow is that these feathers normally incorporate the melanin pigment and almost no yellow pigment. This causes the flight feathers on a normal caique to be black to blue in color. Thus, if there is damage to the follicle that prevents melanin deposition, these feathers grow in a very pale yellow or white. Mayaud (251) even suggests that if the trauma is severe enough it can prevent the deposition of both pigments, the follicle will produce white feathers on other parts of the body. However, I am unaware of any reports of this for caiques or any other parrot.

Another aspect of this may be the appearance of yellow feathers on older caiques. On some older birds there are large numbers of yellow feathers on their backs while on others only a scattered few. I suspect this may be due to incidental follicle damage happening during the course of aging. This may be akin to the appearance of gray hair on people, something le Vaillant suggested at the turn of the seventeenth century (217).

This may be a hybrid of a yellow-thigh caique with a black-headed caique. It is thirteen years old and probably a male since it has never laid an egg. The black feathers on the head form a broad chevron with apricot feathers in front and the typical apricot colored feathers on his nape. The feathers on his thighs are a yellow-green and his beak departs from the usual coloration. The top portion of the upper beak is pale flesh color, but it is dark in the commisure area. (Photo courtesy of Scott Blum.)

Adventitious or Cosmetic coloration

Nearly all of the museum caique specimens collected from the wild exhibit a chestnut staining of their breast feathers. This contrasts with the snowy white feathers on captive-reared birds. This seems particularly pronounced for the *P. m. pallidus* specimens in the Carnegie Museum. Seeing these birds, one understands why Barraband prepared one of his two illustrations of the black-headed caique with chestnut fringing of its breast feathers. (See Le Vaillant (216), plate No. 120.) Some early descriptions refer to caiques having a breast that is "Isabel" colored—this being a shade of yellow-brown.

This may be the result of caiques cosmetically altering the color of their feathers in the wild. Adult captive bred caiques have snow-white breasts; however, observers of caiques in the wild noticed they invariably have "dirty" yellow-brown breasts. We think this is the result of the bird's habit of leaf bathing or rubbing against tree twigs and branches exposing their feathers to sap and tannins. If you examine the feathers of specimens in museum collections that naturalists have collected from the wild, the staining of the outer fringe of the feather is usually greater than the rest of the feather. When I pointed this out to one museum curator, she tried to wash one of these feathers with soap and water but the stain remained. This leads one to suspect that a chemical-like dye, probably a tannin, in the food, sap or leaves specifically reacts with their feathers. This may be the reason Barraband, who based some of his illustrations on bird skins in the collections of his benefactors, painted a *P. m. melanocephalus* showing the edges of the breast feathers with a shade of orange (217). This may be another example of a rare phenomenon among birds in which the bird itself cosmetically changes the color of its feathers (271).

Hybridization

Another way of producing atypical feather colorations is to hybridize the different subspecies of caiques. Parrot aviculturists usually frown upon hybridization (119), and, strange as it may seem, at least one state, New Jersey, has a law forbidding hybridization. This is not particularly rational, and seems to reflect the view of people involved in species conservation rather than people breeding birds for the pet trade. I concur with the view of limiting hybridization at this stage of caique aviculture in order to establish pure bloodlines. Still, hybridization is already occurring and will occur more frequently in the future. It is difficult to

make a rational argument against it when a bird is going to become a pet. In the past, caique hybridization often occurred because of the scarcity of mates of the same subspecies. This led to the hybridization of the green-thighed white-bellies (*P. l. leucogaster*) with the black-headed (*P. m. melanocephalus*) at Busch Gardens in Tampa, FL, one of the earliest caique breeding successes[25] . The progeny of these caiques have since entered the breeder gene pool in the United States and occasionally one encounters an atypically colored bird that may be the progeny of these birds. Even now, there are so few green-thighed white-bellies (*P. l. leucogaster*) in the North America; some breeders mate them with yellow-thighed white-bellies (*P. l. xanthomerius*). Yet species purists castigate these breeders to the extent that they are reluctant to disclose that their chicks are hybrids. Thus, they have not shared any information on the genetics of caique coloration. Further complicating this is the fact that even in the wild there is a wide variation in feather coloration particularly in the clinal zones between the ranges of the subspecies. Despite the purists, at the 1989 show of the Long Island Parrot Society, the judges awarded a yellow-thighed caique (*P. l. xanthomerius*) with "Best of Show" even though it clearly had green frosting on its thigh feathers (105). These feathers should have been a clear lemon color.

Most of what we know about the genetics of caiques comes from casual observations. Dr. George Smith (393, 407) noted that the inheritance of the paler coloration, such as seen for *P. leucogaster*, which has less melanin in its feathers, is a dominant trait. Thus, one would expect hybrids of *P. leucogaster* and *P. melanocephalus* to have a greater resemblance to *P. leucogaster* than *P. melanocephalus*. The only published report germane to this hybridization, however, is a single chick resulting from the second known breeding of caiques in captivity. At a time when caiques were nearly unobtainable, Lady Poltimore (318) paired a pallid male (*M. m. pallidus*) with a green-thighed female (*P. l. leucogaster*). This pair hatched four chicks but only one survived. The plumage of this chick was the same as the pallid male parent except that its thighs were green and the salmon color on the back of its neck was more intense. In private conversations with persons breeding mixed pairs, they noted that the green-thigh trait seems to be genetically dominant when the green-thighed caique is crossed with a yellow-thighed caique. Unfortunately, all these reports are for young birds,

---

[25] You may find this breeding data in the International Zoo Yearbook, 1967 through 1972.

and we do not know if this coloration changes when they reach maturity.

Atypically colored birds

This brings us to the topic of birds in the wild that do not conform to the standard descriptions of the different species and subspecies. There are black-headed caiques (*P. m. melanocephalus*) with light flesh colored periorbital skin, and yellow-thighed caiques (*P. l. xanthomerius*) with black periopthalmic skin. There are museum specimens of both black-headed (*P.m. melanocephalus*) and pallid (*P.m. pallidus*) caiques with green tinged thighs. I have also received a report of a domestically bred black-headed caique with green vent feathers; something unreported for any of the subspecies. Further, among the green-tailed caiques, there is considerable variation in the extent of yellow on the tips of the tail feathers. Some have none, while on others the yellow creeps up from the end of the tail a centimeter or so. We do not really know how these variants arise. One would expect some variation to arise from the interbreeding of the subspecies in the clinal zones between the species and subspecies ranges (159, 286). This, however, cannot explain all variants since some, such as a black-headed caique with the greenish thighs, were collected in French Guiana well away from range of the green-thighed caiques. Such birds are reasonably frequent in aviculture. One of my own birds, a male yellow-thighed caique greater than ten years old, has intermediate gray colored periopthalmic skin that seems to be becoming darker as he ages. A picture provided by Gloria Balaban shows the extreme form in which the periopthalmic skin is quite black. There are probably other variant forms. All these differences, whether seen on captive or wild origin birds, demonstrates that the coloration of caiques should not be regarded as fixed. Indeed, an astute breeder may one day use them to advantage and breed interesting new color forms of caiques.

Mutations

Presently, I am confident of the existence of at least one color mutation of the caique, although there may be others. Dr. Smith reported (399) that someone imported a lutino form into England shortly after World War II but kept it as a pet instead of breeding it. A bit later, he reported on a lutino form of the *P. l. leucogaster* subspecies that might have resulted from inbreeding because of its rarity in Europe (395). I suspect these two reports are for the same bird. The mutation I feel confident about is still only a chick and its owner needs to confirm this by breeding it. It is an aberrantly colored black-headed caique. The nature of the mutation has yet to be determined, but it appears to be a gray green or melanistic form, although, a "dark" or olive mutation cannot be ruled out (245). There is a picture of this bird at the end of this section.

Several breeders have contacted me through my website indicating they might have a "pied" mutation. Proving that the pied condition is due to a mutation, however, is very challenging. As noted earlier, I purchased what appeared to be a pied hen but its pied appearance reverted to a normal plumage after I changed its diet. As I already noted, fatty diets and certain treatments of the feather follicles can induce a scattering of yellow feathers on a bird's back. Further, the genetics of the pied trait in parrots is complex (245) and there are at least two forms of pied phenotype. In one form, individual yellow feathers are scattered through the green plumage. In the other, the yellow feathers occur in patches. Complicating this is that some normal birds develop a pied appearance as they age. This phenotype is due to a defect in melanin synthesis or deposition and certain stresses are able to abrogate melanin deposition on a feather-by-feather basis.

Of all the reports I have received of a pied mutation, I believe only one has any merit. There is a picture of it at the end of this section. In this particular instance, the male but not female birds of a pair housed in the same cage expresses the pied appearance. Further, it did not develop the trait until it reached sexual maturity. This is consistent with the sex-linkage of the pied trait in other parrots (406). The owner, however, has no plans to confirm that this is a mutation because it is in a green-thigh caique, and they are difficult to secure.

A possible specimen of a melanistic form may exist in the Academy of Sciences in Philadelphia, but I suspect its appearance is due to its feathers absorbing oils during transport rather than it being a mutant. In due course, more color mutants will appear. I only hope their owners chose to breed them.

Lateralization

Lateralization refers to departures from the normal bilateral structure of higher animals. This can be physical or behavioral. Most physical lateralization of birds is internal and not immediately noticeable. Examples for people are our appendix located inside our body in the lower right of our abdomen, and our heart, in which the left and right chambers have different functions. An important example of this for birds is that the female reproduction system develops asymmetrically within the body. A complete ovary and oviduct develops on the left side and the matching sexual apparatus on the right side becomes vestigial. However, in the brief period with surgical sexing was routine, veterinarians were sometimes surprised to find the ovary of some female parrots developed on the opposite side.

While physical lateralization is interesting, researchers think behavioral lateralization may offer insight to brain function (145, 357).The most common of these is handedness and, as we know, no amount of training can force a left-handed person to become a truly right-handed person. There is a similar phenomenon among parrots. A study of black-headed caiques found that they are more frequently right-footed than left footed (408, 411). This appears to be opposite from the observations for most other parrots species which are usually left-footed (134, 165, 357). Footedness for a parrot refers to the foot it most frequently uses to grasp and manipulate its food. When offered a tasty morsel from the left, 62 percent of the time caiques will grasp it with the right foot. Offered from its right side this increases to 96 percent of the time. There are questions about the reason for this phenomenon (165). Since one usually observes this behavior when the bird is perching, it may be the bird needs the stronger foot to clasp the perch while it uses the other to manipulate its food. On the other hand, the bird may be innately more adept with one foot than it is with the other. There are other explanations for why parrots favor one foot over the other. These include skeletal asymmetry, internal organ position, and a disproportionate distribution of the blood supply to the brain. None is very convincing (165).

The above two pictures are of same pair of the yellow-thighed caiques. The upper picture is how they appear under white light. The one below shows how they fluoresce in visible light range when illuminated with near ultraviolet light not visible to people. (Photos of author's birds by Prof. Davidhazy, Rochester Institute of Technology.)

The chick in the upper right appears to be a "dark" or "olive" mutation of the black-headed caique. This chick is a male and hatched in 2005. Unfortunately this chick died. (Photo courtesy of birds' owner who wished to remain anonymous.)

This is a breeding pair of green-thighed caiques. The bird on the right with the "pied" phenotype is the male. We suspect this may be a sex-linked mutation expressed only when the male reaches sexual maturity. However, we need more information to confirm this is a true mutation. (Photo courtesy of Terry Irwin.)

Appendices

Appendix A. Notes on the preparation of some the caique's favorite foods.

Apple. Caiques like apples, but most get bored with them if you serve them too regularly. I serve them as a coarse dice leaving on the skins. You may feed the whole fruit if you do not mind it going to waste. An entertaining use of apple peels resulting from your regular human cooking is to drape a few over their cage bars. The bird will drag them off and chew on them. There is no need to remove the seeds. The Carolina Parakeet, considered an agricultural pest at one time, would destroy whole apples just to get at the seeds (187). Low (229) noted that the main attraction of apples for caiques is their seeds. Because the ancestor of parrots was a seedeater, one has to wonder if they evolved in a manner that renders them resistant to the toxins in the seeds that affect mammals.

Banana. Most caiques do not like fresh banana. They do seem to like the sweetened dried banana pieces.

Blackberries. They love them, but you will have a blue splatter decor if you feed too many. No preparation required, just add a few of them to the bowl. Be prepared for blue droppings.

Blueberries. Prepare same as for blackberries. Like blackberries, they can make a big mess with them.

Broccoli and **cauliflower**. Most caiques will eat broccoli and, to a lesser extent, cauliflower. Break off the florets and serve, and do not forget the stalks. Slice the stalks into sticks and serve them too. These vegetables belong to a larger group called either the cruciferous or the brassica group of vegetables. This group includes the cabbages, kale, mustard greens, rutabagas, and turnips. You can feed all of these to your birds.

Cherries. Not all caiques like these, but those that do, love them. Just drop the whole cherries in the bowl. To get them started, you sometimes have to cut them in half to expose the flesh. Caiques cannot crack the pits, so there is no need to seed them.

Corn. Caiques like both fresh and frozen corn on the cob. They tend to turn up their bill at canned corn. You do not need to cook corn. If frozen on the cob is used, let it defrost over night in the refrigerator. To serve corn on the cob, chop it into chunks that they can pick up with their foot. Giving them a whole ear is wasteful. Chopping chunks of corn on the cob requires a little skill. You need a large heavy knife and a cutting board.

It is easiest to cut it across the diameter of the cob. To cut, place the tip of the knife on the board, and then rock it down on the cob using the palm of your other hand to press through the cob. If the cob seems particularly tough, microwave it for a minute. If you are providing fresh corn on the cob, be sure to inspect it carefully. Discolored kernels are a sign of fungal infection and you should discard that cob. Finally, give the husk to the birds for them to play with.

Carrots. Andy, one of my males, loves carrots no matter how I prepare them—fresh or cooked. The rest of my caiques are less enthusiastic. Usually they just chew carrots into tiny pieces without taking much nourishment from them. Chop carrots any way you please so that they can pick it up in their claw. If you buy carrots with tops, give them too. You can hang the tops in the cage at perch level to provide entertainment in addition to nourishment.

Cheese. I give each bird a ½-inch cube of mild yellow cheddar cheese twice a week. Most, but not all caiques like cheese. Some are especially fond of it and you need to limit it because of its fat content. Do not spend too much money on cheese. The chief factor affecting caique cheese preference is color. They prefer yellow and ignore the white cheeses.

Cranberries. A major favorite! I just pick over the berries to remove the brown and soft ones and serve. Caiques tend to waste these, they like the little seeds more than the flesh. Still, they like them so much I buy a few extra bags while they are in season and freeze them. They freeze as individual berries, and you defrost them by dropping them into warm water.

Flowers. For a change in pace you can feed your birds flowers. Some varieties of nasturtiums are grown for their edible flowers. Other flowers you may serve include pansies, roses, hibiscus and marigolds. Be sure the flowers are free of insecticide.

Grapes. One of the standard fresh fruits I serve my birds. Grapes seem to be available in all seasons unlike other fruits. Normally I feed table grapes, but you can feed the viniferous or wine grapes too. Caiques tend to prefer table grapes. If you have a choice, buy the sweetest grapes. Do not worry about the color or whether they have seeds. For some unknown reason, parrots tend to avoid intact grapes. My one serving instruction is to slice grapes in half until they accept them whole. Sliced grapes are particularly useful for weaning chicks onto solid foods. A grape is one of the first foods my chicks eat by themselves.

If you feed grapes, you need to exercise more caution than with other fruits. Molds growing on them can produce a mycotoxin called ochratoxin A. Ochratoxin A is a nephrotoxin and carcinogen for people. Chickens fed ochratoxin A develop kidney and liver diseases (213, 442). Thus, it is particularly important to avoid feeding moldy grapes, ones with loose skins, or otherwise do not look normal.

Greens. Most commercially available greens belong to either the brassica (Brassicaceae) or goosefoot (Chenopodiaceae) families. Cabbage, kale and radishes are brassicas, while beets, chard, and spinach are chenopodias. I do not usually put these in the bird's fruit bowl, instead I place whole leaves near their favorite perch. To serve greens with long stems like Swiss chard, I lower the stem through the bars on the top of the cage so they dangle supported by the bulk of the leaf. They will usually chew on the stems, then pull the leaf through and chew on it. If you have a shelf or clip in the cage, they may be used. While on Swiss chard, caiques do not like the red form in this instance. I suspect it looks too much like a snake.

Kiwi. Not every caique likes the kiwi fruit. The ones that do, however, relish them. Sometimes the ones sold in stores are as solid as rocks and if you taste them, they are not sweet. Kiwi's are best served when they are slightly soft. If they are not ready, allow them to sit at room temperature until they just begin to turn soft. To serve, leave on the skin and cut them into foot-sized wedges. To a caique, the little black seeds are the best part.

Mango. I slice mangos the same as when I prepare them for myself, i.e., slice parallel to the flat side of the fruit along the large flat seed to remove the pulp. Leave the hide on, slice into chunks, and serve. One word of caution, some people are allergic to the skin of this fruit.

Melons. Caiques are not very fond of melons. They do like a piece of sweet watermelon on occasion. Just like people, they eat the red part and leave the rind. Chop into chunks. Be sure to leave the seeds in.

"Nectar." In the wild, caiques take nectar from flowers. Nectar is an aqueous solution comprised mostly of glucose and fructose, but caiques also seem to like sucrose, i.e., regular table sugar. Caiques will accept the commercial nectars meant for Lories, and this is a good choice if they are not getting complete nourishment from their regular diet. I provide my pet caiques with a few teaspoons of ginger ale or clear juice such as cranberry juice in a small cup as a treat when they are out on their stand.

Nuts. Caiques like all kinds of nuts. Just avoid the salted ones. You should not feed too many because of their high fat content. Caiques need to have the harder shelled nuts cracked for them. They can open peanuts easily. I like to give an occasional almond in the shell. They can get into the nut, but it is a challenge that can entertain them for a long time. I give nuts as a treat. Even my breeders take them directly from my hand. A reliable sign that my breeders are going to nest is when the female refuses this treat.

Okra. Some caiques relish this vegetable while others dislike it. They prefer the older pods over the young pods. I sometimes find large spiny pods at a farmer's market. They were a great hit with my birds even though most people would not have tolerated them. This is probably because the birds prefer the seeds. To prepare okra, either cut the pods across the diameter to form disks or lengthwise into quarters. When preparing my fresh food bowls, I always prepare okra and hot peppers last. The reason for doing okra last is the slime it leaves on the knife. The birds probably do not care, but I like to wash my knife before I slice other foods.

Oranges and Grapefruits. Oranges, grapefruits, kumquats and occasionally lemon are accepted by caiques. As with all fruits, caiques tend to prefer the sweeter citrus fruits. Like apples, chop them into foot-sized chunks. I tried blood oranges once, but these were not accepted. I suspect the ones I served were not sweet enough.

Papaya. It is hard to know when to buy this fruit. They pick papayas green for the northern markets and they sometimes never develop a good sweet taste. This is particularly true of the larger papaya varieties. Of the two smaller varieties, caiques prefer the sweeter orange-fleshed form to the yellow-fleshed form. The problem is that often one cannot distinguish them apart until you cut them open. Sometimes, they have been in the store long enough to have ripen, but equally as often they are still green. A good quality ripe papaya should be blemish free and barely soft in your hand. If it is still hard, allow it to sit at room temperature, preferably in a paper bag, until it just starts to turn yellow and soften. To prepare, slice the papaya in half-lengthwise to expose the seeds. There is no need to peel. Cut into chunks, and serve it seeds and all. The birds will eat the flesh and drop the skin and most of the seeds.

111

Peas. The best peas for caiques are sugar snap peas. Shell peas in the pod are accepted, but they prefer them young and sweet. They like snow peas, but since the bird only eats the seed, these are a waste. Snap peas are usually sweet and their seeds nice and plump. They are also easy to prepare. Just drop them in the bowl. I find caiques do not particularly like the frozen or canned shelled peas.

Peppers. Caiques have a taste for peppers—both the mild and hot varieties. Some bird shops sell the dried chilies. There are two general rules covering the caique's preferences in peppers. They like them red and they like them with plenty of seeds. Of the mild ones, they prefer the red bell peppers. They chew out the flesh and leave the skin. However, they have a special fondness for the seeds. Anytime you are preparing peppers for yourself, always save the inner core of seeds for your birds. The red colored hot peppers are the most preferred, but they will eat the long green seed filled chilies too. Do not worry that feeding your parrot hot peppers is cruel. Birds do not have the same response to them as mammals (202, 205). In fact, it is thought that the existence of capsaicin in hot peppers evolved as a way for the plant to limit its eating to birds (431). Studies at the Virginia Tech University indicate that if you feed capsaicin to chickens it protects them from *Salmonella enterica*. This bacterial species causes food poisoning of people. Because only birds seem to be able to tolerate hot peppers, some people add them or their juice to their wild birdseed to keep the squirrels and other vermin from eating it. (The hot Chinese type mustard is the only food I have noticed that gets the bird shaking its head in revulsion.) As with the other foods, chop them into chunks. Take care not to touch your eyes, nose, lips and your personal mucosal surfaces after you have prepared the hot varieties. If you feed the red ones, do not be alarmed when you see red droppings.

Persimmon. There are reports that persimmon can be toxic for parrots (76). I have not had any problem, but this may be because I only feed them occasionally and in small amounts. The reason I do not serve them more often is that they are very messy to prepare. This fruit has to be very soft before you can serve it to either birds or people. If it is not, it is very astringent. It is best when you are able to let it ripen on the tree and pick it just after it softens. Even then, be sure that it is completely soft before offering them to your birds or eating them yourself. Most people, however, have to buy persimmons at their local market. The fruit offered there is usually hard and very astringent. There are two ways to make these persimmons edible. The first way is to allow it to sit at room temperature until completely soft. The second way is to freeze it solid and allow it to defrost <u>completely</u>. Either way, its flesh will become jelly-like. To serve it to my birds, I do my best to chop it into suitable portions trying to keep it in the fruit's skin. This can be a challenge.

Pomegranate. This is a major favorite but messy. Pomegranates are usually only commercially available in the autumn unless you are lucky enough to live in a warm area and have your own tree or bush. To serve these, I use a large knife and slice them in half. I then place the cut side of the half on the cutting board and slice it into sections and then across the sections to form wedges or some semblance of wedges. I slice them this way because pomegranates are very juicy and during the slicing the juice gets sprayed all around. You can prevent this by trying to keep all the slices together with your hand while you are cutting. I drop the wedges, hide and all into the bowls. I usually prepare pomegranates last because they are so messy. The juices will run all over if you are not careful. Pomegranate seeds, or rather the dried fruit cells, are available at Indian groceries under the name anardana seeds. Alternatively, you can freeze the fruit cells. To do this, make shallow incisions through the hide that are not deep enough to cut into the cells. Then submerge the fruit under water and remove the hide. The juice laden seed cells will sink and separate from the husk remnants.

Prickly pear or **Cactus pear**. The prickly pear is the fruit of the *Opuntia* genus of cactus. There are several species of this cactus. The fruit from all of them are edible for people. Some are sweeter than others are and these are the ones we occasionally find in our northern markets. As for most fruits, chop them, hide and all, into foot-sized chunks.

Pumpkin. While it is hard to persuade caiques to partake of the gargantuan Halloween pumpkins, they do like the small mini-pumpkins. I give these a quick heating in a microwave oven for 30 seconds. Then I chop it into foot sized pieces seeds and all.

Raspberries. Raspberries are another major favorite. They like the red and black ones better than the yellow ones. No preparation required. I give these as treats. The main problem with raspberries, as with blackberries and blueberries, is the mess.

Soybeans. I sometimes serve fresh soybeans. You need to cook all beans, not just soybeans, to detoxify them. To prepare them, blanch the whole unshelled bean for five minutes in boiling water. Cool and keep in the refrigerator until ready to serve. They sometimes call these blanched soybeans edamame, and are a nice treat for people too. In recent years, feeding soy-based products to birds has come under fire. Some suggest that soy is a source of unwanted hormones and toxins capable of seriously affecting parrots (70).

Sprouted seeds. I occasionally give my caiques sprouts, but they tend to ignore them. If you provide these, be warned. The CDC reports that some people have acquired *Escherichia coli* O157:H7 and *Salmonella* from organic sprouts. These bacteria can cause death of the very young, the elderly and immunocompromised persons. This is probably one case where you best avoid products labeled as organically grown. There is no way of completely avoiding these bacteria without the use of some chemical agent. If you prepare your own sprouts, pretreat the seeds with calcium hypochlorite (not bleach which is sodium hypochlorite) to reduce the danger of contracting these deadly bacteria.

Strawberries. These are a major favorite, but wasteful treat. Caiques like the little seeds on the outer surface and seldom eat the berry itself. Leave the stem on and cut the larger berries into pieces they can handle with their feet.

Sweet potatoes and Yams. You can serve sweet potatoes and yams raw or cooked. Just chop it into "bite" sized pieces.

Tomatoes. The tomatoes' seeds are what caiques like best and for their size, cherry tomatoes have more than regular tomatoes. When I serve cherry tomatoes, I just cut them in half. I chop larger tomatoes into chunks. Be sure to remove stems since there are reports they are toxic. As per their normal color preference, red is best.

Twigs and buds. Some parrot owners, especially in Europe, make a special effort to provide fresh twigs so their birds can strip off their bark and eat their buds. I provide apple twigs in winter. One German breeder provides his parrots with willow twigs and another with fruit and ash buds (111). There are two important cautions. First, never give your birds twigs from trees that are thought to be toxic such as cherry or avocado. Second, take care to avoid twigs from trees sprayed with insecticides.

A more complete list of foods you may feed caiques is provided in Appendix B

Appendix B. Human foods you may feed caiques.

Fruits

Apple[a]	Apricots (dried)	Banana (dried)	Blackberries
Cherries	Crabapples	Cranberries[a]	Currants
Dates	Elderberries	Figs	Gooseberries
Grapefruit	Grapes[a]	Hawthorn fruit	Kiwi[a]
Lemon	Mango	Melons	Orange[a]
Papaya[a]	Pears	Persimmon	Plums
Pomegranate[a]	Prickly pear	Raisins	Raspberries[a]
Rose hips	Strawberries[a]		

Vegetables

Asparagus	Beans[b]	Beet	Bok Choi
Broccoli	Brussels sprouts	Cabbage	Carrots[a] & tops
Cauliflower	Celery	Cooked dry beans	Corn[a]
Cucumber	Dandelion leaves	Endive	Kale
Mustard greens	Okra[a]	Peas	Peppers[a]
Plantain	Pumpkin	Radish pods[a]	Radishes
Rapini	Rutabagas	Soy beans[b]	Spinach
Sprouts (all types)	Sweet potato	Swiss Chard	Tomatoes[c]
Turnip	Watercress	Yam	

Other

Bones[a] (cooked)	Bread	Butter*	Cereals
Cheese*	Cooked fish	Cooked meats[a]	Eggs (cooked)
Flowers	Ginger ale[a]	Insect grubs[d]	Jellies
Margarine[a]	Nuts[a]	Pasta	Peanut butter
Quinoa	Tofu	Tree twigs[d]	

[a] Caiques are usually fond of these foods.
[b] Beans and soybeans need to be cooked to render them non-toxic.
[c] The stem of the tomato can cause violent reactions in some people, so it is wise to remove them.
[d] Twigs may be from any of the safe trees including maple, willow and fruit trees.
[e] You can feed a number of different insect grubs. These include waxworms, mealworms, and flour moth grubs. You can buy some of these at pet shops specializing in reptiles.

Do not feed these! These are human foods known or thought to be toxic[a].

Alcoholic beverages	Avocado	Chocolate
Coffee beans	Coriander	Dendé oil
Eggplant	French sorrel	Garlic[b]
Jack beans (fresh or dried)	Lima beans (fresh or dried)	Onions[b]
Parsley	Potato shoots	Rapeseed[c]
Rhubarb leaves	Tobacco	

[a] The evidence for the toxicity of some of these is poor. Further, their toxicity is dose dependent.
[b] All members of the allium family of plants should be considered toxic.
[c] The rapeseed used for the pressing of canola oil is non-toxic and acceptable. You sometimes find rapeseed in wild birdseed mixes.

Appendix C. Plants caiques eat in the wild.

Scientific name	Common name[a]	Part eaten	Reference
Alchornea Sp.(Euphorbiaceae)		Fruit	Schwartz[b] (374)
Apocynaceae sp.		Fruit	Davis (99)
Astrocaryum tucumoides (Drude)	Awarra		McLoughlin (257)
Bursera inversa	Resbalamono	Fruit pulp	Stevenson (416)
Byrsonima coriacea var. spicata (Malpighiaceae)	Hitia	Fruit	Schwartz[b] (374), McLoughlin (257)
Caraipa densiflora	Tamaquare Dakudu (Ye'kwana)	Seed	Desenne (110), Juniper (204), Collar (83)
Caryocar Linn. (Caryocaracea)		Fruit	Schwartz[b] (374)
Chrysophyllum prieurii		Ripe fruit	van Roosmalen[c]
Clusia grandiflora	Jadahada (Ye'kwana)	Seed and pulp	Desenne (110), Juniper (204), Collar (83)
Cynometra hostmanniana		Pulp	Juniper (204), Collar (83)
Dacryodes chimantensis		Fruit	Parrado-Rosselli (300)
Dialium guianensis	Jutahy Dede (Ye'kwana)	Pulp	Desenne (110), Juniper (204), Collar (83)
Euterpe oleracea	Açai	Seed	Moegenburg (268, 269)
Euterpe precatoria	Chonta (palm tree) Wajo (Ye'kwana)	Fruit pulp	Desenne (110), Collar (83), Juniper (204)
Eschweilera sp.	Manbarklak Odoma (Ye'kwana)	Flower	Desenne (110), Collar (83)
Eschweilera subgrandulosa	Tawadi (Ye'kwana)	Flower, pollen?	Desenne (110),
Erisma uncinatum	Cambara	Flower	Guide, Cristalino Lodge
Erythrina fusca		Nectar, anthers, seeds	Cotton (87)
Erythroxylum sp. Browne (Erythroxylaceae)		Fruit	Schwartz[b] (374)
Ficus spp.	Wild figs	Fruit/seeds	McLoughlin (257)
Guarea grandiflora	American muskwood Jasudu (Ye'kwana)	Seed	Desenne (110), Juniper (204), Collar (83)
Gutteria sp.			Rasmussen (333)
Hevea benthamiana	Rubber tree Katajai (Ye'kwana)	Seed	Desenne (110), Juniper (204), Collar (83)
Hymenaea courbaril	Jatoba, Jiguitiba	Fruit/seeds	Guide, Cristalino Lodge
Inga laterifolia	Shirada Poixdoux Wüwü (Ye'kwana)	Flower, nectar	McLoughlin (257), Desenne (110), Juniper (204), Collar (83)

Maximilianea regia (Mart.)	Cocorite		McLoughlin (257)
Micropholis mensalis	Grumixava Wakadu (Ye'kwana)	Seed	Desenne (110), Juniper (204), Collar, 1997
Micropholis melinoneana	Grumixava Kadiye (Ye'kwana)	Pulp	Desenne (110), Juniper (204), Collar (83)
Myristicaceae spp.	Nutmeg tree	Immature fruit	Job advertisement[d]
Norantea	Liana	Flower	Juniper (204), Collar (83), Tostain, 1992 Sigrist (388)
Oenocarpus batauá	Batauá palm	Fruit	Peres (311)
Ocnocarpus bacaba	Kujedi (Ye'kwana)	Seed (tentatively identified eating seed.)	Desenne (110)
Oryza sativa	Rice	Seed heads	Smith (400)
Parkia pendula		Young seeds	Peres (312)
Platonia insignis	Bacuri	Nectar	Maués (250)
Pouroma guianensis	Mangabe Sadajoi (Ye'kwana)	Seed, pulp	Desenne (110), Juniper (204), Collar (83)
Pouteria anomala		Ripe pulp	van Roosmalen[c]
Pradosia cochlearia		Immature seeds	van Roosmalen[c]
Protium sp. (?) *Protium* Burm (Burseraceae)	Kudawäma (Ye'kwana)	Fruit; seed	Desenne, 1994; Schwartz[b] (374)
Psidium guajava	Guava	Fruit	McLoughlin (257)
Sterculia excelsa		Leaves	Juniper (204), Collar, 1997
Symphonia globulifera	Chewstick	Flower	Juniper (204), Collar (83), Tostain, 1992 Sigrist (388)
Tapirira quianensis	Warimia tree	Fruit	Bourne (35), McLoughlin (257)
Tetragastris altissima		Seed	Ratiarison, 2005

[a] The common name may differ from one place to another.
[b] Fruits eaten by five bird species including *P. melanocephalus*.
[c] These data were from an excellent web page written by Marc Roosmalen with illustrations by Betty Roosmalen-Blijenberg. Unfortunately this web page is no longer available.
[d] Advertisement for volunteer to monitor nutmeg trees in Ecuador in winter of 2004 placed by Simn Queesnborough, Univ. Aberdeen, Scotland. (http://www.primate.wisc.edu/pin/jobs)

Appendix D. Some safe and unsafe ornamental plants.

These lists are modified from the somewhat arbitrary lists given by C.A. Johnson-Delaney (198), Ludeman et al (236), and Jeanne Smith (409). The lists are far from complete and their accuracy questionable. I would not be too concerned if your bird ate or chewed a small amount of any of them. Just be sure to watch the bird carefully if it does. For example, the toxic component of many of these plants is oxalic acid, and the bird would have to eat a very large amount of the plant for there to be any toxic effect.

Plants you may plant in an aviary if you do not mind them being chewed.

Acacia	African violet	Aloe	Baby's tears
Bamboo	Begonia	Bougainvillea	Chickweed
Christmas cactus	Cissus (Kangaroo vine)	Coffee	Coleus
Corn plant	Crabapple	Dandelion	Dogwood
Donkey tail	Dracaena varieties	Ferns (all types)	Figs (all types)
Gardenia	Grape ivy	Hen and Chickens	Jade plant
Kalanchoe	Magnolia	Marigolds	Monkey plant
Mother-in-law's tongue	Nasturtium	Natal palm	Norfolk Island pine
Palms (all types)	Pepperomia	Petunia	Pittosporum
Pothos	Prayer plant	Purple passion	Schefflera
Sensitive plant	Spider plant	Swedish ivy	Thistle
Wandering Jew	White Clover	Zebra plant	

House plants to avoid.

Amaryllis	Anthurium	Arum lily	Avocado
Azalea	Bird of Paradise	Bittersweet	Bulbs (most all)
Caladium	Calla lily	Castor Bean	Chrysanthemum
Coriander	Crocus	Croton	Crown of thorns
Dieffenbachia	Eucalyptus	Hydrangea	Ivy (most)
Jerusalem cherry	Lantana	Lily of the Valley	Marijuana
Mistletoe	Moonseed	Oleander	Oxalis
Philodendrons	Poinsettia		

Tree branches you may use for perches.

Almond	Apple	Ash	Citrus (any)
Dogwood	Elm	Guava	Madrona
Magnolia	Manzanita	Maple	Nectarine
Nut (see exclusions)	Peach	Pear	Pine
Plum	Sassafras	Sycamore	Thurlow
Willow (any)			

Tree branches and limbs you need to avoid as perches.

Apricot	Azalea	Black[a] and honey locust	Cherry
Chinaberry	Clematis[a]	Elderberry	Flame tree
Horse chestnut	Linden (basswood)	Mock orange	Mountain laurel
Oak (any kind)	Oleander[a]	Poinciana	Poison Ivy
Privet	Pyracantha	Rhododendron[a]	Virginia Creeper
Yew[a]			

[a] Shropshire et al (385) experimentally showed these plants to be poisonous for budgies.

117

Appendix E. Commercial sanitizers and disinfectants.

Agent	Brand names	Comments
Detergents/soaps	Various brands	While some soaps are formulated with antibacterial agents, e.g. Dial soap, most have little bactericidal activity. These are best used in conjunction with sanitizers.
Alcohol	Ethanol Isopropanol Hand sanitizers: Germ-X Purell	Both kinds of alcohols are used in clinics to sanitize surfaces. For ethanol, the optimum concentration is 70 percent. The isopropanol purchased at the pharmacy usually comes at the correct concentration. To use, spread it on the surface and allow it to dry. The drying action is what kills. Ethanol pads are sold for sanitizing the skin and cleaning wounds. Alcohol is also the active ingredient in some hand sanitizers. Inactivates polyomavirus (351).
Chlorhexidine gluconates	Nolvasan Virosan Hibitane Hibistat	Used as antiseptic to clean both surfaces and wounds. Effective against most bacteria and yeasts, but not viruses, bacterial spores or the bacterium *Pseudomonas aeruginosa*. Add it to the water in incubators and brooders to prevent growth.
Sodium hypochlorite	Clorox Purex *etc.*	Bleach. This is a very effective against bacteria, yeast, fungi, and viruses. It can be quite corrosive. Never use it at full strength since the vapors can kill parrots(461). Avoid prolonged exposure to metals. It is wise to wear latex or other waterproof gloves with this sanitizer. The Centers for Disease Control recommends a 1:100 dilution (2.5 tablespoons per gallon) for killing *C. psittaci*. Inactivates polyomavirus at a 1:10 dilution (351). Cheap!
Stabilized chlorine dioxide	Oxyfresh Dent-A-Gene	Considered superior to bleach for disinfecting and does not have the odor. Effective against viruses and bacteria. Do not use in concentrated form. Not deleterious to one's hands at the low concentrations used for sanitation, i.e., at a 1:200 dilution. Inactivates polyomavirus at a dilution of 1:400 (351).
Gluteraldehydes	Wavecide Cidex Sporcide Banacide Sterol Sonacide Cybact MC-25	Effective against nearly all pathogens. Can be corrosive to metals and can cause skin damage. Use these in a well-ventilated area.
Iodophors	Wescodyne Vanodine Betadyne Mikroklene Povidone Scrubodyne	These are detergents containing iodine. Effective against most pathogens but not polyoma virus, psittacine beak and feather virus or *Ps. aeruginosa*. Often used to clean skin and wounds. Will stain your skin.
Phenols	Lysol One Stroke O-syl Avinol-3 LPH Matar Amerse Environ Staphhene	Phenols are one of the most effective disinfectants. After chlorine bleach, these are the cheapest. Leaves residual odor on plastics. Take care about handling and ventilation. Reputed to be toxic to cats and reptiles. Avinol-3 inactivates polyomavius at a concentration of 1:256 (351).
Quaternary Ammonium Compounds	Roccal-D Quitacide Parvosol Hitor Omega Barquat Merquat Cetylcide A-33 Floquat Zephiran	Effective against most, but not all pathogens. Effective against most bacteria, including chlamydia, as well as some viruses. Not effective against fungi, spore forming bacteria, and hydrophilic viruses. Difficult to rinse away and its residue may be ingested by birds with disastrous results. The Centers for Disease Control recommends a 1:1000 dilution for killing *C. psittaci*.
Wood Tar Distillates	Pinesol Hexol	These are only effective when mixed with detergents. They are generally safe, but there is an unconfirmed report of young chicks dying from exposure.

118

Appendix F. Dangerous household products

There are many products that human beings tolerate very well but are dangerous for birds. Most are air borne agents. Many reports are anecdotal, and as such, you should regard them with some skepticism. One also must be wary of some claims because radical groups and individuals sometimes disseminate disinformation about the products of certain companies. Where possible, I have tried to document the products that are harmful.

Air fresheners. There are many different kinds of air fresheners. Some are probably innocuous

Aluminum cooking bags. Use of these has been reported to be associated with the death of birds (6).

Aromatic Candles. Do not be tempted to burn lots of these candles. They may make the holiday seasons seem more festive, but they may also be toxic for your bird.

Aromatic oils. These are what provide the scent in the aromatic candles. These oils are sometimes sold for use in lamps and warmers to increase their scent.

Brass keys. Brass keys contain a small amount of lead to facilitate easier cutting when you make a new key. If your bird chews on one too much, there is a danger of it ingesting too much lead.

Carpet cleaners. There have been several reports that the carpet cleaner **Carpet Fresh** sold by Arm and Hammer caused the death of smaller birds including cockatiels, budgies, and finches. The ingredient in the product responsible for the deaths is unknown, but it may be in other similar products. Try to avoid them until we know more about these products.

Clothing freshener. Proctor and Gamble sells a product called **Febreeze** that some have reported to cause the death of small pet birds when they first marketed it. They changed its formulation and now claim it is safe to use around birds. It is still wise to remove your birds from the room when you use any such product.

Detergents and other cleaners. All types of cleaning agents should be regarded as poisonous. These include all detergents, drain cleaners, oven cleaners, toilet bowl cleaners, and polishes.

Drugs and pharmaceuticals. Drugs and pharmaceuticals intended for human use. This includes both over the counter (OTC) and prescription drugs. Some drugs are useful in veterinary medicine, but you should never administer these without consulting a veterinarian.

Evaporative cooling pads. If you live in a dry area such as American Southwest and use an evaporative cooler instead of air-conditioning, you need to be careful not to use certain pads. Pads sold under the names of CELdek, CELdek with Mi-T-edg, Mi-T-Cool, and Mi-T-edg are supplied in a preservative that emits an odor for the first 24 hours. A preliminary report indicates these can kill birds in a matter of hours.

Flame tamer. This product is a plate placed over a gas-stove burner to distribute heat better. These are coated with a polysilicone lacquer that vaporizes and this is thought to be dangerous for your bird (6).

Galvanized chicken wire and hardware cloth. Some grades of galvanized wire mesh can present a hazard to your bird's health. Parrots sometime chew on this wire, and while they do not usually die, they can become

very sick (191, 334). The better grades of this product, however, are used to make cages for parrots. The difference appears to be the capacity of the zinc in the galvanizing to form "white rust." Avoid the hardware cloth sold in hardware stores and home centers. This product appears to be particularly dangerous for parrots.

Hair dryers. Some hair dryers, particularly new ones, produce toxic vapors that are reported to have killed birds. Some older models are also dangerous since they were made with PTFE.

Heat lamps. Many infrared heat lamps are coated with PTFE. Restaurants use these lamps to keep food warm before serving. This coating prevents glass from a broken lamp from falling on the food. There is a report from a Texas zoo that lost a large number of birds when they gathered near some of these lamps during a cold snap.

Insecticides and other pesticides. The aerosol and fog insecticide products are the most dangerous. Those used to fog a house to rid it of fleas are particularly dangerous. If you must spray or fog, remove your birds, and do not bring them back for at least 24 hours. You should keep all fungicides, herbicides, and rodenticides away from your bird.

Irons. Many clothes irons are now coated with PTFE. Avoid these.

Lead. The poisonous effect of lead on birds is well established. Birds like to chew on this metal. It occurs in many forms. A partial list includes lead paint and putty in older houses, lead curtain weights, solder on old water pipes and other metals, older leaded glass lamps and light fixtures, Champagne cork foil, etc. Ceramic dishes used as water bowls can leach lead, especially older or imported dishes. Even car and house keys contain a small amount of lead, particularly those made of brass. Test kits are available to test your dishes if you feel this is a problem. Recent laws now restrict the use of lead in the production of household products, so do not be too concerned if you purchase paint or dishes made in this country if they are of recent manufacture.

Lumber, pressure treated. In the past, manufacturers treated lumber intended for outdoor use with copper arsenic compounds such as chromated copper arsenate (CCA) or ammoniacal copper arsenate (ACA). They forced these chemicals into the wood under pressure. This greatly increased the life of the wood by preventing termite and rot damage. You should never use treated wood for the construction of cages, as perches, its chips as bedding, or burn it as firewood. Indeed, it was so toxic to people, that most home centers that sell it refuse to saw it to size at your request even though they will do this for all other woods. Further, the manufacturers recommended that you use a breathing mask and eye protection when working with this wood. The recommended method of disposal is by burying it in an approved landfill, never by fire. The manufacturers voluntarily ceased making CCA treated wood in 2004.

PTFE coated cooking tools and lamps. There are a number of brand names including Teflon®, Hostaflon, CuFlon, etc. When PTFE is heated to too high of a temperature, it gives off a very toxic gas. Cookware such as skillets, pots, pans, cookie sheets, etc., often has a film of PTFE on them to prevent food from sticking. Particularly dangerous are the coated drip pans under electric stove heating elements. Even heat lamps sometimes have a film of PTFE enshrouding them to contain the glass should shatter. It is sometimes difficult to find cookware that is not PTFE coated. A good place to find PTFE free cookware is a restaurant supply house.

Scented papers. Many bird keepers suspect that scented toilet paper and paper towels are dangerous for birds. No one has confirmed this, but why take the risk.

Self-cleaning ovens. There are reports that some of the newer self-cleaning ovens have caused the death of parrots that had been kept in the kitchen when the self-cleaning feature was used (417). They believe danger is greatest the first few times this feature is used. The high temperature at which they operate causes the release of toxic gases. If you must use this feature, remove your birds from the house.

Solvents. You should regard all types of solvents as poisonous. These include gasoline, kerosene, paint remover, paint thinner, mineral spirits, nail polish remover, etc.

Space heaters. Some manufacturers make space heaters with PTFE. There is a danger these will over heat, do not use them around birds.

Toothbrushes. Most toothbrushes have tiny metal clips that hold the bristles in place. Avoid giving these as a toy. If your birds chew on one, they may ingest these clips. These clips can leach zinc and copper (208).

Appendix G. Methods for determining the sex of monomorphic parrots

Method	Description	Reliability
Behavior, "Roer's rule"	Male and female caiques exhibit differences in behavior. These differences are more obvious in sexually mature birds, even then, they can be difficult to discern because of seasonal variation and bird individuality.	Poor
Witching	There are several versions of this method. The practitioner of this method dangles a small object on a thread over the head of the bird. Depending on the practitioner, the object has to be a steel needle, a gold ring, a wooden ball, etc. If it swings in a circle it is supposed to be a female and if a male in a straight line (402, 419).	Pure bunk
Subtle indications	For caiques, this includes square-headedness, darker eye ring, and lower pitch voice (148). White frosting beneath eye (242)..	Poor
Body weight & wing chord	A difference in size and shape permits the distinguishing the sex of many species of birds; however, such differences are not obvious for caiques.	Poor
Presence of phallus	We cannot apply this to caiques since they do not have a phallus like other genera such as ducks and geese.	Not applicable to caiques
Pubic symphysis	In mature birds, the bones of the pelvic girdle fuse into a mass of fixed dimensions called a pubic symphysis. This structure in the females of some bird species is necessarily wider in order to accommodate egg passage. However, the difference in width is not obvious for caiques of opposite sex.	Poor
Fluorescence	Parrots can see in the near-ultraviolet range (UVA). Pearn (303) showed that reflectance, but not fluorescence due to ultraviolet light can affect mate choice for budgies. In contrast, Arnold et al. (11) indicate that it is fluorescence. This may also play a role in mate selection by zebra finches (194). While the feathers on caiques, particularly the apricot ones on the neck and head fluoresce, I have not been able to discern any differences by either photography or observation under a black light.	Unknown
Reflectance	The plumage of some male and female birds sometimes reflects both visible and ultraviolet light differently. These bird species typically exhibit different patterns of iridescent feather patches. An example of this for visible light is the common starling (93, 303). I had a pair of caiques photographed in reflected UV light and saw no striking difference.	Possible
Multiple-angle Spectrometry	This is another approach to using reflectance for sexing parrots. This method scans the capacity of feathers on different parts of the bird's body over a range of light wavelengths. It works for *Amazona aestiva* (367).	Possible
Ultrasonography	This method is similar to that used to observe unborn human babies.	Possible
Laparotomy	A surgical technique known as a laparotomy was the first reliable method for determining sex. This involved opening the body cavity and inspecting the sexual organs. Arthur Risser pioneered this method, but laparoscopy has supplanted it (419).	Excellent, but traumatic.
Laparoscopy	In this method, one makes a small incision into the body cavity and inserts a laparoscope. You then observe the sex organs directly.	Acceptable
Hormone level	This method involves measuring the level of estrogen or testosterone in either serum or feces (123). This method has a success rate of 87 percent (429).	Acceptable, but there are better methods.
DNA karyotyping	For this assay, one collects whole blood and then examines the blood cells for the presence or absence of the W sex chromosome.	Acceptable
W body staining	The erythrocyte nucleus of some species of female birds contains a dark staining body. This method only works for certain species, it is unknown if this works for caiques (161).	Unknown
DNA restriction fragment identification	This is the most reliable and robust of the current methods for determining the sex of monomorphic bird species. There are a number of forms of this assay.	Excellent, recommended
DNA quantification	This method relies on the fact that the total amount of DNA in a cell is greater in male birds than in female birds due to the smaller size of the W chromosome. The amount of DNA in a cell can be determined with an instrument called a flow cytometer (66).	Promising, but little tested

Appendix H. Breeder cage sizes and nest box sizes and shapes

Cage size (h × w × l) ft	Nest Box Shape[a]	Nest box size[b] (h × w × l) in	Reference
4 to 8 × 3 to 4 × 4 to 7	Slant	11 × 8 × 15	Smith (394)
	Horizontal.	7.9 × 7.9 × 11.8	Deurer-Bury (111)
2 × 2 × 3			Quint (328)
2 × 1.5 × 3			Low (234)
6 × 3 × 6	Vertical	24 × 9 × 9	Blackler (31)
2 × 2.5 × 2.5	Vertical	18 × 9 × 10	Folk (126)
6 × 4 × 6	Vertical	9 × 9 × 18	Manning (241)
3 × 3 × 4	Boot	16 × 8 × 16	Gonzales (148)
2 × 4 × 5	Boot or horizontal	Boot 24 × 12 × 12 Horizontal 10 × 10 × 24	Weaver (454)
1.5 × 1.5 × 4			Smith (400)
3 × 2 × 6	Vertical	24 × 12 × 12	Lima (222)
2.5 × 2.5 × 6	Internal ledge		Neufeld (281)
3 × 3 × 4	Vertical	24 × 8 × 8	Hollaway (186)
3.5 × 3.5 × 5	Gamma or internal ledge	13 × 11 × 9	Reillo (338)
3 × 2 to 3 × 3 to 6	Vertical or boot	Vertical 22 × 10 × 10 Boot 12 to 15 × 8 × 14 to 20	Worth (470)
10 ft long	Vertical	8.3 × 8.3 × 15.8	Low (228)
Outdoor[c] 6 × 3 × 9 to 30 Indoor 5 × 3 × 8	Vertical[c]	Diameter = 10, h = 16	Asmus (13)

[a] Shapes are illustrated below by profile. The large dark spot indicates the entrance hole.
[b] Only the largest dimension is provided.
[c] Asmus provides both indoor and outdoor caging year round. He also uses cylindrical nest boxes.

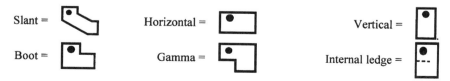

122

References

1. **Abramson, J.** 1992. Legumes in the avian diet. The AFA Watchbird **19**:23-26.
2. **Aengus, W. L., and J. R. Millam.** 1999. Taming parent-reaed orange-winged Amazon parrots by neonatal handling. Zoo Biology **18**:177-187.
3. **Agassiz, L., and E. C. Agassiz.** 1893. A Journey in Brazil. Houghton, Mifflin and Co., New York.
4. **Al Haddad, J.** 2002. A question about feeding meaty bones to parrots. Magazine of the Parrot Sociey **36**:339.
5. **Alderton, D.** 1991. The Atlas of Parrots of the World. T.F.H. Publications, Neptune City, NJ.
6. **Annonymous.** 1998. Product alerts. The North American Parrot Society (N.A.P.S.) Times **3**:6.
7. **Anonymous.** 1997. Dog-bite-related fatalities--United States, 1996-1996. MMWR **46**:463-466.
8. **Anonymous.** 1944. Notes. Avicultural Magazine 5th Series **9**:45.
9. **Anonymous.** 2000. Paranormal? Magazine of the Parrot Society **34**:166.
10. **Anonymous.** 2002. Parrot chicks a first for Paradise Park--after 15 years. Paradise Park Newsletter:1.
11. **Arnold, K. E., I. P. F. Owens, and N. J. Marshall.** 2002. Fluorescent signaling in parrots. Science **295**:92.
12. **Asero, R., G. Mistrello, D. Roncarolo, and S. Amato.** 2004. Airbourne allergy to sunflower seed. Journal of Investigational Allergology and Clinical Immunology **14**:244-246.
13. **Asmus, J.** 2003. Der Rostkappenpapagei. Papageien **11**:368-372.
14. **Astley, H. D.** 1914. My Brown-necked parrot. Avicultural Magazine **6**:110-111.
15. **Atyeo, W. T., J. Gaud, and T. M. Perez.** 1988. Morphotypes of New World Rhytidelasma gaud (Ararina, Pterolichidae), with (re)description of the five named and one new species. Acarologia **29**:175-187.
16. **Atyeo, W. T., and T. M. Peres.** 1990. Feather mites of the Aralichus canestrinii (Trouessart) complex (Acarina, Pterolichidae) from New World parrots (Psittacidae). II. From the genera Aratinga Spix, Deroptyus Wagler, Leptositacca Berlepsch and Stolzmann, Ognorhynchus Bonaparte, Pionites Heine, and Pyrrhura Bonaparte, and conclusions to the study. Fieldiana Zoology (NS) **62**:1-30.
17. **Bates, H. W.** 1864. The Naturalist on the River Amazons. John Murray, London.
18. **Bauck, L.** 1991. Feather problems. American Cage-Bird Magazine **63**:9-12.
19. **Bavelaar, F. J., and A. C. Beynen.** 2004. Atherosclerosis in parrots: a review. Veterinary Quarterly **26**:51-60.
20. **Bavelaar, F. J., J. Kuilen, R. Hovenier, and A. Lemmons.** 2005. Plasma lipids and fatty acid compostion in parrots in relation to the intake of α-linoleni acid from two feed mixtures. Journal of Animal Physiology and Animal Nutrition **89**:359-366.
21. **Bechstein, J. M.** 1837. The Natural History of Cage Birds: Their Management, Habits, Food, Treatment, Breeding and the Methods of Catching Them, English ed. Groombridge and Sons, London.
22. **Beckers, G. J. L., B. S. Nelson, and R. A. Suthers.** 2004. Vocal-tract filtering by lingual articulation in a parrot. Current Biology **14**:1592-1597.
23. **Beissinger, S. R., and E. Bucher, H.** 1992. Sustainable harvesting of parrots for conservation, p. 73-115, New World Parrots in Crisis. Solutions from Conservation Biology. Smithsonian Institution Press, Washington, DC.
24. **Beissinger, S. R., S. Tygielski, and B. Eldred.** 1998. Social constraints on the onset of incubation in a neotropical parrot: a nestbox addition experiment. Animal Behavior **55**:21-32.
25. **Bennett, A. T. D., I. C. Cuthill, J. G. Partridge, and E. J. Maler.** 1996. Ultraviolet vision and mate choice in zebra finches. Nature **380**:433-435.
26. **Berlepsch, H. v.** 1889. Systematisches Verzeichniss der von Herrn Gustav Garlepp im Brasilien und Nord Peru im Gebeite des Obern Amazonas gesammelten Vogelbälge. Journal für Ornithologie **37**:317.
27. **Bertagnolio, P.** 1974. Lories, lorikeets and caiques. Avicultural Magazine **80**:237-238.
28. **Betancourt, J. L.** 2000. The Amazon reveals its secrets--partly. Science **290**:2274-2275.
29. **Birt, T. P., V. L. Friesen, J. M. Green, W. A. Montevecchi, and W. S. Davidson.** 1992. Cytochrome-*b* sequence variation among parrots. Hereditas **117**:67-725.
30. **Bishop, S.** 1992. A pulsating diet. Magazine of the Parrot Society **26**:296-304.
31. **Blackler, R.** 1991. Breeding black headed caiques (*Pionites melanocephala*). Magazine of the Parrot Society **25**:25-26.
32. **Boetticher, H. v.** 1962. Papageien. A. Ziemsen Verlag, Wittenberg.
33. **Boles, W. E.** 1990. Glowing parrots--need for a study of hidden colours. Birds International **3**:76-79.
34. **Bond, C., and L. G. Cleland.** 1996. Rheumatoid arthritis: are pets implicated in its etiology? Seminars on Arthritis and Rheumatism **25**:308-317.
35. **Bourne, G. R.** 1975. The red-billed toucan in Guyana, p. 99-126. *In* D. A. Lancaster and J. R. Johnson (ed.), The Living Bird. Thirteenth annual of the Cornell Laboratory of Ornithology 1974.
36. **Brabourne, W. W. K.-H., and C. Chubb.** 1912. The Birds of South America. R.H. Porter, London.
37. **Breedveld, M.** 2007. Contact calls in Psittacinae. "What is their function in anti-predation?" University of Utrecht.
38. **Brehm, C. L.** 1842. Monographie der Papageien. Schmidt, Jena, Germany.
39. **Bren, L.** 2001, posting date. Pet food: the lowdown on labels. http://www.fda.gov/fdac/features/2001/301_pet.html. [Online.]
40. **Brightsmith, D.** 2004. Avian geophagy and soil characteristics in southeastern Peru. Biotropica **36**:534-543.
41. **Brightsmith, D.** 2000. Blue-and-gold macaws in Peru. BirdTalk **18**:28-31.
42. **Brightsmith, D.** 1999. Cooperative breeding. BirdTalk **17**:74-75.
43. **Brightsmith, D.** 2004. Effects of weather on parrot geophagy in Tambopata, Peru. Wilson Bulletin **116**:134-145.
44. **Brightsmith, D.** 2004. Macaw and clay lick studies at Tambopata Research Center, Peru. The AFA Watchbird **30**:34-35.
45. **Brightsmith, D.** 2005. Parrot nesting in southeastern Peru: seasonal patterns and keystone trees. Wilson Bulletin **117**:296-305.
46. **Brightsmith, D.** 2005. Parrot nesting in Southeastern Peru: seasonal patterns and keystone trees. Wilson Bulletin **117**:296-305.
47. **Brightsmith, D.** 2002. The parrot predator. BirdTalk **20**:34-39.
48. **Broad, S.** 1987. Imports of psittacines into the U.K. (1981-1984). Magazine of the Parrot Society

49. **Brockner, A.** 1999. Haltung und Zucht des Gelbschenkel-Rostkappenpapageien. Papageien **8**:264-267.

50. **Bronson, J. T.** 1950. Parrot Family Birds. Their Training, Care & Breeding, 3rd ed. All-Pets Magazine, Fond du Lac, WI.

51. **Brook, E. J.** 1916. A substitue for fruit. Bird Notes. The Journal of the Foreign Bird Club **7**:162-163.

52. **Brooks, D.** 1990. Twins. Magazine of the Parrot Society **24**:300.

53. **Brouwer, K., M. L. Jones, C. E. King, and H. Schifter.** 2000. Longevity records for psittaciformes in captivity. International Zoo Year Book **37**:299-316.

54. **Brown, C. E.** 1928. Longevity of birds in captivity. The Auk **45**:345-348.

55. **Bruner, A. G., R. E. Gullison, R. E. Rice, and G. A. B. da Fonseca.** 2001. Effectiveness of parks in protecting biodiversity. Science **291**:125-128.

56. **Bucher, E., H.** 1992. Neotropical Parrots as Agricultural Pests, p. 201-219. *In* S. R. Beissinger and N. F. R. Snyder (ed.), New World Parrots in Crisis. Solutions from Conservation Biology. Smithsonian Institution Press, Washington, DC.

57. **Buckley, P. A.** 1969. Genetics, p. 23-43. *In* M. L. Petrak (ed.), Diseases of Cage and Aviary Birds. Lea & Febiger, Philadelphia.

58. **Budden, A. E., and S. R. Beissinger.** 2004. Against the odds? Nestling sex ratio variation in green-rumped parrotlets. Behavioral Ecology **15**:607-613.

59. **Budden, A. E., and S. R. Beissinger.** 2005. Egg mass in an asynchronously hatching parrot: does variation offset constraints imposed by laying order? Behavioral Ecology **144**:318-326.

60. **Buffon, C. G. L. L.** 1793. Herrn von Buffons Naturgeshichte der Vögel. J. Pauli, Berlin.

61. **Buffon, C. G. L. L.** 1783. Histoire naturelle des oiseaux, vol. 7. De l'Imprimerie royale, Paris.

62. **Burns, K. C., and J. L. Dalen.** 2002. Foliage color contrasts and adaptive fruit color variation in a bird-dispersed plant community. Oikos **96**:463-469.

63. **Cabral, D.** 1993. Catching escaped pet birds. The AFA Watchbird **20**:45-47.

64. **Canaday, C.** 1997. Loss of insectivorous birds along a gradient of human impact in Amazonia. Biological Conservation **77**:63-77.

65. **Canaday, C., and J. Rivadeneyra.** 2001. Initial effects of a petroleum operation on Amazonian birds: terrestrial insectivores retreat. Biodiversity and Conservation **10**:567-595.

66. **Canon, N. R., L. A. Tell, M. L. Needham, and I. A. Gardner.** 2000. Flow cytometric analysis of nuclear DNA for sex identification in three psittacine species. American Journal of Veterinary Research **61**:847-850.

67. **Caparroz, R., and J. M. Barbanti Duarte.** 2004. Chromosomal similarity between the Scaly-headed parrot (*Pionus maximiliani*), and the short-tailed parrot (*Graydidascalus brachyurus*) and the yellow-faced parrot (*Salvatoria zanthrops*) (Psittaciformes: Aves): a cytotaxonomic analysis. Genetics and Molecular Biology **27**:522-528.

68. **Casky, K.** 2000. Co-parenting macaws: a comparative study of parent-raised and hand-raised siblings, p. 31-36, 2000 Conference Proceedings. American Federation of Aviculture, Los Angeles, CA.

69. **Castells, M., S. Martin, V. Sanchis, and A. J. Ramos.** 2005. Fate of mycotoxins in cereals during extrusion cooking: a review. Food Additives and Contaminates **22**:150-157.

70. **Chamberlain, S.** 2003. Bird-safe Gardening; soy for birds. BirdTalk **21**:12-16.

71. **Chapman, F. M.** 1917. The distribution of bird-life in Columbia; a contribution to a biological survey of South America. Bulletin of the American Museum of Natural History **36**.

72. **Chubb, C.** 1916. The Birds of British Guiana, Based on the Collection of Frederick Vavasour. B. Quaritch, London.

73. **Clark, E.** 1999. Would you believe twins? The AFA Watchbird **26**:30-31.

74. **Clements, J. F.** 1992. Birds of the World, a Check List, 4 ed. Ibis Publishing Co., Vista, CA.

75. **Clipsham, R.** 1997. Sex ratios in nondomestic avian species. Bird Breeder **69**:11-15.

76. **Clipsham, R.** 1998. Sweet but deadly: How toxic is that persimmon you're feeding your bird? BirdTalk **16**:86-89.

77. **Clubb, S., T. Tully, and H. Hoeffer.** 1997. Heavy metal toxicosis. Journal of Avian Medicine and Surgery **11**:115-118.

78. **Clubb, S. L.** 1992. The role of private aviculture in the conservation of Neotropical psittacines, p. 117-131. *In* S. R. Beissinger and N. F. R. Snyder (ed.), New World Parrots in Crisis. Solutions from Conservation Biology. Smithsonian Institue Press, Washington, D.C.

79. **Clubb, S. L.** 1997. The science of providing good nutrition for pet birds. Magazine of the Parrot Society **31(Sept.):**302-304.

80. **Clubb, S. L., K. Clubb, D. Skidmore, S. Wolf, and A. Phillips.** 1992. Psittacine neonatal care and hand-feeding, p. 11-1--11-12. *In* R. M. Schubot (ed.), Psittacine Aviculture. Perspectives, Techniques and Research. Avicultural Breeding and Research Center, Loxahatchee, FL.

81. **Clubb, S. L., and L. Karpinski.** 1998. Aging in macaws. Cyanopsitta **June(49):**4-5.

82. **Cole, G., and M. Murray.** 2005. Presented at the 26th Annual Convention of Expo of the Association of Avian Veterinarians, Monterey California, August 4-11, 2005.

83. **Collar, N. J.** 1997. Family Psittacidae, p. 280-477. *In* J. Del Hoyo, J. A. Elliott, and J. Sargatal (ed.), Handbook of the Birds of the World, vol. 4. Lynx Edicions, Barcellona.

84. **Collette, J. C., J. R. Millam, K. C. Klasing, and P. S. Wakenell.** 2000. Neonatal handling of Amazon parrots alters the stress response and immune function. Applied Animal Behavior Science **66**:335-349.

85. **Corrier, D. E., A. Hilton, R. L. Ziprin, and J. R. DeLoach.** 1990. Effect of dietary lactose on *Salmonella* colonization of market-age broiler chickens. Avian Disease **34**:668-676.

86. **Corrier, D. E., A. Hilton, R. L. Zoprin, R. C. Beier, and J. R. DeLoach.** 1990. Effect of dietary lactose on cecal pH, bacteriostatic volatile fatty acids and *Salmonella typhimurium* colonization of broiler chicks. Avian Disease **34**:617-625.

87. **Cotton, P. A.** 2001. The behavior and interactions of birds visiting Erythrina fusca flowers in the Columbian Amazon. Biotropica **33**:662-669.

88. **Cougill, S., and Marsden.** 2003. Variability is roost size in an Amazon parrot. implications for roost monitoring. Journal of Field Ornithology **75**:67-73.

89. **Cracraft, J.** 1988. Deep-history biogeography: Retrieving the historical pattern of evolving continental biotas. Systematic Zooolggy **37**:221-234.

90. **Cracraft, J.** 1985. Historical biogeography and patterns of differentiation within the South American avifaunas: Areas of endemism. *In* P. A. Buckly (ed.), Neotropical Ornithology. Ornithology Mongraphs, Washington, DC.

91. **Cracraft, J.** 1988. Patterns and processes of diversification: Speciation and historical congruence in some Neotropical birds. Evolution **42**:603-620.

92. **Cray, C., C. J. Roskos, and K. Zielezienski-Roberts.** 2005. Detection of cotine, a nicotine metabolite, in the plasma of birds exposed to secondhand smoke. Journal of Avian Medicine and Surgery **19**:277-279.

93. **Cuthill, I. C., A. T. D. Bennett, J. G. Partridge, and E. J. Maier.** 1999. Plumage reflectance and the objective assessment of avian sexual dichromatism. American Naturalist **153**:183-200.

94. **Cutler, B. A., T. E. Roudybush, and K. D. Shannon.** 1986. Storage of cockatiel eggs prior to incubation. Avicultural Bulletin:8-10, 23-25.

95. **Cutler, B. A., T. E. Roudybush, and K. D. Shannon.** 1985. Viability of Cockatiel (*Nymphicus hollandicus*) eggs stored up to ten days under several conditions, p. 104-106, 34th Western Poultry Disease Conference.

96. **Darwin, C. R.** 1868. Variation of animals and plants under domestication. John Murray, London.

97. **Daustin, W. C.** 1934. Breeder Secrets. By the author, Redlands, CA.

98. **David, N., and M. Gosselin.** 2002. Gender agreement of avian species names. Bulletin of the British Ornithologists' Club **122**:257-282.

99. **Davis, E. W., and J. A. Yost.** 1983. The Ethnobotany of the Waorani of Eastern Ecuador. Botanical Museum Leaflets **29**:161-202.

100. **Davis, T. A. W.** 1953. An outline of the ecology and breeding seasons of birds of the lowland forest region of British Guiana. The Ibis **95**:450-467.

101. **Dawkins, M. S.** 2000. Animal minds and animal emotion. American Zoologist **40**:883-888.

102. **Dawson, C. R.** 1915. Some Colony Birds. Timehri: The Journal of the Royal Agricultural and Commercial Society of British Guiana. 3rd Series **3**:270-278.

103. **Dawson, R. D.** 2004. Efficacy of diatomaceous earth at reducing populations of nest-dwelling ectoparasites in tree swallows. Journal of Field Ornithology **75**:232-238.

104. **de Moll, E. T.** 1983. Rare hybrid. Magazine of the Parrot Society **27**:162-163.

105. **Decoteau, A. E.** The white-bellied caique. 1990. Journal of the Society of Parrot Breeders and Exhibitors **4**:12-15.

106. **Denton.** 2003. White-bellied caique. PsittaScene Magazine **15**:20.

107. **Derscheid, J. M.** 1936. A food for lorikeets. Avicultural Magazine 5th Ser **1**:166-167.

108. **DeSchauensee, R. M., and E. Eisenmann.** 1966. The species of birds of South America and their distribution. Academy of Natural Sciences (Philadelphia), Narberth, PA.

109. **DeSchauensee, R. M., and W. H. Phelps.** 1978. A Guide to the Birds of Venezuela. Princeton University Press, Princeton, NJ.

110. **Desenne, P.** 1994. Estudio preliminary de la dieta de 15 especies de pistácidos en un bosque siempreverde, cuenca del Rio Tawadu, Reserva Forestal el Caura, Edo, Bolivar, p. 25-42. *In* G. Morales (ed.), Biología y conservación de los psitácidos de Venezuela, Caracas.

111. **Deuer-Bury, C.** 1972. Zucht des Grünzügelpapageis. Gefiederte Welt **96**:1-5.

112. **Doane, B. M.** 1991. The Parrot in Health and Illness. Howell Book House, New York.

113. **Drew, P.** 1993. Hand-rearing for the non-professional. Magazine of the Parrot Society **27**:167-169.

114. **Duchin, P.** 1996. Ghost of a Chance. A Memoir. Random House, New York, NY.

115. **Dunn, T.** 2002. To Bolivia and back. Zoogoer **31**.

116. **Dyck, J.** 1971. Structure and spectral reflectance of green and blue feathers of the rose-faced lovebird (*Agapornis roseicollis*). Biologiske Skrifter **18**:5-65.

117. **Edling, T. M.** 2000. Basic psittacine pediatrics. Veterinary Medicine **95**:378-385.

118. **Edwards, G.** 1751. A Natural History of Uncommon Birds. College of Physicians in Warwick-Lane, London.

119. **Elgas, B.** 1992. Straight talk regarding hybridization. The AFA Watchbird **19**:12-13.

120. **Engen, P. C.** 1979. Fly larvae. an easy and odorless way. AFA Watchbird 6.

121. **Enkerlin-Hoeflich, E. C.** 1995. Comparative ecology and reproductive biology of three species of Amazona parrots in northeastern Mexico. Texas A&M University, Kingsville, Texas.

122. **Enkerlin-Hoeflich, E. C., N. F. R. Snyder, and J. W. Wiley.** 2006. Behavior of wild *Amazona* and *Rhynchopsitta* parrots, with comparative insights from other psittacines, p. 13-25. *In* A. U. Luescher (ed.), Manual of Parrot Behavior. Blackwell Publishing, Oxford, UK.

123. **Erb, L., and A. B. Bercovitz.** 1980. Fecal steroid analysis: non-disruptive technique for psittacine endocrine studies, p. 65-71. *In* R. F. Pasquier (ed.), Conservation of New World Parrots. Proceeding of the ICBP Parrot Working Group Meeting. Smithsonian Institution Press, St. Lucia.

124. **Finger, E., and D. Burkhardt.** 1992. Avian plumage colors: origin of UV reflection in a black parrot. Naturwissenschaften **79**:187-188.

125. **Finsch, O.** 1868. Die Papageien Monographisch, vol. 2 (Part 1). Bearbeitet. E.J. Brill, Leiden.

126. **Folk, D.** 1991. The black-headed caique. Parrot World **8**:5-7.

127. **Forshaw, J. M.** 1973. Parrots of the World. Lansdowne Press, Melbourne, Australia.

128. **Forsyth, A., and K. Miyata.** 1984. Tropical Nature. Touchtone, New York.

129. **Forys, E. A., and C. R. Allen.** 1999. Biological invasions and deletions: community change in South Florida. Biological Conservation **87**:341-347.

130. **Fox, A. R., and J. R. Millam.** 2004. The effect of early environment on neophobia in orange-winged Amazon parrots (*Amazona amazonica*). Applied Animal Behavior Science **89**.

131. **Fox, M. R. S., and G. M. Briggs.** 1959. Effects of dietary lactose upon chicks fed a purified diet. Poultry Science:964-968.

132. **Francisco, M. R., V. O. Lunardi, and P. M. Galetti.** 2001. Chromosomal evidences of adaptive convergence in the tail morphology of Neotropical psittacidae (Aves, Psittaciformes). Cytologia **66**:329-332.

133. **Friedman, S. G.** 2005. Alternatives to breaking parrots: reducing aggression and fear through learning, p. 58-62, 2005 Conference Proceedings. American Federation of Aviculture, Los Angeles, CA.

134. **Friedmann, H., and M. Davis.** 1938. "Left-handedness" in parrots. The Auk **55**:478-480.

135. **Friston, D.** 1981. Danger from non-stick pan fires. Magazine of the Parrot Scoiety **15**:135.

136. **Fry, C. H.** 1970. Ecological distribution of birds in north-eastern Mato Grosso State, Brazil. Anais da Academia Braziliera de Ciências **42**:275-318.

137. **Furner, A. C.** 1936. A Derby member's aviaries. Aviculture Magazine. 5th Ser **1**:6-10.

138. **Garner, J. P., C. L. Meehan, T. R. Famula, and J. A. Mench.** 2006. Genetic, environmental, and neighbor effect on the severity of stereotypies and feather picking in orange-winged Amazon parrots (*Amazona amazonica*): an epidemiological study. Applied Animal Behavior Science **69**:153-168.

139. **Garner, J. P., C. L. Meehan, and J. A. Mench.** 2003. Stereotypies in cages parrots, schizophrenia and autism: evidence for a common mechanism. Behavioral Brain Research **145**:125-134.

126

140. **Garner, M. M., S. L. Clubb, M. A. Mitchell, and L. Brown.** 2008. Feather-picking psittacines: histopathology and species trends. Veterinary Pathology **45**:401-408.

141. **Garrod, A. H.** 1874. On some points in the anatomy of the parrots which bear on the classification of the suborder. Proceedings of the Zoological Society of London:586-598.

142. **Gilardi, J. D., and C. M. Munn.** 1998. Patterns of activity, flocking, and habitat use in parrots of the Peruvian Amazon. Condor **100**:641-653.

143. **Gilardi, J. D., Sean S. Duffey, Charles A. Munn and Lisa A. Tell. . 25:897-922.** 1999. Biochemical functions of geophagy in parrots: detoxification of dietary toxins and cytoprotective effects. Journal of Chemical Ecology **25**:897-922.

144. **Gill, G. E., R. T. Fowler, and S. A. Mori.** 1998. Pollination biology of Symphonia globulifera (Clusiaceae) in central French Guiana. Biotropica **30**.

145. **Glick, S. D.** 1985. Cerebral Lateralization in Nonhuman Species. Academic Press, Orlando, FL.

146. **Goldsmith, T. H., and B. K. Butler.** 2005. Color vision of the budgerigar (Melopsittacus undulatus) hue matches, tetrachromacy, and intensity discrimination. Journal of Comparitive Physiology. A. **191**:933-951.

147. **Goldsmith, T. H., and B. K. Butler.** 2003. The roles of receptor noise and cone oil droplets in the photopic spectral sensitivity of the budgerigar, Melopsittacus undulatus. Journal of Comparitive Physiology **189**:135-142.

148. **Gonzales, F.** 1996. Caiques. The AFA Watchbird **23**:45-46.

149. **González, J. A.** 2003. Harvesting, local trade, and conservation of parrots in the Northeastern Peruvian Amazon. Biological Conservation **114**:437-446.

150. **Gosling, S. D.** 2001. From mice to men: What can we learn about personality from animal research? Psychological Bulletin **127**:45-86.

151. **Gottlieb, G.** 1997. Synthesizing nature-nurture: prenatal roots of instinctive behavior. Erlbaum, Mahwah, NJ.

152. **Graham, J., T. F. Wright, R. J. Dooling, and R. Korbel.** 2006. Sensory capacities of parrots, p. 33-41. In A. U. Leuscher (ed.), Manual of Parrot Behavior. Blackwell Ames, IA.

153. **Grajal, A.** 2000. The Neotropics (Americas), p. 98-151. In N. Snyder, D. McGowan, J. Gilardi, and A. Grajal (ed.), Parrots: Survey and Conservation Action Plan 2000-2004, Gland, Switzerland.

154. **Grau, C. R., T. E. Roudybush, P. Vohra, F. H. Kratzer, M. Yang, and D. Nearenberg.** 1989. Obscure relations of feather melanization and avian nutrition. World's Poultry Science Journal **45**:241-246.

155. **Gray, G. R.** 1849. The Genera of Birds, vol. 1. Longman, Brown, Green and Longmans, London.

156. **Grimes, J. E.** 1987. Zoonoses acquired from pet birds. Veterinary Clinics of North America: small Animal Practice **17**:209-218.

157. **Haffer, J.** 1978. Distribution of Amazon forest birds. Bonner Zoologische Beiträge **29**:38-78.

158. **Haffer, J.** 1969. Speciation in Amazonian forest birds. Science **165**:131-137.

159. **Haffer, J.** 1977. Verbreitung und Hybridisation der Pionites papageien amazoniens. Bonner Zoologische Beiträge **28**:269-278.

160. **Hales, R. J.** 2000. Stamp your parrots. Magazine of the Parrot Society **34**:299-301.

161. **Halverson, J.** 1990. Avian sex identification by recombinant DNA technology, p. 256-262, Proceedings of the Annual Conference of the Association of Avian Veterinarians.

162. **Hanks, C. K.** 2005. Spatial patterns in Guyana's wild bird trade. University of Texas.

163. **Harcourt-Brown, N.** 2004. Development of the skeleton and feathers of dusky parrots (Pionus fuscus) in relation to their behavior. Veterinary Record **154**:42-48.

164. **Hargis, V. A., E. Stauber, S. Casteel, and D. Eitner.** 1989. Avocado (Persea americana) intoxication in caged birds. Journal of the American Medical Association **194**:64-66.

165. **Harris, L. J.** 1989. Footedness in parrots: three centuries of research, theory, and mere surmise. Canadian Journal of Psychology **43**:369-396.

166. **Harris, R.** 1988. Grey-cheeked parakeets--goin, going... Parrotworld **6**:33-35.

167. **Hau, M.** 2001. Timing of breeding in variable environments: tropical birds as model systems. Hormones and Behavior **40**:281-290.

168. **Hausmann, F., K. E. Arnold, N. J. Marchall, and I. P. F. Owens.** 2003. Ultraviolet signals in birds are special. Proceedings of the Royal Society B **270**:61-67.

169. **Haverschmidt, F.** 1948. Bird weights from Surinam. Wilson Bulletin **60**:230-239.

170. **Haverschmidt, F.** 1968. Birds of Surinam. Oliver & Boyd, London.

171. **Hawley, J.** 1997. Bernard Roer, olde master aviculturist. The AFA Watchbird **24**.

172. **Hawley, S. B.** 1994. Food toxicosis in birds. Caged Bird Hobbyist **2**:10-13.

173. **Heath, J.** 1993. Hand-rearing mixture. Magazine of the Parrot Scoiety **27**:15-16.

174. **Heath, L. A., S. E. Wilkie, J. K. Bowmaker, and D. M. Hunt.** 1997. The red and green opsins of two avian species, the budgerigar, Melopsittacus undulatus, and the mallard duck, Anas platyrhyncus. Gene **204**:121-126.

175. **Heine, F., and A. Reichnow.** 1882-1890. Nomemclator Musei Heineani ornithologici. Friedlander & Sohn, Berlin.

176. **Hellmayr, C. E.** 1907. On a collection of birds from Teffé, Rio Solimóes, Brasil. Novitates Zoologicae **14**.

177. **Henke, S. E., V. C. Gallardo, B. Martinez, and R. Bailey.** 2001. Survey of aflatoxin concentrations in wild bird seed purchased in Texas. Journal of Wildlife Diseases **37**:831-835.

178. **Herndon, W. L.** 1853. Exploration of the Valley of the Amazon made under the direction of the Navy Department by William Lewis Herndon and Lardner Gibbon, Lieutenants United States Navy. Robert Armstrong, Washington, D.C.

179. **Hess, L., G. Mauldin, and K. Rosenthal.** 2002. Estimated nutrient content of diets commonly fed to pet birds. The Veterinary Record **150**:399-404.

180. **Hile, A. G., T. K. Plummer, and G. F. Stiedter.** 2000. Male vocal imitation produces call convergence during pair bonding in budgerigars, Melopsittacus undulatus. Animal Behavior **59**:1209-1218.

181. **Hilty, S.** 1994. Birds of Tropical America, a Watcher's Guide to Behavior, Breeding and Diversity. Chapters Pub. Ltd., Shelburne, VT.

182. **Hilty, S. L.** 2003. Birds of Venezuela, 2 ed. Princeton University Press, Princeton, NJ.

183. **Hilty, S. L., and W. L. Brown.** 1986. A Guide to the Birds of Columbia. Princeton University Press, Princeton, NJ.

184. **Hogan, L. S.** 1991. Nutritional benefits of Canola rapeseed. American Cage-bird Magazine **63**:16-17.

185. **Holland, J. R.** 1971. The Amazon. A.S. Barnes and Co., London.

186. **Hollaway, B., and V. Hollaway.** 1999. Calling all caiques. BirdTalk **17**:42-49.

187. **Holmes, E.** 1857. Birds injurious of agriculture. Agriculture, Washington, DC.

188. **Homberger, D. G.** 1981. Functional morphology and evolution of the feeding apparatus in parrots, with special

reference to the Pesquet's parrot, *Psttrichas fulgidus* (Lesson), p. 471-485, Conservation of New World Parrots. Smithonian Instition Press, Washington, D.C.

189. **Hoorn, C.** 2006. The birth of the mighty Amazon. Scientific American **294**:52-59.

190. **Hopkinson, E.** 1914. English names for the parrots. Avicultural Magazine **6**:43.

191. **Howard, B. R.** 1992. Health risks of housing small psittacines in galvanized wire mesh cages. Journal of the American Veterinary Medical Assciation **200**:1667-1674.

192. **Hoyo, J. d., A. Elliot, J. Sargatal, and N. J. Collar.** 1992. Handbook of the Birds of the World, vol. 4. Lynx Edicions, Barcelona.

193. **Hughes, J. M., and M. L. Cohen.** 1998. Compendium of measures to control Chlamydia psittaci infection among humans (psittacocic) and pet birds (avian chlamydiosis) 1998. MMWR **47**.

194. **Hunt, S., I. C. Cuthill, A. T. Bennett, S. C. Church, and J. C. Partridge.** 2001. Is ultraviolet waveband a special communication channel in avian mate choice? Journal of Experimental Biology **204**:2499-2507.

195. **Ireland, T.** 1988. Caiques (Audio recording), Convention of the American Federation of Aviculture.

196. **Jansen, A., A. Vermeulen, P. H. Dieges, and A. W. v. Toorenenbergen.** 1996. Allergy to pine nuts in a bird fancier. Allergy **51**:741-744.

197. **Johns, A. D.** 1991. Responses of Amazonian rain forest birds to habitat modification. Journal of Tropical Ecology **7**:41-437.

198. **Johnson-Delaney, C. A.** 1990. Choosing safe plants. BirdTalk:40-46.

199. **Johnson, K. A.** 1992. 1991 Psittacine captive breeding survey. A survey of private Aviculture in the United States. TRAFFIC USA, Washington, D.C.

200. **Johnston, W. B., and e. al.** 2000. Compendium of measure to control Chlamydia psittaci infection among humans (psittacosis) and pet birds (avian chlamydiosis). MMWR **49**:1-17.

201. **Jordan, R.** 1989. Parrot Incubation Procedures. Silvio Mattacchione and Co., Pickering, Ontario.

202. **Jordt, S.-E., and D. Julius.** 2002. Molecular basis for species-specific sensitivity to "hot" chili peppers. Cell **108**:421-430.

203. **Jullien, M., and J.-M. Thiollay.** 2001. The adaptive significance of flocking in tropical understory forest birds. Nouragues: Dynamics and Plant-Animal Interaction in a Neotropic Rainforest, p. 143-165. *In* F. Bongers (ed.). Springer.

204. **Juniper, T., and M. Parr.** 1998. Parrots. A Guide to Parrots of the World. Yale University Press, New Haven, CN.

205. **Kaiser, J.** 1999. Getting to the roots of carbon loss, chili's gain. Science **285**:1198-1199.

206. **Karsten, P.** 2002. Raising waxworms as food insects. The AFA Watchbird **29**:37-38.

207. **Kelly, B., and M. London.** 1983. Amazon. Harcourt, Brace, Jovanovich, New York.

208. **Kersting, D.** 2006. Presented at the Proceedings of the Annual Conference of Avian Veterinarians.

209. **Kollias, G. V.** 1986. Relationships of avian structure and function to infectious dieases, p. 313-318. *In* G. J. Harrison and L. R. Harrison (ed.), Clinical Avian Medicine and Surgery including Aviculture. W.B. Saunders, Philadelphia, PA.

210. **Krebs, E. A.** 1999. Last but not least: nestling growth and survival in asynchronously hatching crimson rosellas. Journal of Animal Ecology **68**:266-281.

211. **Kubitzki, K.** 1985. The dispersal of forest plants, p. 192-206. *In* G. T. Ghilean and T. E. Lovejoy (ed.), Amazonia. Pergamon Press, New York.

212. **Kuhl, H.** 1820. Conspectus Pisttacorum. Nova acta Leopoldina Bonn **10**:1-104.

213. **Kumar, A., N. Jindal, C. L. Shukla, R. K. Asrani, D. R. Ledoux, and G. E. Rottinghaus.** 2004. Pathological changes in broiler chickens fed ochratoxin A and inoculated with Escherichia coli. Avian Pathology **33**:413-417.

214. **Latham, J.** 1821. A General History of Birds, vol. 2. Jacob and Johnson, Winchester, England.

215. **Latham, J.** 1790. Index ornithologicus, sive Systmea ornithologiae; complectens avium divisionem in classes, ordines, genera, species, ipsarumque varietates, vol. 1, Londonini.

216. **Le Vaillant, F.** ca. 1801. Histoire Naturelle des Perroquets., vol. 2. Levrault, Schoell & Company, Paris.

217. **Le Vaillant, F.** 1989. Natural History of Parrots. The Pot Still Press Proprietary Ltd, Sydney, Australia.

218. **Lear, E.** 1997. The Family of Parrots: Illustrations by Eward Lear. Pomegranate Artbooks, New York.

219. **Lee, G.** 1939. Hand-rearing gray parrots. Aviculture Ser. 3 **9**:117.

220. **Lepperhoff, L.** 2001. Gelbschenkel-Rostkappenpapageien im Regenwald Westamazoniens. Gefiederte Welt:114-117.

221. **Lesson, R. P.** 1833. Les trochilidees, ou les colibris et les oiseaux-mouches. Arthus Bertrand, Paris.

222. **Lima, R.** 1996. The care and breeding of caiques. The AFA Watchbird **23**:34-38.

223. **Lindsay, J.** 2000. Tale of the missing caiques. Magazine of the Parrot Society **34**:157-158.

224. **Linné, C. v.** 1758. Systema naturae. Per regna tria, secundum classes, ordines, genera, species, cum charachteribus, differentiis, synonymis, locis, vol. 2. Holmiae. Impensis L. Salvii.

225. **Lloyd, C. A.** 1895. Some Guiana parrots. Timehri: The Journal of the Royal Agricultural and Commercial Society of British Guiana Series 2. **9**:273-278.

226. **Lorenz, K. Z.** 1937. The companion in the bird's world. The Auk **54**:245-273.

227. **Lorenz, K. Z.** 1988. Here am I--Where are you? Harcourt Brace Jovanovich, Publishers, New York.

228. **Low, R.** 2002. Auffallend und Beliebt-Grüzugel- und Rostkappenpapageien. Gefiederte Welt **August**:271-273.

229. **Low, R.** 2003. Caiques. DONA Publishing, Czech Republic.

230. **Low, R.** 1991. Feeding fruits to parrots. American Cage-Bird Magazine **63**:46-49.

231. **Low, R.** 1987. Hand-Rearing Parrots and Other Birds. Blandford Press, London.

232. **Low, R.** 1972. The Parrots of South America John Gifford Ltd., London.

233. **Low, R.** 1988. Parrots. Their care and breeding., 3rd ed. Blandford Press, London.

234. **Low, R. a.** 1988. The Complete Book of Parrots. Barron's, New York.

235. **Loye, J., and S. Carroll.** 1995. Birds, bugs and blood: avian parasitism and conservation. Trends in Ecology and Evolution **10**:232-235.

236. **Ludemann, L., L. Graham, and S. L. Clubb.** 1992. Poisonous plants, p. 6.1-6.9. *In* R. M. Schubot, K. J. Clubb, and S. L. Clubb (ed.), Psittacine Aviculture. Perspectives, Techniques and Research. Avicultural Breeding & Reseach Center, Loxahatchee, FL.

237. **Lüling, K. H.** 1986. Meine seltenen Papageien aus Südamerika. Die Gefiederte Welt April, May:110-111, 141-143.

238. **Lunardi, V. O., M. R. Francisco, G. T. Rocha, B. Goldschmidt, and P. M. Galetti.** 2003. Kayotype description of two Neotropical psittacidae species: the endangered hyacinth macaw, *Anodorhychus hyacinthinus*, and the hawk-headed parrot *Deroptyus accipitrinus*

(Psittaciformes: Aves), and its significance for conservation plans. Genetics and Molecular Biology 26:283-287.

239. **Macwhirter, P. J., and R. Mueller.** 1998. Comparison of immediate skin test reactions in clinically normal and self-mutilating psittaciformes. *In* K. S. Latimer and W. L. Steffans (ed.), International Virtual Conferences in Veterinary Medicine. Diseases of psittacine birds, http://www.vet.uga.edu/ivcvm/1998/.

240. **Mancianti, F., S. Nardoni, and R. Ceccherelli.** 2002. Occurrence of yeast in psittacine droppings from captive birds in Italy. Mycopathologia **153**:121-124.

241. **Manning, A.** 1994. The icing on the caique. Parrot Magazine:52-54.

242. **Manning, A. F.** 1991. Characteristics of the black headed caique. Magazine of the Parrot Society **25**:129-130.

243. **Marshall, T.** 1995. Captivating caiques. The AFA Watchbird **22**:8-9.

244. **Marshall, T.** 1989. Captivating caiques. Bird Talk:14-17.

245. **Martin, T.** 2002. A Guide to Colour Mutations & Genetics in Parrots. ABK Publications, South Tweeds Head, Australia.

246. **Martuschelli, P.** 1994. Maroon-bellied conures feed on gall-forming homopeteran larvae. Wilson Bulletin **106**:769-770.

247. **Masin, S., R. Massa, and L. Bottoni.** 2004. Evidence of tutoring in the development of subsong in newly fledged Meyer's parrots *Poicephalus meyeri.* Anais da Academia Brasileira de Ciências 76:231-236.

248. **Maslin, M. A., and S. J. Burns.** 2000. Reconstruction of the Amazon basin effective moisture availability over the past 14,000 years. Science **290**:2285-2287.

249. **Massie, M. J., and S. L. Clubb.** 1998. Presented at the IV International Parrot Convention, Tenerfie.

250. **Maués, M. M., and G. C. Venturieri.** 1997. Pollination ecology of *Platonia insignis* Mart. (Clusiaceae), a fruit tree from eastern Amazon basin. Acta Horticulturae 437:255-259.

251. **Mayaud, N.** 1950. Téguments et phanères. Traité de Zoologie 15:4-77.

252. **Mayle, F. E., R. Burbridge, and T. J. Killeen.** 2000. Millennial-scale dynamics of southern Amazonian rain forests. Science **290**:2291-2294.

253. **McGrath, J.** 1992. The value of feeding lupins to your parrots. The AFA Watchbird **19**:22.

254. **McGraw, K. J., G. E. Hill, R. Stradi, and R. S. Parker.** 2001. The influence of carotenoid acquisition and utilization on the maintenance of species-typical plumage pigmentation in male American goldfinches (*Carduelis tristis*) and northern cardinals (*Cardinalis cardinalis*). Physiological & Biochemical Zoology 74:843-852.

255. **McGraw, K. J., and M. C. Nogare.** 2004. Carotenoid pigments and the selectivity of psittacofulvin-based coloration in parrots. Comparative Biochemistry and Physiology B **138**:229-233.

256. **McGraw, K. J., and M. C. Nogare.** 2004. Distribution of unique red feather pigments in parrots. Biology Letters (online).

257. **McLoughlin, E.** 1983. The black-headed caique-field notes. Avicultural Magazine **87**:43-46.

258. **McMillan, R. J.** 2002. Legal identification of stolen parrots. Magazine of the Parrot Society **36**:93-95.

259. **Mee, M.** 2004. Margaret Mee's Amazon: Diaries of an Artist. Antique Collector's Club/The Royal Botanic Gardens, Kew, London.

260. **Meehan, C. L., J. P. Garner, and J. L. Mench.** 2003. Isosexual pair housing improves the welfare of young Amazon Parrots. Applied Animal Behavior Science **81**:73-88.

261. **Meehan, C. L., and J. A. Mench.** 2002. Environmental enrichment affects the fear and exploratory responses to novelty of young Amazon parrots. Applied Animal Behavior Science **79**:75-88.

262. **Mendez, A., R. E. Vargas, and F. I. Michelangeli.** 1998. Effects of concanavalin A, fed as a constituent of jack bean (*Canavalia ensiformis* L.) seeds, on the humoral immune response and performance of broiler chickens. Poultry Science 77:282-289.

263. **Mettke-Hofmann, C., H. Winkler, and B. Leisler.** 2002. The significance of ecological factors for exploration and neophobia in parrots. Ethology **108**:249-272.

264. **Millam, J. R.** 1999. Husbandry and care of research parrot colonies. Poultry and Avian Biology Reviews **10**:85-89.

265. **Mine, Y., C. Oberle, and Z. Kassaify.** 2003. Eggshell matrix proteins as defense mechanism of avian eggs. Journal Agricultural and Food Chemistry 51:249-253.

266. **Mistrello, A. R., G. Roncarolo, and S. Amato.** 2004. Airborne allergy to sunflower seed. Journal of Investigative Allergology and Clinical Immunology **14**:244-246.

267. **Mitchell, P. C.** 1911. On longevity and relative viability of mammals and birds: with a note of the theory of longevity. Proceedings of the Zoological Society of London:425-548.

268. **Moegenburg, S. M., and D. J. Levey.** 2003. Do frugivores respond to fruit harvest? An experimental study of short-term responses. Ecology Letters **84**:2600-2912.

269. **Moegenburg, S. M., and D. J. Levey.** 2002. Prospects for conserving biodiversity in Amazonian extractive reserves. Ecology Letters 5:320-324.

270. **Monaghan, P., and N. B. Metcalfe.** 2000. Genome size and longevity. Trends in Genetics 16:331-332.

271. **Montgomerie, R.** 2006. Cosmetic and adventitious colors, p. 399-427. *In* G. E. Hill and K. J. McGraw (ed.), Bird Coloration, vol. 1. Harvard University Press.

272. **Morabia, A., S. Stellman, L. H. Lumey, and E. L. Wynder.** 1998. Parakeets, canaries, finches, parrots and lung cancer. British Journal of Cancer 77:501-504.

273. **Morton, E. S.** 1975. Ecological sources of selection on avian sounds. American Naturalist **109**:17-34.

274. **Mudge, G. P.** 1902. On the myology of the tongue structure of parrots, with a classification of the order, based on the structure of the tongue. Transactions of the Zoological Society of London 16:211-272.

275. **Munn, C. A.** 2006. Parrot conservation, trade, and reintroduction, p. 27-31. *In* A. U. Leuscher (ed.), The Manual of Parrot Behavior. Blackwell Publishing, Oxford, UK.

276. **Munshi-South, J., and G. S. Wilkinson.** 2006. Diet influences life span in parrots (Psittaciformes). The Auk **123**:108-118.

277. **Myers, S. A., J. R. Millam, T. E. Roudybush, and C. R. Grau.** 1988. Reproductive success of hand-reared vs. parent-reared cockatiels (*Nymphicus hollandicus*). The Auk **105**:536-542.

278. **Nager, R. G., P. Monaghan, R. Griffiths, D. C. Houston, and R. R. Dawson.** 1999. Experimental demonstration that offspring sex ratios varies with maternal condition. Proceedings of the National Academy of Science 96:570-573.

279. **Naka, L. N.** 2004. Structure and organization of canopy bird assemblages in Central America. The Auk **121**:88-102.

280. **Nemesio, A.** 2001. Colour production and evolution in parrots. International Journal of Ornithology 4:75-102.

281. **Neufeld, L.** 1996. The wonderful world of caiques, Canadian Parrot Symposium, Toronto, Canada.

282. **Newton, A.** 1877. Notes. May 15, 1877. Proceedings of the Zoological Society of London:418-419.

129

283. **Nicholson, J.** 1929. Brock's Book on Birds, 13 ed. Nicholson and Brock Limited, Toronto.

284. **Nitsan, Z.** 1977. A comparative study of the nutritional and physiological significance of raw and heated soya beans in chicks and goslings. British Journal of Nutrition **37**:81-91.

285. **Nores, M.** 1999. An alternative hypothesis for the origin of Amazonian bird diversity. Journal of Biogeography **26**:475-486.

286. **Novaes, F. C.** 1981. A estrutura da especie nos periquitos do genero Pionites Heine. (The species structure of the parrot genus Pionites psittacidae aves). Boletim do Museu Paraense Emilio Goeldi (Zool.):1-21.

287. **O'Neill, J. P.** 1980. Comments on the status of parrots occurring in Peru, p. 419. *In* R. F. Pasquier (ed.), Conservtion of New World Parrots. Smithsonian Institution Press, Wachington, DC.

288. **Ohtani, Y., K. Kojima, Y. Sumi, M. Sawada, N. Inase, S. Miyake, and Y. Yoshizawa.** 2000. Inhalation provocation tests in chronic bird fancier's lung. Chest **118**:1382-1389.

289. **Oliphant, L. W.** 1987. Pteridines and purines as major pigments of the avian iris. Pigment Cell Research **1**:129-131.

290. **Olivera Pinto, O. M.** 1938-1944. Catalogo das aves do Brasil e lista dos exemplares que as representam no Museu Paulista. Museu Paulista, Sao Paulo.

291. **Ologhobo, A., R. Mosenthin, and O. O. Alaka.** 2003. Histological alterations in the internal organs of growing chicks from feeding raw jackbean and limabean seeds. Veterinary and Human Toxicology **45**:10-13.

292. **Oniki, Y., and E. O. Willis.** 1983. A study of breeding of the Belém area, Brazil: II. Psittacidae to trochilidae. Ciência e Cultura **35**:956-964.

293. **Ouboter, P.** 2001. Assessment of traded wildlife species. WWF Guianas Report #GFECP07.

294. **Owen, D. J., and J. M. Lane.** 2006. High level of corticosterone in feather-picking parrots (*Psittacus erithacus*). Veterinary Record **158**:804-805.

295. **Pacheco, M. A., M. A. Garcia-Amado, C. Bosque, and M. G. Dominguez-Bello.** 2004. Bacteria in the crop of the seed-eating green-rumped parrotlet. Condor **106**:139-143.

296. **Page, R. K., S. Vezey, O. W. Charles, and T. Hollifield.** 1977. Effects of feed consumption and egg production of coffee bean seed (*Cassia obtusifolia*) fed to white leghorn hens. . Avian Disease **21**:90-96.

297. **Palmer, M.** 1995. Letter to the Editor. Magazine of the Parrot Society **29**:364-365.

298. **Parker, T. A.** 1982. Observations of some unusual rainforest and marsh birds in southeastern Peru. Wilson Bulletin **94**:477-493.

299. **Parker, T. A., S. A. Parker, and M. A. Plenge.** 1982. An Annotated Checklist of Peruvian Birds. Buateo Books, Vermillion, SD.

300. **Parrado-Rosselli, A.** 2005. Fruit availability and seed dispersal in terra firma rain forests of Colombian Amazonia. University of Amsterdam, Amsterdam.

301. **Patel, A. M., J. H. Ryu, and C. E. Reed.** 2001. Hypersensitivity pneumonitis: current concepts and future questions. Journal of Allergy and Clinical Immunology **108**:661-670.

302. **Payne, C. M.** 1960. On the hardiness of caiques. Avicultural Magazine **66**:44-45.

303. **Pearn, S. M., A. T. Bennett, and I. C. Cuthill.** 2001. Ultraviolet vision, fluorescence and mate choice in a parrot, the budgerigar Melopsittacus undulatus. Proceedings of the Royal Society of London. Series B: Biological Sciences **268**:2273-2279.

304. **Pearson, D. L.** 1975. The relation of foliage complexity to ecological diversity of three Amazonian bird communities. Condor **77**:453-466.

305. **Pearson, D. L.** 1971. Vertical stratification of birds in a tropical dry forest. Condor **73**:453-466.

306. **Pearson, J. T.** 1998. Development of thermoregulation and posthatching growth in the altricial cockatiel *Nymphicus hollandicus*. Physiological Zoology **71**:237-244.

307. **Pelzeln, A. v.** 1873. On the birds in the Imperial collection at Vienna obtained from the Leverian Museum. The Ibis **3**, Series **3**:117.

308. **Pelzeln, A. v.** 1871. Zur Ornithologie Brasiliens. A. Pichler's Wite & Sohn, Wein.

309. **Penard, F. P.** 1908. De vogels van Guyana, Paramaribo.

310. **Pepperberg, I. M.** 1999. The Alex Studies. Cognitive and Communicative Abilities of Grey Parrots. Harvard University Press, Cambridge, MA.

311. **Peres, C. A.** 1994. Composition, density, and fruiting phenology of arborescent palms in an Amazonian terrarei firme forest. Biotropica **26**:285-294.

312. **Peres, C. A.** 2000. Identifying keystone plant resources in tropical forests: the case of gums from Parkia pods. Journal of Topical Ecology **16**:287-317.

313. **Perry, G. C.** 2002. Wasps--do you have problems? Magazine of the Parrot Scoiety **36**:293.

314. **Peters, J. L.** 1937. Check-List of Birds of the World, vol. 3. Harvard University Press, Cambridge, MA.

315. **Phalen, D. N.** 1998. Avian polyomavirus: my thoughts. The AFA Watchbird **25**:28-39.

316. **Pini, E., A. Bertelli, R. Stradi, and M. Falchi.** 2004. Bilogical activity of parrodienes, a new class of polyunsturated linear aldehydes similar carotenoids. Drugs Experimental Clinical Research **30**:203-206.

317. **Poltimore, L.** 1958. Black-headed x white-bellied caique hybrid and some notes about the wild birds of Southern Rhodesia. Avicultural Magazine **64**:89-90.

318. **Poltimore, L.** 1936. Breeding of the black-headed and white-breasted caiques. Avicultural Magazine. 5th series **1**:294-296.

319. **Pranty, B.** 1994. Florida Field Naturalist **20**:57-68.

320. **Prestwich, A. A.** 1955. Caiques. Avicultural Magazine **61**:154-167.

321. **Prestwich, A. A.** 1963. "I name this parrot..." Kent, England.

322. **Prestwich, A. A.** 1949. Records of parrot-like birds bred in the United States of America, London.

323. **Prodanovic, H. C., H. C. Raherison, J. M. Vernejoux, J. M. Tunon de Lara, and A. Taytar.** 2002. [Does the presence of a pet at home influence the prevalence of asthma and rhinitis?] Revue des Maladies Respiratoires **19**:735-740.

324. **Prum, R. O.** 2006. Anatomy, physics, and evolution of structural colors, p. 295-353. *In* G. E. Hill and K. J. McGraw (ed.), Bird Coloration, vol. 1. Harvard University Press, Cambridge, MA.

325. **Prum, R. O., J. D. Kaplan, and J. E. Pierson.** 1996. Display behavior and natural history of the yellow-crowned manakin (*Heterocercus flavivertex:* pipridae). Condor **98**:722-735.

326. **Prus, S. E., and S. M. Schmutz.** 1987. Comparative efficiency and accuracy of surgical and cytogenetic sexing in psittacines. Avian Diseases **31**:420-424.

327. **Pryor, G. S.** 2003. Protein requirements of three species of parrots with distinct dietary specializations. Zoo Biology **22**:163-177.

328. **Quint, L. M.** 1986. Take a peek at the caique. BirdTalk:57-61.

329. **Racheli, L., and T. Racheli.** 2003. Historical relationships of Amazonian areas of endemism based on raw

distributions of parrots (Psittacidae). Tropical Zoology **16**:33-46.

330. **Raffles, H.** 2002. Amazonia: A Natural History. Princeton University Press, Princeton.

331. **Ralph, C. L.** 1969. The control of color in birds. American Zoologist **9**:521-530.

332. **Rance, L.** 2002. Deaths in parakeets and cockatoos caused by adult ticks. Magazine of the Parrot Society **36**:259-260.

333. **Rasmussen, C.** 1999. Flock sizes of parrots recorded in the terra firme lowland rainforest in Parque Nacional Yasuni, Ecuador. Papageienkunde:141-145.

334. **Reece, R. L., D. B. Dickson, and P. J. Burroes.** 1986. Zinc toxicity (new wire disease) in aviary birds. Australian Veterinarian Journal **63**:199.

335. **Regal, P. J.** 1977. Ecology and evolution of flowering plant dominance. Science **196**:622-629.

336. **Reichnow, A., H. v. Boetticher, J. Steinbacher, and G. Mützel.** 1955. Vogelbilder aus feren Zonen--Papageien. Gottfries Helene, Pfungstad

337. **Reillo, P. R., and K. A. McGovern.** 2000. White-bellied caique PMP. AZA Annual Report on Conservation and Science 1997-98:262.

338. **Reillo, P. R., K. McGowan, R. Meyerson-McCormick, and A. Coons.** 1998. A Management Guide for the White-Bellied Caique Parrot (*Pionites leucogaster xanthomeria*). Rare Species Conservatory Foundation, Loxahatchee, FL.

339. **Remsen, J. V., and M. A. Traylor.** 1989. An Annotated List of Birds of Bolivia. Buteo Books, Vermillion, SD.

340. **Renton, K.** 2002. Influence of environmental variability on the growth of lilac-crowned parrot nestlings. The Ibis **144**.

341. **Renton, K.** 2001. Lilac-crowned parrot diet and food resource availability: resource tracking by a parrot seed predator. Condor **103**:62-69.

342. **Renton, K.** 2002. Seasonal variation in occurrence of macaws along a rainforest river. Journal of Field Ornithology **73**:15-19.

343. **Renton, K., and A. Salinas-Melgoza.** 1999. Nesting behavior of the lilac-crowned parrot. Wilson Bulletin **111**:488-493.

344. **Ridgely, R. S.** 1980. The current distribution and status of mainland Neotropical parrots, p. 233-334. *In* R. F. Pasquier (ed.), Conservation of New World Parrots. Smithsonian Institution Press.

345. **Ridgely, R. S.** 1980. Presented at the Proceedings of the ICBP Parrot Working Group Meeting, St. Lucia.

346. **Ridgely, R. S., and P. J. Greenfield.** 2001. The Birds of Ecuador, vol. 1. Cornell University Press, Ithaca, NY.

347. **Ridgely, R. S., and M. B. Robbins.** 1988. *Pyrrhura orcesi*, a new parakeet from southwestern Ecuador, with systematic notes on the *P. melanura* complex. Wilson Bulletin **100**:172-343.

348. **Ripple, P. L.** 1990. Crawfish add protein to bird's diet. Journal of the Society of Parrot Breeders and Exhibitors **4**:14-15.

349. **Risdon, D. H. S.** 1973. The eating of meat by parrots. Avicultural Magazine **79**:87-88.

350. **Ritchie, B. W., F. D. Niagro, K. S. Latimer, and e. al.** 1991. Polyomavirus infections in adult psittacine birds. Journal of the Association of Avian Veterinarians **7**:202-206.

351. **Ritchie, B. W., N. Pritchard, K. S. Latimer, and P. D. Lukert.** 1994. Susceptiblity of avian polyomavirus to inactivation. The AFA Watchbird **21**:16-21.

352. **Robinson, J. M.** 2001. The dynamics of avicultural markets. Environmental Conservation **28**:76-85.

353. **Rodner, C., M. Lentino, and R. Restall.** 2000. Checklist of the Birds of Northern South America. Pica Press, Sussex.

354. **Roet, E. C., D. S. Mack, and N. Duplaix.** 1980. Presented at the Proceedings of the ICBP Working Group Meeting, St. Lucia.

355. **Rogers, C. H.** 1969. Pet Library's Parrot Guide. The Pet Library Ltd., New York, NY.

356. **Rogers, K. L.** 1989. Experience of one parent families in the parrot world. Magazine of the Parrot Scoiety **23**:239.

357. **Rogers, L. J.** 1980. Lateralization in the avian brain. Bird Behavior **2**:1-12.

358. **Rooy, J. v.** 1983. Charcoal. Magazine of the Parrot Society **17**:195.

359. **Roudybush, T.** 1993. Milk products for birds. Parrot World **11**.

360. **Rowley, I.** 1980. Parent-offspring recognition in a cockatoo, the galah, Cacatua roseicapilla. Australian Journal of Agricultural Research **28**:445-456.

361. **Rull, V.** 2006. Quaternay speciation in the Neotopics. Molecular Ecology **15**:4257-4259.

362. **Russ, K.** 1879-1899. Die fremdländischen Stubenvögel, ihre Naturgeschichte, Pflege and Zucht, vol. 3. C. Rumpler, Hanover, Germany.

363. **Rutter, W. J., P. Krichevsky, H. M. Scott, and R. G. Hansen.** 1953. The metabolism of lactose and galactose in the chick. Poultry Science **32**:706-715.

364. **Sakurai, F., M. Hamamatsu, R. Takahashi, N. Tsushima, Y. Ohta, and T. Ishibashi.** 1998. Endogenous amino acids in budgerigars (*Melopsittacus undulatus*). Experimentation Animale **47**:189-194.

365. **Salvadori, T.** 1906. Notes on Parrots. The Ibis, Series 8 **6**:652-653.

366. **Salvadori, T. E.** 1891. Catalogue of the birds in the British Museum, vol. 20.

367. **Santos, S. I. C. O., B. Elward, and J. T. Lumeij.** 2006. Sexual dichromatism in the blue-fronted Amazon parrot (*Amazona aestiva*) revealed by multiple-angle spectrometry. Journal of Avian Medicine and Surgery **20**:8-14.

368. **Schmid, R., M. G. Doherr, and A. Steigera.** 2006. The influence of breeding method on the behaviour of adult African grey parrots (*Psittacus erithacus*). Applied Animal Behaviour Science **98**:293-307.

369. **Schmidt, V., S. Schneider, J. Schlomer, M. E. Krautwald-Junghanns, and E. Richter.** 2008. Transmission of tuberculosis between men and pet birds: a case report. Avian Pathology **37**:589-592.

370. **Schneebaum, T.** 1969. Keep the River on Your Right: A Modern Cannibal Tale. Grove Press.

371. **Schomburgk, M. R.** 1922. Richard Schomburgk's Travels in British Guiana, 1840-1844, vol. 1. Daily Chronicle, Georgetown, British Guiana.

372. **Schroeder, D.** 2002. Flowers with flavor. BirdTalk **20**:66-67.

373. **Schubot, R. M., K. J. Clubb, and S. L. Clubb.** 1992. Psittacine Aviculture. Perspectives, techniques and Research. Avicult. Breed. Res. Cent, Loxahatchee. FL.

374. **Schwartz, M. J., D. Rosane, F. I. Michelangeli, and R. Rodriguez.** 1999. Chemical ecology of food items of five frugivorous Amazonian birds. Emanations 1.

375. **Sclater, P. L.** 1862. Catalogue of a Collection of American Birds. N. Trubner and Co., London.

376. **Sclater, P. L.** 1873. Nomenclator avium neotropicalium, Londinin.

377. **Sclater, P. L.** 1857. On a collection of birds transmitted by Mr. H.W. Bates from the upper Amazon. Proceedings of the Zoological Society of London:261-268.

378. **Sclater, P. L.** 1879. Remarks on some parrots living in the society's gardens. Proceedings of the Zoological Society of London:299-301.

379. **Sclater, W. L.** 1887. A few notes on British Guiana and its birds. The Ibis. Series 5 **5**:315-319.

131

380. **Shade, R.** 2000. Bronze-winged pionus research project. Part II. Original Flying Machine:42-45.
381. **Sharpe, R. B.** 1900. A Hand-List of the Genera and Species of Birds, vol. 2,, London.
382. **Shaw, G.** 1809-1812. General Zoology, or Systematic natural History, vol. 8, Part 2. Kearsley, London.
383. **Shawkey, M. D., and G. E. Hill.** 2004. Feathers at a fine scale. The Auk **121:**652-655.
384. **Sheldon, B. C.** 1999. Sex allocation: at the female's whim. Current Biology **9:**R487-R489.
385. **Shropshire, C. M., E. Stauber, and M. Arai.** 1992. Evaluation of selected plants for acute toxicosis in budgerigars. Journal of the American Veterinary Medical Association **200:**936-939.
386. **Sick, H.** 1993. Birds in Brazil. A Natural History. Princeton University Press, Princeton.
387. **Sick, H.** 1960. Tukani. Eriksson-Taplinger Co., New York.
388. **Sigrist, T.** 2006. Aves do Brasil. Uma Visão Artistica. Fosfertil, São Paulo, Brazil.
389. **Silva, T.** 1993. Feral bird populations - are they on the increase? Magazine of the Parrot Scoiety **27:**325-327.
390. **Silver, A.** ca. 1933. The Parrot Book. The Marshall Press, Ltd., London.
391. **Simone-Freilicher, E.** 2008. Recurrent smoke-induced respiratory infections in a ruby blue-headed pionus parrot (*Pionus menstrus rubrigulris*). Journal of Avian Medicine and Surgery **22:**138-145.
392. **Smith, A.** 1971. Mato Grosso. Last Virgin Land. E.P. Dutton and Co., New York.
393. **Smith, G. A.** 1976. Bird hybrids. Avicultural Magazine **82:**216-219.
394. **Smith, G. A.** 1971. Black-headed caiques. Avicultural Magazine **77:**202-218.
395. **Smith, G. A.** 1991. The Caique. The AFA Watchbird **18:**49-51.
396. **Smith, G. A.** 1991. The Caique. Magazine of the Parrot Society **25:**191-197.
397. **Smith, G. A.** 1990. The Caique in Captivity. Part II. The A.F.A Watchbird **17:**19-22.
398. **Smith, G. A.** 1991. The Caique. Magazine of the Parrot Society **25:**191-197.
399. **Smith, G. A.** 1990. The Caique. Part I. The A.F.A Watchbird **17:**27-32.
400. **Smith, G. A.** 1996. The Caiques. Caged Bird Hobbyist **4:**22-25.
401. **Smith, G. A.** 1998. Dietary requirements for parrots. Magazine of the Parrot Society **32:**95-97.
402. **Smith, G. A.** 2000. Dogma. Magazine of the Parrot Society **34:**25-26.
403. **Smith, G. A.** 1997. Myths: part 1. Soya, rearing foods, and milk. Magazine of the Parrot Society **31:**145-148.
404. **Smith, G. A.** 1997. Myths: part 2. The parrot egg. Magazine of the Parrot Society **31:**217-221.
405. **Smith, G. A.** 1993. A new disease? Magazine of the Parrot Society **27:**217-218.
406. **Smith, G. A.** 1999. Pied ringnecks. Magazine of the Parrot Society **33:**165-167.
407. **Smith, G. A.** 1975. Systematics of parrots. The Ibis **117:**18-68.
408. **Smith, G. A.** 1971. The use of the foot in feeding, with special reference to parrots. Avicultural Magazine **77:**93-100.
409. **Smith, J.** 2001. Toxicosis. Exotic Bird Report **13:**6.
410. **South, J. M., and T. F. Wright.** 2002. Nesting sex ratios in the yellow-naped Amazon: no evidence for adaptive modification. Condor **104:**437-440.
411. **Sparks, J., and T. Soper.** 1990. Parrots a Natural History. Facts On File, Inc, New York.
412. **Speed, N. (ed.).** 2003. Juvenile interaction in the nursery.
413. **Spix, J. B. v.** 1824-1825. Avium species novae, quas in itinere per Brasiliam annis MDCCCXVII-MDCCCXX. Franc. Seraph. Hubschmanni, Monachii (Munich).
414. **Spoon, T. R.** 2006. Parrot reproductive behavior, or who associates, who mates, and who cares?, p. 63-77. *In* A. U. Leuscher (ed.), Manual of Parrot Behavior. Blackwell Publishing, Oxford, UK.
415. **Stanford, M.** 2006. Effects of UVB radiation on calcium metabolism in psittacine birds. Veterinary Record **159:**236-241.
416. **Stevenson, P. R., A. Link, and B. H. Ramirez.** 2005. Frugivory and seed fate in *Bursera inversa* (Burseraceae) at Tinigua Park, Columbia: implications for primate conservation. Biotropica **37:**431-438.
417. **Stoltz, J. H., F. Galey, and B. Johnson.** 1992. Sudden death in ten psittacine birds associated with the operation of a self-cleaning oven. Veterinary and Human Toxicology **34:**420-421.
418. **Stoodley, J., and P. Stoodley.** 1984. Pionus Parrots. Bezels Publications, Portsmouth, England.
419. **Stromberg, L.** 1977 (revised 2002). Sexing all fowl, baby chicks, game birds, cage birds. Stromberg Pub. Co., Pine River, MN.
420. **Sweeney, R. G.** 1997. "Home made" calcium supplement blocks used at Loro Parque. Magazine of the Parrot Society **31:**33.
421. **Swicegood, C.** 1998. Feeding the flock. The AFA Watchbird **25:**52-56.
422. **Taczanowski, W.** 1884-1886. Ornithologie du Pérou, vol. 3, Rennes.
423. **Talan, D. A., D. M. Citron, F. M. Abrahamian, G. J. Moran, and E. J. C. Goldman.** 1999. Bacteriologic analysis of infected dog and cat bites. New England Journal of Medicine **340:**85-92.
424. **Tauer-Reich, I., G. Fruhmann, A. B. Czuppon, and X. Baur.** 1994. Allergens causing bird fancier's asthma. Allergy **49:**448-453.
425. **Tavares, E. S., A. J. Baker, S. L. Pereira, and C. Y. Miyaki.** 2006. Phylogenetic relationships and historical biogeography of Neotropical parrots (Psittaciformes: Psittacidae: Arini) inferred from mitochrondrial and nuclear DNA sequences. Systematic Biology **55:**454-470.
426. **Taylor, T. D., and D. T. Parkin.** 2008. Sex rations observed in 80 species of parrots. Journal of Zoology **276:**89-94.
427. **Teixeira, D. L. M.** 1983. Tapiragem. Ciência hoje; revista de divulgação da Sociedade Brasileira para o Progresso da Ciência **2:**42-46.
428. **Teixeira, D. M.** 1992. Perspectivas da etno-ornitologia no Brasil: O exemplo de um estudo sobre a "tapiragem." Boletim do Museu Paraense Emílio Goeldi. Serie Zoologia **8:**113-121.
429. **Tell, L. A., and B. L. Lasley.** 1991. An automated assay for fecal estrogen conjugates in the determination of sex in avian species. Zoo Biology **10:**361-367.
430. **Terbough, J., S. K. Robinson, T. A. Parker, C. M. Munn, and N. Pierpont.** 1990. Structure and organization o an Amazonian forest bird community. Ecological Monographs **60:**213-238.
431. **Tewksbury, J. J., and G. P. Nabhan.** 2001. Directed deterrence by capsaicin in chillies. Nature **412:**402-403.
432. **Them, P.** 1988. Caiques. Clown of the parrots. The A.F.A. Watchbird **15:**20-26.
433. **Thiollay, J.-M.** 1997. Disturbance, selective logging and bird diversity: a Neotropical forest study. Diversity and Conservation **6:**1155-1173.
434. **Thompson, D. R.** 1988. Hybridization. American Cage-Bird Magazine **60:**64.
435. **Thomsen, J. B., and T. A. Mulliken.** 1992. Trade in Neotropical psittacines and its conservation implications,

p. 221-239. *In* S. R. Beissinger (ed.), New World Parrots in Crisis. Solutions from Conservation Biology. Smithsonian Institution Press, Washington, DC.

436. **Todd, W. E. C.** 1925. Four new birds from Brazil. Proceedings of the Biological Society of Washington **38**:111-114.

437. **Todt, D.** 1975. Social learning of vocal patterns and modes of their applications in grey parrots. Zeitschrift für Tierpsychologie **39**:178-188.

438. **Traylor, M. A.** 1958. Birds of northeast Peru. Fieldiana Zoology (NS) **35**:87-141.

439. **Turner, F. J.** 1978. Parrot keeping in Paraguay. Some disasters and their cures. Magazine of the Parrot Society **12**:121-122.

440. **Vaughan, C., N. M. Nemeth, J. Cary, and S. Temple.** 2005. Response of a scarlet macaw *Ara macao* population to conservation in Costa Rica. Bird Conservation International **15**:119-130.

441. **Verheyen, R.** 1956. Analyse du potentiel morphologique et projet d'une nouvelle classification des Psittaciformes. Bull. Inst. R. Sci. Nat. Belg **32**:1-54.

442. **Verma, J., T. S. Johri, B. K. Swain, and S. Ameena.** 2004. Effect of graded levels of aflatoxin, ochratoxin and their combinations on the performance and immune response of broilers. British Poultry Science **45**:512-518.

443. **Vice, T. E., and M. E. Mainster.** 1984. Feeding your caged bird. Texas Veterinary Medical Journal:30-31.

444. **Vickers, W. T.** 1991. On the track of the road: changes in subsistence hunting in a Brazilian Indian territory. *In* J. G. Robinson and K. H. Redford (ed.), Neotropical Wildlife Use and Conservation. University of Chicago Press, Chicago, Ill.

445. **Vilella, G. G.** 1968. Carotenóides de penas de algumas aves Amazônicas. Anais da Academia Brasileira de Ciências **40**:391-399.

446. **Vogler, B. K., and E. Ernst.** 1999. *Aloe vera*: a systematic review of its clinical effectiveness. British Journal of General Practice **49**:823-828.

447. **Völker, O.** 1937. Ueber Fluoreszierende, gelbe Federpigmente bei Papa gaien: Eine neue Klasse von Federfarstoffen. Journal für Ornithologie **85**:136-146.

448. **Voren, H.** 1995. The use of human electrolyte solutions for hatchlings, brooding temperatures. Bird Breeder **67**:10-11.

449. **Wade, L. L., and S. J. Newman.** 2004. Hemoglobinuric nephrosis and hepatosplenic erythrophagocytosis in a dusky-headed conure (*Aratiga weddelli*) after ingestion of garlic (*Allium sativus*). Journal of Avian Medicine and Surgery **18**:155-161.

450. **Wallace, A. R.** 1853. A Narrative of Travels on the Amazon and Rio Negro. Reeve and Co, London.

451. **Walther, B. A.** 2002. Grounded ground birds and surfing canopy birds: variation of foraging stratum breadth in Neotropical birds and tested with simulation models using boundary constraints. The Auk **119**:658-685.

452. **Walther, B. A.** 2002. Vertical stratification and use of vegetation and light habitats by Neotropical forest birds. Journal of Ornithology **143**:64-81.

453. **Watson, W. H.** 1890. Change of colour caused by food. Zoologist **13**:394.

454. **Weaver, N. S.** 1995. Having fun breeding the black-headed caique. Bird Breeder:16-19.

455. **Weisman, R. G., M. G. Njegovan, M. T. Williams, J. S. Choen, and C. B. Sturdy.** 2004. A behavior analysis of absolute pitch: sex, experience, and species. Behavioral Processes **66**:289-307.

456. **Wenner, A. S., and D. H. Hirth.** 1984. Status of the feral budgericar in Florida. Journal of Field Ornithology **55**:214-219.

457. **Werquin, G. J., K. J. deCock, and P. G. Ghysels.** 2005. Comparison of the nutrient analysis and caloric density of 30 commercial seed mixtures (in toto and dehulled) with 27 commercial diets for parrots. Journal of Animal Physiology and Animal Nutrition **89**:215-221.

458. **Wheatley, N.** 1995. Where to watch birds in South America. Princeton University Press, Princeton, NJ.

459. **Whitney, B. M.** 1996. Flight behavior and other field characteristics of the genera of the Neotropical parrots. Cotinga **5**:32-42.

460. **Whitney, B. M., T. A. Parker, C. A. Budney, C. M. Munn, and J. W. Bradbury.** 2002. Voices of New World Parrots. Cornell Laboratory of Ornithology.

461. **Wilson, H., C. A. Brown, C. B. Greenacre, D. Fontenot, and K. P. Carmichael.** 2001. Suspected sodium hypchlorite toxicosis in a group of psittacine birds. Journal of Avian Medicine and Surgery **15**:209-215.

462. **Wilson, H. R.** 1997. Effects of maternal nutrition on hatchability. Poultry Science **76**:134-143.

463. **Winkler, H., and M. Preleuthner.** 2001. Behaviour and ecology of birds in tropical rain forest canopies. Plant Ecology **153**:193-202.

464. **Wissman, M. A.** 1999. The Birds and the Bees. BirdTalk **17**:50-60.

465. **Wissman, M. A.** 2005. Feather color changes & health. BirdTalk **23**:28.

466. **Wissman, M. A.** 2007. Gaga for baby food? BirdTalk **25**:46.

467. **Wolf, P., and J. Kamphues.** 2003. Hand rearing of pet birds - feeds, techniques, and recommendations. Journal of Animal Physiology and Animal Nutrition **87**:122-128.

468. **Wolters, H. E.** 1975. Die Vogelarten der Erde. Parey, Berlin.

469. **Woodward, K.** 1918. Aviculture in the U.S.A. Bird Notes. The Journal of the Foreign Bird Club **1**. Series **3**:28.

470. **Worth, G. J.** 1998. Breeding aspects of caiques and pionus parrots. The AFA Watchbird **25**:37-39.

471. **Wright, A.** 1987. Chocolate toxicity. AAV Today **1**:12.

472. **Wright, T. F., and M. Dorin.** 2001. Pair duets in the yellow-naped Amazon (Psittaciformes: *Amazona auropalliata*): responses to playbacks of different dialects. Ethology **107**:111.

473. **Wright, T. F., C. A. Toft, E. Enkerlin-Hoeflich, J. Gonzales-Elizondo, M. Albbornoz, A. Rodríguez-Ferraro, F. Rojas-Suárez, V. T. Sanz, A., S. R. Beissinger, V. Berovides, X. Gálvez, A. T. Brice, K. Joyner, J. Eberhard, J. Gilardi, S. E. Koenig, S. Stoleson, P. Martuscelli, J. M. Meyers, K. Renton, A. M. Rodríguez, A. C. Sosa-Asanza, F. J. Vilela, and J. W. Wiley.** 2001. Nest poaching in Neotropical parrots. Conservation Biology **15**:710-720.

474. **Yantz, J.** 1987. Toxicity of live food. American Cage-Bird Magazine **59**:42-43.

475. **Yates, E., and** 1976. Parrots at liberty in the home. Magazine of the Parrot Society **10**:5-7.

476. **Ziprin, R. L., D. E. Corrier, A. Hinton, R. C. Beier, G. E. Spates, and J. R. deLoach.** 1990. Intracloacal *Salmonella typhimurium* infection of broiler chickens: reduction of colonization with anaerobic organisms and dietary lactose. Avian Disease **34**:749-753.

133

Index

40539473R00084

Made in the USA
Lexington, KY
10 April 2015